6/7/19

To my dearest
friend Sooze,
Thank you for your
unwavering love, support
and creativity durin'
this climb....
Love you Forever an

Going to
Empty

Going to
Empty

Through the Tunnel of Jealousy

Di Ucci

Palmetto Publishing Group
Charleston, SC

Going to Empty
Copyright © 2019 by Di Ucci
All rights reserved

First Edition

Printed in the United States

ISBN-13: 978-1-64111-323-6
ISBN-10: 1-64111-323-5

To my soul mate Mark who offers endless opportunities for growth,
My children Keegan and Gwen who inspire me in their becoming

and

Any and all who have wrestled with the green-eyed monster...

The way out is through, and the way through is in.
Michael Brown, *The Presence Process*

Prologue

A deluge of adrenaline flooded through my system as I sprawled out on the settee in our bedroom. It was late afternoon in April and the light was fading as my husband packed for his first overseas ice climbing expedition. The sound of his caribiners clicking against one another conjured images of his ongoing thirst for freedom, adventure and challenge. I shuddered in anticipation, not about an accident, or even a fatal fall, but about a possible encounter with some awesome female climber that might take my place in the seat of his heart. As he carefully rolled his yellow rain gear into a small, compact shape, I gave space to the feeling. My body twinged painfully in response. Pulling the afghan around my shoulders, I attempted to cloak the gnawing anxiety. This time his departure would not be marked by conflict, like past scenarios. I was determined to keep the demons at bay. Reaching into the basket alongside the bed, I randomly selected a magazine and started thumbing through it, though it was impossible to concentrate. Passing a photograph of an athletic, bronze skinned woman with firm thighs, another wave traveled through me. *This was the type*, I thought to myself, someone like her will wash the features from my face.

"What are you reading, sweet one?" He looked up from his duffel bag.

"Just looking at the latest and greatest in walking shoes," I fibbed to keep things on an even keel.

"You in the market for a new pair?" He was so casual, convinced that I was *actually* thinking about shoes.

"No, just seeing what's out there. You know me, always on the lookout." *But do you really know me at all,* I wondered, yet part of me felt as if I'd known this man for more than this lifetime.

~

If you asked either of my two children about that man, their response would be determined by which memory they tapped into. Regardless of which scenario they found themselves wandering back through, they would both agree on one thing, the day I allowed myself to be shamed on that small New England island, all our lives changed forever.

Marrying their father Dane Hanson was, perhaps, the easiest thing I'd ever done. There was no vacillation, doubt or the usual butterflies in the belly the day we tied the knot. I was so comfortable that morning I consumed a tall stack of pancakes without hesitation. Not only was Dane boyishly handsome, but he was good medicine for the heart. His enduring patience and acceptance were as appealing as his lean, tight athletic body and sandy brown hair. He was a physical therapist by day and sculptor by night. He had chosen a profession and art form that were tactile because his long, slender fingers created magic wherever they went, and that spell was cast out at sea.

Chapter One

Island living was not something I imagined as part of my future. But after two years attending graduate school in California, I decided to head back to my roots in the northeast. I had my fill of "new age" life, tofu, Tai Chi, body painting parties, and guerrilla theatre. The lack of structure and boundaries had finally gotten to me. I longed for something that felt more solid and defined. My studies and field work in psychology consisted of clients that came and went, and with them any certainty about the impact I had on their lives. I longed for something more tangible.

My decision to move back east was fraught with hesitation, knowing I did not want to be too close to my parents, Charlene and Frederick, still living in New Jersey. I had disengaged three years ago and didn't want to become enmeshed in their emotional turmoil once again. After all, it had taken me so long to break away.

One foggy April morning facing the great Pacific I sat on the stone bench in the back of my narrow, pink cottage that I rented during graduate school. With a cup of coffee the size of a small soup bowl, I watched the early risers running along the shore and the fanatical surfers bobbing in the distance. I coveted this ritual each morning before encountering my roommate Danine, who needed at least two cigarettes and a strong dose of caffeine before she was even remotely civil. Today I knew I had to move forward. I opened the map of the eastern United States that I had placed beside me. Closing my eyes, I randomly brushed my finger across its surface, stopping about a quarter of an inch off the coast of Maine. I picked it up and looked closer to see where it had landed. "Algonquin Island," I said aloud.

I had long held a mild fascination with Native American culture and history. In college, when I returned deeply bronzed from spring break in the Bahamas, my English professor Dr. Roland began calling me Pocahontas. I also dated an athletic poet that year who would refer to me as "squaw" while he gently traced his fingers down my tanned belly. The thought of going to a place with a name like Algonquin, neither too close nor too far from family, had just the right appeal, spiced with a sprinkle of intrigue. I finished my last sip of coffee and folded the map. My fate was sealed with a single impulsive gesture.

That impulsive nature fell in line with being raised by two Italians with a reputation for being an extremely volatile couple. My parents had a whirlwind romance, married less than a year later and added five children to an already unstable emotional equation. I was second in line; though most people say I behaved more like a first child. To avoid getting swept into my parent's fiery spiral, I became the family mediator always trying to keep the peace. When I succeeded it made me feel like a comet bursting forth from the whirling DeMarco constellation.

As I packed my 1969 viper green beetle, now over a decade old, the night before my cross country journey, I planned a series of farewell rituals. This would allow me to let go of this west coast chapter of my life. Much had transpired here that had tremendous influence on me and I wanted to put it in its proper place before moving on. I liked marking passages in my life so I could be sure they really happened, that I hadn't dreamt or imagined them.

I awoke about an hour before sunrise the morning of my departure so I could complete everything with a grand finale at dawn. In green shorts and a t-shirt, I jogged down the road. First stop was the white stucco dormitory I lived in when I began my graduate studies. My mind intentionally conjured images of old neighbors, their pets, and gatherings in the common area. The marshmallow roast was my first taste of African drumming and dancing which lasted all night around a huge bonfire. Next, I came to the geodesic dome-shaped house surrounded by golden poppies where I allowed myself to explore my life through the lens of celestial objects. Jenna was an outrageously talented harmonica player that I had seen at an outdoor concert. When she announced that she also did astrology charts I decided to pursue it and we set a date for one Sunday afternoon. I found myself so drawn to Jenna's ethereal presence and perspective, we ended up spending the entire afternoon together, going to levels I never envisioned. It was a timeless space among stars, planets and other heavenly objects, and their placement at the time of my birth. My time with this star woman had left me feeling more complete on some level, so I bowed, smiled and moved on toward the ocean.

I made it to the water's edge just as the sun's crimson slivers pierced the horizon. As I disrobed, I flashed back on my first day at the beach and how startled I was seeing all the tanned naked bodies sprawled across the sand. It was a mixture of pregnant women, children, and sturdy college volleyball players. On this nude beach I wrestled with the imperfections of my body as I compared it to those younger and leaner. Now I stood naked and alone, except for a passing jogger, feeling how all the exposure had freed me up. I took a deep breath, counted to three and plunged into the depths of the mighty Pacific, allowing myself to be held in one last parting cool, wet embrace. While living by the ocean I came to know her as the "Great Mother" and my Aries fire was soothed away by rocking in her waves.

Chapter Two

The trip cross country was fairly uneventful for a woman traveling close to three-thousand miles alone. There were a few truck stop encounters that left something to be desired, but the journey as a whole had gone rather smoothly. My finest moments came while driving in the wee hours of the morning, sun roof open, pumped up on caffeine with good music on the radio. I never felt completely alone when I had a song to sing along with, and a rhythm to tap out on the steering wheel. Occasionally I tuned into President Carter's latest comments regarding the American hostage situation in Tehran. When I finally made it outside of Boston early one Saturday morning, my body was ready for a good stretch and a long, hot shower. My cousin Angie lived thirty miles west of the city and I felt comfortable enough spontaneously contacting her about a short visit. She was delighted to hear from me, and in typical Italian fashion, she cooked me a grand breakfast and tried coaxing me into spending the night.

"Olivia, it's been so long since we had a visit. Can't you stay just one night? What's the hurry?" But I was clearly on a mission.

"I really want to get to the island before it explodes with summer people so I can find a place to live. I double checked the ferry schedule to Algonquin and if I continue south at a good clip, I can make the last one out tonight."

"All right, all right. You always were headstrong. At least stay long enough for me to pack you some lunch." I was grateful for her generosity as she sent me off with large portions of pasta salad, peaches and black olives.

When the ferry pulled away from the mainland I remained on deck and watched it slowly become smaller and smaller, until it resembled a postcard image. When it disappeared altogether there was nothing but the vastness of ocean everywhere. When Algonquin became visible it was enveloped in the evening fog, like April's lace was holding her in an embrace of tranquility, before the tourist invasion began in a few short weeks. According to the travel guide this lasted until the beginning of December when folks came to glean some of its quaint Christmas tradition. As I disembarked it felt like stepping into a place that had not yet entered the pace and complications of the twenty-first century. There were rows of small shingled cottages set back comfortably from the road, covered with ivy and mossy patches on their roofs. Some had flower boxes, others clay pots on tree stumps with spring flowers anxious to bloom. It was the sort of place gnomes could easily inhabit.

Everything unfolded easily from my first stop at the local newsstand and beyond. I secured a room and board situation in exchange for my limited yet convincing culinary abilities. The essentials: food, housing and compensation, had been satisfied. I felt grateful and relieved as I unpacked my bags in the musty attic of the Mosses' historic home. I was already composing an ad in my head to tack on the kiosk to find additional employment working with my hands.

The Mosses were well established on Algonquin and their family had owned property for several generations. They knew just about everyone there was to know on the island. When I told Mrs. Moss at breakfast my first morning what I was hoping to do in my spare time, she said she might be able to put me in contact with just the right person.

"Our dear friends the Hansons who live down the road have a son named Dane who is finishing his internship in physical therapy at the local hospital. He's also a sculptor on the side. To earn extra money while he's still in school he usually does carpentry in the summer. Perhaps he needs an assistant."

"That sounds promising; I'll give him a call." One afternoon shortly after serving the Mosses their Scarsdale diet lunch of Melba toast and fresh fruit, I retrieved the piece of paper with Dane Hanson's phone number on it. It was blurred from the fruit juices that lingered on my finger tips and I could barely make out my own handwriting. Even under the best of circumstances it was only slightly legible.

The plan was to meet in town at the Allagash Café. I would keep it brief and businesslike over coffee. I would have an easy escape route should our conversation about employment reach a dead end.

It was dusk when I arrived at the cafe. I was obviously the first one there, so I waited on the bench outside, feeling a little nervous about meeting Dane. His phone voice had a gentle quality with a somewhat alluring pitch which had me fantasizing about what he might look like. I watched different men approach the cafe imagining which one might be him. Growing impatient, I glanced down at my watch. It was already twenty minutes past our designated meeting time. I got up to relieve some of my nervous energy by walking over to the menu encased in glass at the entrance of the cafe.

"Are you Olivia?"

I turned to face a man of medium stature, sandy hair with snug, faded jeans and light brown, weathered boots. We moved toward each other and simultaneously extended our hands. With a brisk, firm shake, he looked me in the eye with a pleasant, relaxed expression.

"I'm Dane Hanson. Am I late?"

I broke loose from our handshake noting how strong it felt, yet his fingers were long, delicate and finely shaped. But there was something different about his blue eyes.

"Not to worry. I was enjoying people watching and checking out the menu."

He walked over, and standing rather close to it, he quickly scanned the menu.

"Looks like they have cappuccino. Care for one?" I nodded and followed him through the yellow louvered doors leading into the cafe. He nodded to a few customers as we made our way to a corner table by the window.

"Decaf or the real thing at this hour of the night?" Dane said with a soft smile brushing across his boyish face.

"Definitely decaf. I serve breakfast to the Mosses at seven forty-five sharp. I get up at about six so I can stretch, walk down to the wharf and have my first cup of coffee alone to start my day." *Probably more than he needed to know*, but the conversation unfolded easily. Before I realized it more than an hour had gone by and we hadn't touched on the subject of working together.

"So, what is this I hear about you wanting to do some carpentry?" It was as if he read my concern. He leaned forward in his chair and looked right into my eyes. I again noticed something unusual about his eyes.

"I'm looking for something tangible to do with my hands, something I can look at and touch, stand back and see a finished product. Most of what I've done in the world up to this point is counseling and dance, neither of which can be easily measured. I never really know what kind of impact I've had. With dance the movement happens and then it's gone."

My voice trailed off as I remembered the final performance I had directed with a group of middle school students. I could almost hear the thunder of applause in the auditorium. I interned with the Gilroy Alternative School for a semester while in graduate school. The students had started out very self-conscious and awkward in their movement, but with warmth, acceptance and enthusiasm they all blossomed into wonderful dancers, gliding gracefully across the floor during their recital. I often tried to picture them in their now adult bodies, wondering if any of them had gone on and joined the ranks of Alvin Ailey, or perhaps the Rockettes.

Chapter Three

From the first day Dane and I worked together the chemistry between us was charged yet playful. I was gradually seduced by his quiet, patient nature as he methodically took me through the basics of carpentry. I was fascinated by his abilities despite a visual impairment that was a result of a biking accident in college. The way he so generously shared his talents with such humility was rather endearing.

It was my first real attempt at working with my hands in a disciplined, coordinated way so initially it was a clumsy dance. I made mistakes along the way that had to be corrected or done over. It was Dane's acceptance of my pace and awkwardness that eventually took over my heart. I had never known such ease and patience when it came to my shortcomings, and rather slow, gradual learning curve.

Growing up in a household of unrealistically high expectations always made me feel like no matter what I did or how I did it, it was never quite good enough. A judgmental and critical haze loomed over our colonial home during my youth. Even extra pounds that crept onto my body during adolescence were something to get rid of, and rolls with butter were forbidden when dining out at Palazzo's. Grades that weren't above average were unacceptable and greeted with a stern demeanor from my father. His familiar mini-lecture always concluded with, "Input equals output," and me making a quick exit to the refuge of my bedroom on the third floor.

Our flirtation on the job led to spending time together outside of work. I soon found myself lying in the lumpy old mattress at the Mosses fantasizing about being with him on a more long term basis. I would let my mind run wild like Mustangs in the wind, with thoughts of far away, exotic travels or settling down in a cottage by the woods. I could hear Dane playing his classical guitar by the fire at night and see me writing in my journal. I imagined finely toned, naked bodies sprawled across a thick rug where we would create lovemaking positions that no one had ever thought of, sounds no one had ever heard, enter places no one had ever been.

Dane did introduce me to some of the finer subtitles of my sexuality that summer on Algonquin. Tucked away on a blanket in the pine forest I first learned the exquisite pleasure of multiple climaxes. His continued acceptance allowed me to go beyond the traditional, unleashing a myriad of ways for our bodies to come together. One morning, shortly after sunrise, Dane nuzzled against my thick mane of hair. We had spent the night on the deck of a beach house that was still under construction.

"Time to get moving, wild one," he smiled softly as he hinted about last night's erotic activities. With sleep goobers in my eyes yet passion reawakening in my body I rolled over and pulled him down, hugging him with an intensity and strength that surprised me. I had never been so comfortable, so much myself with a man. It was a new way of being and I was basking in the luxury and tenderness of it all, like a stack of pancakes covered with warm butter and syrup. But the day had broken and the carpenters on the job would be arriving soon. We gathered the moth-eaten army blanket we had grabbed from the back of his dad's old Land Rover and walked toward town, the sun cresting over the harbor behind us. When we got to the intersection where we had to head in separate directions, he squeezed my hand firmly, "See you on the job site."

"Be there," I winked in response and began to jog toward the Mosses wondering what they thought about me not coming home last night. But it was but a fleeting consideration as I flashed on the night before in all its sensual glory.

Chapter Four

Each summer day unfolded into the next, as I cooked breakfast and dinner for the Mosses, and did carpentry with Dane in the afternoons. When I finished washing the Lenox china by hand, I would meet Dane and go off somewhere. We were always engaged in deep conversation or lovemaking in some new location. By the end of August, we had probably discovered every possible place where such interludes could take place without intrusion. Dane had gently coaxed me into sexual escapades beyond what I imagined were possible.

The only area that didn't feel safe and comfortable was entering the cool, scrutinizing chambers of Dane's family. His father Bill was a retired executive from Prudential and they owned a house on the water that had been in their family for decades. They had summered there ever since Dane was born, with his father commuting up from Boston on the weekends. They were old money, prep schools and ivy league colleges, competitive, athletic and intelligent. A sensitive, outspoken Italian woman was not exactly what they had in mind for one of their sons. My strong, extroverted presence and spontaneity seemed unnerving for them as they sat back in distant amazement watching our relationship unfold.

After one particularly long drawn out dinner with his family, when no one seemed at all interested in *my* life, I became sullen and discouraged. I had had it with their superficial, social chatter about the Colgate reunion and the next dance at the country club. As Dane walked me home that night, he slid his hand easily into my back pocket and made light of my concerns.

"You'll get used to them. They don't mean any harm, it's just their way. Besides, they like you. They just don't know how to show it like you Italians." He squeezed my buttock through my linen pants attempting to rub away my newly sprouting concerns.

"How do you know they like me? They hardly asked me anything about my life."

"They're just getting warmed up. It takes them awhile." He was very convincing.

"Okay, I guess I just have to give it some time. You know them, I don't."

"Trust me Olivia. It will all work out." And in that moment under the streetlight I believed those eyes and surrendered to that touch.

The connection and ease between us became even more secure as summer spilled into fall and plans shifted. I had expected to have a *real* job lined up in Bangor by the end of the season, but in mid-August we began the conversation about living together. Originally, he was going to stay with his folks until he completed his internship, but we decided to look for our own place. Dane's unexpected change in plans sent his family into a real swivel and did nothing to endear me in their eyes. He was making sudden changes without their usual input and approval and this would not do at all, not for the Hansons.

One night when we were scheduled to meet someone about a rental Dane called to say he would have to postpone it. He was unusually vague when I questioned him.

"Some old friends of my parents came in unexpectedly." He mumbled.

"So, you won't be able to get away?" I was hoping that our search for housing would be his priority.

"My folks just want me to hang around for a while. These people haven't seen me for years." He became a little defensive.

"But what if we lose the rental?" I was suddenly feeling less special.

"Look Olivia, it's not going to make that much difference if we delay the meeting for a day or two." I was a little disappointed in how easily he was giving into his parents.

"Well I hope they can see us in the next few days because rentals don't last long around here. Aren't you the one who told me that?"

"Yes, but it's the end of the summer and the winter market is just opening up. We'll be fine."

"I hope so. Call me tomorrow after you've had your visit." I had an edge, but he went along with his plans anyway. That night I lay in bed trying to read but I kept cycling back to it in my mind. *Why hadn't he been more assertive with them?* I chalked it up to him being accommodating, and that was a good thing.

My parents had issues of their own about us moving in together, just a different variation from the Hansons. Dane's intern status and along with a visual impairment was of great concern to my high achieving, domineering father. One night on the phone he really grilled me.

"Olivia, I'm very concerned about what you're embarking on here. I don't see an engagement ring on your finger or either of you with a full-time job."

"Dad, Dane is very motivated and once he finishes his internship, he'll have a full-time job as a physical therapist. We'll be fine!" I came back with a vengeance, but he wasn't convinced. Try as he and my mother might, they could not persuade me to reconsider about Dane. Despite the odds and the dual family disapproval, our feelings for one another never wavered.

Chapter Five

Early in October the island was gradually deserted by the tourists and we secured a winter rental through his family's connections. It was a wonderful old clapboard cottage set back from the road nestled in the pines. It gave the illusion of being secluded, yet it was conveniently close to town. It met my need to hear the wind whisper through the trees and Dane's to have his Great Pyrenees Blizzard move in with us. As our first habitat, it worked. Moving day went off without a hitch. The next morning as I filled a vase on our small, round oak table, I watched Dane putting up some shelves.

"Do you love it?" I asked looking for confirmation after the huge leap we had made only knowing each other a few short months.

"It's perfect, just perfect." He blew me a kiss and went back to banging nails.

As time went on, I became more determined to understand what it was that Dane actually saw as he viewed the world with only a single, partially damaged eye. At the end of the day as we took one of our frequent strolls with Blizzard, I would prod him.

"Tell me what you see. Describe it to me."

I wanted to climb inside and look out there, crossing boundaries and entering his world.

Boundaries had been an issue for me since I was about ten years old and my mother unknowingly crossed mine. She confided in me about my father's indiscretions and flirtations, treating me more like a confidante than a child. My dad had been a wanderer from day one. After their brief courtship, my mother naively thought that once they were married it would all change. This handsome, Italian football hero would only have eyes for her, but his gregarious charm and seductive brown eyes drew women to him that he rarely discouraged.

One morning her frustration spilled out and poured all over me like hot bacon grease. They had attended a family wedding at Preakness Hills Country Club. My mother was hardly the picture of insecurity as she rocked back and forth on our porch swing in her elegant apricot silk blouse and black linen capris. She was a sensual, striking woman who knew how to dress for any occasion. As I rounded the corner with my jump rope that day, my mother patted the seat next to her on the swing.

"Olivia, come sit next to me" I reluctantly coiled up my red, white and blue fourth of July rope and set it on the steps. I nestled into the folds of my mother's curvaceous body.

"So how was the wedding, mommy?" She turned toward me and slid her arm around my shoulder. My mother's brown eyes strayed out to the front lawn as she responded in a tired and defeated voice.

"Your father spent most of the night dancing with Connie McCrary, an old high school girlfriend." Her words felt like a damp, cold rag landing on my shoulders. I moved restlessly, my eyes drawn to the jump rope draped over the railing. My body wiggled and my youthful innocence went with it.

"Did daddy dance with you too?"

My mother responded wistfully as she looked past the two huge maple trees that bordered our property. "Yes, at one point I was able to lure him away to cha cha. He's such a good dancer and everyone was watching and clapping as we went by. Your daddy loves to be the center of attention you know."

"Mommy, what does *lure* mean?" My mother smiled as she reached over and tousled my unruly hair, now cut into a short manageable bob.

"It's what you do when you are fishing with bait at the end of your hook. You are trying to draw the fish to your rod to take a bite."

"What was your bait mommy?"

She laughed out loud. "I promised your father if he danced with me that we would have a good time when we got home."

For me "good times" meant going for soft ice cream at "Ollie's" when daddy came back from one of his long business trips or riding the Ferris wheel beside him at the fireman's bazaar on a cool summer evening. I remember a vague feeling of contentment knowing my parents had a good time, whatever that meant. But I had lost interest in my jump rope for the moment. My legs suddenly felt too heavy to lift into the air.

I soon learned that being in Dane's world was like an Impressionist painting, full of color and soft images. I loved to go there and attempt to become part of what no one else but Dane ever saw. Living with him was becoming a creative challenge and I longed to share it with someone else.

In order to stay in shape for my new man I joined the health club and took some dance classes. There I met Miranda Quinn, a stunning blond, and we hit it off immediately. She had grown up about an hour from my hometown in New Jersey. On our first walk together, we babbled on about our mutual landmarks and the conversation flowed easily into more personal areas. She was married to a musician named Ruben who was very high strung, and they were having some problems. She was tired of always having a house full of his groupies.

"Actually Miranda, I have quite a different situation. Dane is such a loner, sort of in his own world and I want to bring *more* people into our lives."

"Well perhaps we'll have you over and you can meet our collection of friends. Maybe you can take some of them off my hands." We both laughed while maintaining our stride.

As I began to learn the limits of Dane's vision, I found myself ready to defy them. I devoured everything that related to the functioning of the eye, talking to people in the field, and attempting to uncover new possibilities.

One evening while we sat warming our feet by the fire, I was thumbing through a New Age magazine when I stumbled upon an article about psychic healers in Indonesia.

"Listen to this, Dane. Psychic healers in the back country of Indonesia heal fatal injuries and diseases of people from the States. Hands-on miracles defy modern medicine." Dane shifted his glance from the fire which had him totally captivated. He had a slight grin on his face.

"What are you reading honey, *The National Inquirer?*"

"No, it's a new age quarterly publication called *Transformation* that I saw at the health club. This article is amazing. People with cancer, leukemia and other serious illnesses were healed. Maybe they can help with your eye." He didn't respond as he got down from his chair and squatted in front of the fire. His body was so limber that he could remain in that position indefinitely and still be comfortable. As he stared blankly into the flames, I couldn't read his reaction to my out of the box suggestion.

"Give me the magazine. I'll read it and let you know what I think."

I was persistent, and for the next two days whenever Dane emerged from the bathroom, I would jump on him. I was getting impatient with his leisurely pace and wanted him to be operating at the same speed I was.

"Well, did you finish it yet?"

Finally, on the third day Dane emerged with the magazine rolled up in his hand. He came into the kitchen where I sat on one of the old red caned chairs sipping coffee and writing in my journal. "So, when do we leave for Indonesia?" he said with that youthful grin on his handsome face as he rubbed my shoulders. I sprang out of my seat and threw my arms around him.

"Are you serious Dane? How will we swing it financially?"

"Hey, at this point anything is worth a try. Nothing in the good old USA has helped, so why not? I'll use the cash surrender value in my life insurance policy."

I went into action. I called the number listed in the magazine and explained all the details of Dane's visual condition, only pausing long enough to hear what had to be done next. It came so naturally, felt so good and totally energized me to have a mission.

There were so many details to make the trek to Indonesia; they kept me buried in a flurry of activity for months. Details were not

Dane's strong point. He moved in a more abstract world where time and place were of no great importance, consequently he was often late for scheduled meetings or arrived on the wrong day. He rarely wore a watch and an appointment book was like foreign matter. He planned only a few days in advance. But this worked beautifully while he was sculpting in a timeless space and I saw to it that his lack of long range planning didn't interfere with how he operated in the world where it counted. With my hypervigilance he was able to stay on track at the hospital, while he finished his internship and continued with his art. I was balancing everything behind the scenes and loving it.

One afternoon when I was at the veterinarian's making reservations for Blizzard to board while we were in Indonesia, I ran into Dane's mom Audrey. She was there with her Scottish terrier for his rabies shot.

"Hello Olivia, what brings you here? Is Blizzard ailing?" She was still so formal with me.

"Actually, I was scheduling some time at the kennel for him."

"Oh, are you and Dane off somewhere?" Her words were ice-capped. I was totally caught off guard. Dane had told me he was going to mention Indonesia to his parents weeks ago.

"I thought Dane had told you already. We're going to be gone for two weeks in March." I didn't want to get into anything more, so I grabbed my calendar and car keys from the counter.

"Where are you going, somewhere warm I hope?" She tried to disguise her obvious disappointment in her son. I backed out toward the door.

"Dane will tell you all about it when he calls tonight." I was disappointed as I got into the car. *How could Dane forget to tell them, or was it intentional?*

When he got home from the hospital that night I was still agitated. All the Hansons needed was another excuse to disapprove of my influence on their son. They would blame it all on me.

"Hey lady, how are all the travel plans coming?" I spun around before he even got his last syllable out.

"Dane, I ran into your mother at the vet's today. I thought you told them about Indonesia weeks ago!" His expression became sheepish and he broke eye contact. There was my answer.

"You put me in a real awkward position with her. Are you afraid to tell them? You are a grown man and it is your life!" I went back to madly peeling carrots for the salad that night, while flying orange-colored skins flew and hit the wall.

"I just didn't want them to have too much lead time, that's all."

"Why, are you afraid they would try to talk you out of it?"

"Maybe, I don't know! I just didn't want to have a whole series of conversations. Psychic healers aren't exactly in their repertoire, Olivia."

"Well, I told her you would call them tonight and tell them all about it."

"Great, thanks." There was a slice of sarcasm in his voice.

He was obviously in no great hurry to make the call because he took Blizzard for an extra long walk after dinner. While he was gone, I called Miranda to get her perspective.

"Sounds like he's still hooked on their approval. He's going to have to get past that," she commented.

"I know but when?"

"I guess whenever he becomes totally his own person and doesn't need it anymore. We are all doing that to some extent, don't you think?"

Chapter Six

It was a hazy, cool March morning the day we departed for San Francisco heading to Indonesia. Neither family endorsed this trip halfway around the world. My father inquired more than once about how they could possibly have more advanced medical procedures than those in the United States. Dane's parents went from shock to pleading with him about this "preposterous idea." But my fierce determination and blind hope about improving Dane's vision pumped me up to the point that I once again turned deaf ears on comments and questions that did not support the path we were embarking on.

Dane was quiet and self-contained on the first leg of the journey westward. He stared out the window while I vacillated between journal writing and stroking his hand. We made our first stop in Hawaii in the middle of the night. I leaned toward him and whispered,

"We're almost there, closer than ever." Dane responded by surrounding my hands with his while he looked out at the tropical, darkened landscape.

"Who knows what awaits us. We shall see," he said. We both silently pondered the magnitude of the next twenty-four hours and what would unfold.

When we finally arrived in our hotel room in downtown Jakarta on Java, we fell into bed with exhaustion and excitement after nineteen hours of traveling. What seemed like only moments after we closed our eyes the phone violently jarred us out of a deep sleep.

"Is this room of Mr. Hanson?" The person spoke in somewhat broken English.

Out of a groggy haze, I responded. "Yes, yes. Who is this?"

In a short, choppy manner the voice said, "It is time for first healing. Come to Room 1173 on the eleventh floor." I hung up and immediately became giddy with fear and anticipation, not to mention sleep deprivation. I quickly rolled over and nuzzled Dane who had not stirred at all. He was a very sound sleeper. When he didn't respond I became more persistent, pulled the covers down and started kissing his neck, ears and chest to wake him. Finally, he rolled over and snuggled up, probably wondering what I had in mind at this ungodly hour.

When we finally pulled our sweatpants and shirts on, splashed cold water on our faces and headed for the elevator, the reality of what we were about to enter into hit us hard. The door slid open and we simultaneously turned to each other, clutching hands and Dane said,

"I'm scared, you?"

"Well, it all seems so strange and sudden, eerie in a way." Just as I finished my sentence the elevator came to a stop and the door opened at the eleventh floor. I steered Dane in the direction of room 1173.

When we entered the room, my senses were on high alert. I immediately had an uneasy feeling as I took a sweeping glance around the room. Off in a corner were four men playing cards and wearing tight black pants and white cropped shirts. There was a faint smell of stale smoke in the air and the window was cracked open. I hid my initial discomfort from Dane. One of the men from the table got up, introduced himself as "Brother Timone" and told Dane to remove his shirt, shoes and socks. Pointing to the window he motioned for him to lie down on the bed next to it. On the night stand was a medium sized orange bowl filled halfway with water. I followed Dane closely and stood next to him as he cautiously went through the motions. My protective instinct was pulsating through my body as I hovered over him, taking in every strange detail.

He lay down and Brother Timone dipped his hands in the bowl of water and began rubbing Dane's temple. Without warning he then flicked his wrist and pulled something seemingly from the back of Dane's head, a rubbery, flesh colored substance. He plunked it in the bowl of water and quickly covered it with a white washcloth, and another man whisked it away to the bathroom. He came back with a new bowl and muttered something I couldn't decipher.

"This is blockage, bad for eye. Removed some. Good start." He told Dane to lie still for a moment and then he disappeared back into the cluster of men, whispering so softly I couldn't make it out, even with my excellent hearing.

I walked over and rested my hand on Dane's shoulder, startling him slightly because his eyes were still closed. He grabbed it and slowly opened his eyes. My chest tightened, my breath quickened as I anticipated what he might see after this first "healing." His eyes fluttered quickly and then shut tightly in disappointment. He released my hand and turned over on his side. His silence told me all I needed to know. I sensed the air of charlatans as soon as we entered the room but refused to acknowledge it after traveling half way around the world to get here. Somehow, I would have to remain open for Dane's sake, but the healings changed nothing for him. There was even a trip in outrigger canoes to a Dayak long house. It was surrounded by pigs, chickens and all the smells that went with them. Here a nun named Sister Kederi was the revered healer in the area. She was a young woman whose poor hygiene became a distraction for me, making it hard to focus on what she was actually doing. Those who came up to her lay on a wooden rectangular box on the altar where she laid hands on the areas that needed to be cleansed of illness or malfunction.

"Where the demons lay," she would say as her hands hovered over different body parts. By this time Dane had lost all faith in the process, wishing he had more sense than to have pursued this whole sham. We left very little in Sister Kederi's basket marked 'Healing Donations' and boarded the bus in silence. We left Jakarta before the rest of the group. There were still members with hope left in their hearts and we didn't want to destroy it for them.

When we got back, I tried contacting the magazine with the article on the 'healers' but no one ever returned my calls. Dane slid into a downward spiral and I caught a glimpse of what he referred to as his "blue funks". Walking and talking with Miranda helped me deal with this other side of Dane that appeared morose and defeated. Fortunately, our love was still new enough to keep me from becoming too discouraged.

Chapter Seven

Surviving the tumultuous Indonesian journey had managed to create *more* of an emotional bond between us. One morning shortly after our return Dane spoke of marriage while we sipped coffee and ate chocolate croissants in bed. The idea slid down into my being like the chocolate melting on my tongue. It felt warm and sweet inside.

"It feels good to me." I grabbed his hand.

"All right lady, when, where and how?" He seemed relieved and excited by my response.

"How about as soon as possible, on the mainland, just the two of us?" I even surprised myself with this suggestion.

"Why just the two of us? That will definitely get both the Hansons and the DeMarcos in an uproar!"

"I know but it's so much simpler that way. Besides, they can throw a big party for us after we've had our own private ceremony."

He brought me close and kissed the top of my head. "I guess that would work."

I was genuinely surprised by his relaxed acceptance of my spontaneous wedding plan. I thought he would hesitate more without having his parents' blessing. I could hear the voices of my own parents screaming inside my head about my next impulsive move. But my heart opened wider and silenced them as I responded more to Dane's acceptance than my fears.

Less than two weeks later in mid-May we quietly slipped away to the mainland and married in the small, quaint town of Belshire. While Dane slept, I dressed before dawn's first light in my lavender muslin gown that buttoned all the way to the floor. When I finished brushing my hair, I tied it back and put a silk iris in it. When I was done, I ran my fingers along my hips and felt utterly feminine, soft and flowing. I turned once more time to look upon him sleeping peacefully on this morning that would alter the course of both our lives.

Our plan was for me to get ready then set the alarm, slipping away to the beach where we would meet the local magistrate Marion Sherman. She was flexible enough to marry us at sunrise at the water's edge. Dane would join me there so he could be surprised by my bridal attire. As he appeared at the top of the hill, a slight wind blew through my hair and I looked over to him and waved. Since he didn't know what I was wearing it was probably difficult for him to distinguish which woman was his bride. I watched him carefully maneuver his way down the cliff and realized this visual challenge would be in my life forever. One part of me welcomed it while the other wished it could change it, but the part that embraced who he was moved swiftly to the foreground as he came toward me grinning from ear to ear.

After the ceremony we each devoured a huge stack of Maine's famous blueberry pancakes and link sausage. When those appetites were satisfied, we took to feeding the other back in our queen-sized canopy bed where our union was consummated over and over.

When we arrived back on the island the following evening bursting with the news, both families reacted very strongly about our haste and secrecy. I was dumbfounded when Dane's parents invited *him*, not us, to lunch the next day, using the polite excuse of family matters that simply couldn't wait.

"But Dane, I'm your wife now which makes me part of the family! Why am I being excluded from this lunch meeting?"

"Honey, I've told you how private they are. They need time to adjust to our being married." I was astounded and confused by his passivity.

"Dane, wouldn't you think they'd want to celebrate with us together instead of excluding me at a time like this?

"Olivia, you are taking it too personally. Whatever they need to talk about must be rather important."

"Well I can't imagine what's more important than our getting married!" When he got back from lunch, he was vague, saying it had something to do with their estate. No matter what he said I remained in a posture of disappointment and uneasiness about all of it.

But within a few days whatever concerns they had about our marriage were overridden by their social graces. Audrey Hanson contacted my mother and together they planned an elegant dinner party held at the country club on Algonquin. Once this formal ritual took place with family members from both sides mingling appropriately, everyone managed to settle into a more comfortable place about our union.

Charting our course from that point on was another matter. How and where we would make a permanent life for ourselves presented more of a challenge than we realized. Dane had completed his internship and there were no openings at Algonquin's only hospital, and I needed to be closer to a city to get my professional life back on track. I had dabbled in carpentry but now I needed to get *serious* again.

After spending a full day brainstorming with huge pieces of newsprint posted on the wall listing pros and cons of all our ideas, we knew we had to leave the security of the island. We would try to stay close to the ocean for it soothed our souls in chaotic times. Rockland was a town just north of where the ferry came in, which would give us continued access to Algonquin. It was big enough to have two hospitals where he could do physical therapy, and I could find work in the mental health area, yet it felt manageable and friendly. So, with a meager financial cushion and great expectations we forged ahead.

Finding a suitable place to live was not easy due to our need to be close to town and public transportation, as well as a place where we could have Blizzard. Very few landlords in town would even consider pets, let alone one of his size. After much searching, we found an apartment on the first floor of a weathered Victorian house, just four short blocks from a bus stop that took you to the center of town. It had a small backyard where the owners said Blizzard could spend his days tied up if there weren't any complaints from neighbors, and we were diligent about cleaning up after him.

Setting up our first real unfurnished household together, mixing our possessions and histories, sharing stories as we hung paintings and unpacked boxes was pleasurable and easy. I clearly had more of a need for order and completion, but Dane's ability to function surrounded by boxes and books allowed me to be more relaxed about the process. I had a compulsive tendency to do away with clutter and make immediate sense of my surroundings. Dane's artistic mentality was to have some disarray and gradually over time, create something handsome from it. After settling in I soon became restless and delved into the classifieds while Dane seemed much less driven. After a week I secured an interview with a group of clinicians looking for someone to do public relations and marketing for their group practice. After two interviews with the director, and one with the group of clinicians, they offered me the job. It wasn't the ideal fit, but we were just about out of money, so it was very timely.

Dane's pursuit of employment was not as direct nor as quick. He perused the papers but did not act on anything without me prodding him along. Once I started working, I would sometimes come home on my lunch hour to motivate him.

"How goes the search, honey?"

"Oh, all right. There's a physical therapy assistant opening in the classifieds, but I would have to switch buses to get to that office. Besides I don't really want to be an assistant. I spent all that time in school to be an ace physical therapist."

"I know but you have to start somewhere." I was annoyed with his attitude. I picked up my plate and wiped the crumbs abruptly from the table.

"Suit yourself, but we do need the money," and I was out the door. No one was back from lunch when I got to the office, so I slipped in a call to Miranda, venting some of my frustrations. She was having her own difficulties with Ruben. They were discussing a separation, so we commiserated together.

Driving home that evening my annoyance with Dane moved to another level. I felt like he wasn't trying hard enough and when he finally got around to responding to the ad, the job was filled, and so were several others. After six weeks he realized he might have to consider carpentry until something opened up again in physical therapy. They were taking a large chunk of my paycheck out for our medical insurance and we had other expenses as well.

He answered an ad that required a vehicle, but I convinced him to try based on his extensive experience. He called when I was there for lunch and the owner happened to be in. His name was Vic

Spoleto, an Italian fellow with a small remodeling business. He told Dane he could see him that day after work, so I rushed home to get him there on time. Dane was obviously nervous.

"So, when we get to the part about transportation, what do you suggest?"

I thought carefully before I responded. I took one hand off the steering wheel and touched his shoulder, knowing the delicacy of this ongoing issue.

"I suppose the truth wouldn't hurt. He'll figure it out eventually, right?"

Dane was able in his quiet, solid way to convince Vic to give him a try. Early the next morning with lunch box in hand and his tool belt resting on his hip I watched him cross the street to Vic's office, scanning as he went. I always got a lovely, sensual tingle when Dane appeared in snug jeans and work boots. His body was lean and tight like a dancer's and you could see his thigh muscles move through the faded denim. I sat for a moment reviewing the directions back to downtown. When I was about to pull away from the curb Dane reappeared flagging me down. He must have forgotten something. As he approached the car with lunch box still in hand, his facial expression indicated he was very disturbed. He opened the car door and said rather abruptly,

"Let's get out of here." Puzzled, I took the car out of park and slid her into drive.

"What's going on? What happened Dane?"

"Vic's wife, who takes care of all the books and the insurance claims, came to the door. Last night she and Vic discussed my "condition" and decided it was too high risk."

I winced inside and quickly lunged forth like a lioness protecting her cub.

"What the hell do they think they're doing, not even giving you a chance to prove yourself? Did you ask to talk to Vic?"

"No, I did not! I told you, Olivia, people have a hard time dealing with someone who is limited, now drive please."

I realized that the car was running but I hadn't released my foot from the break because I was floored by his return. I headed toward the water. I would call work and make some excuse so we could find solace by the sea and formulate another plan for Dane. But as I pulled away from the curb something else pushed its way to the forefront.

"Dane, don't you think it would have been worth speaking directly with Vic?"

"No, I don't. It was obviously a done deal."

"But you don't know that for sure."

"Look Olivia, let's face it, they didn't want to take a risk!"

Yes, and neither did you, I thought.

Things didn't improve. Physical Therapists apparently loved their jobs and rarely left them. There were no openings, even as assistants, which Dane was more than willing to take at this point. After a year of disappointment and longer lasting blue funks, Dane began to turn back toward Algonquin, the place where he had history and connections, a place where people knew and respected him. They knew about his biking accident and its results, and because he was one of the Hanson boys, they embraced him. It was an unspoken code of ethics in the social network his parents traveled in for all those summers.

Chapter Eight

Packing boxes again one dismal, rainy afternoon in late June after giving my reluctant notice at work, I felt resentment begin to stir inside of me. I was beginning to enjoy the marketing aspects of my job and it could have led to greater possibilities, but now I would have to put it aside to meet Dane's needs. I crumpled some newspaper into a ball and tossed it into the box, trying to release some of my emerging discontent along with it. My father's words about Dane echoed in my head, but fortunately I could still taste our sweet, uncomplicated beginnings which helped drown out his stern voice. We would make a life back on Algonquin, settle in and have that home with a crackling fire, friends stopping by, and most important within walking distance of all the necessities. I closed the box and sealed any misgivings about our move tightly inside.

Prior to our arrival on Algonquin, Dane made some calls and had located a place for us to live. This was almost unheard of at the beginning of the tourist season, but his parents were out there networking for us. It was a large old clapboard house facing the water situated on the edge of a bluff. You had to travel down a winding dirt road to get there. Surrounded by scrub pine it was an ideal spot for deer to come through in the early morning. The owners were friends of the Hansons, and they were happy to have the newly-weds, but not without a few favors on the side. They had some work that needed to be done on the house in exchange for rent.

I reinvented myself yet one more time. This time it was with a tool belt securely fastened to my coveralls and a handful of nails in my pocket. We tore off the old wooden gutters and replaced them with fresh smelling pine. Dane and I had conversations from one ladder to the other and took coffee breaks on the bluff overlooking the Atlantic. It was an easy, peaceful summer as one day gently rolled into the next.

But when the September winds began to rustle through the trees, my restless nature kicked in. It unexpectedly came in the form of loneliness. Living so far out of town and working with Dane on the house I began to feel isolated. I needed to incorporate something more involving social interaction. Miranda's was living on her own now, so I saw her weekly, along with some other women she had introduced me to who joined us for our power walks. Dane encouraged me to pursue my need for people in whatever way I could though he did not share in it. His limited visual world had created an experience that set him apart, and he was comfortable out there. He had been betrayed and deceived on occasion so a part of him had closed off. The part that remained trusting and open to human connection seemed adequately filled by me.

So, I ventured away from the house on the bluff searching for a place where I could socially revive myself. One morning when I went to get a paper and coffee and be out among more people, I noticed the kiosk fluttering with various scraps of paper. I stopped to explore the possibilities and watch people setting about their day, with hard rolls and *New York Times* in hand. I spotted a small ad on ivory paper bordered in red crosses: "Volunteers needed at the Community Hospital. Read to patients, make beds, and assist with meals." The image of sitting at someone's bedside and reading aloud to fill their day with some meaning resonated inside me. I dug deep into my leather bag and finally found a pen to jot down the contact number. When I was finished tucking the piece of paper into my wallet, I headed down the street to the harbor. But not without my usual trip past the import store to see their latest display of sweet grass baskets from Senegal. I loved the texture and shapes of baskets, and it was the one thing that I consistently collected whenever I traveled. At some point I would take a class and learn to make them myself. While studying the color tones in one of the larger baskets, a blue Ford F-150 pick-up truck rumbled up the cobblestone street toward me. As I looked up, the driver turned toward me and waved. I didn't recognize him though his attractive, rugged face seemed like one I should remember. Perhaps he had mistaken me for someone else. As he headed up the street, I caught a glimpse of his clever bumper sticker "Is there life before coffee?" I chuckled to myself, *now there's a man after my own heart.*

Without really registering that response, my awareness shifted to my love affair with coffee. Drinking it each morning was such an important ritual for me, starting with the smell as it traveled through the kitchen and into our bedroom. I loved to lie in bed listening for the coffee maker to stop bubbling, knowing that the silence meant its efforts were complete and my coffee was now sufficiently, richly brewed.

My work as candy striper of sorts at Algonquin's only hospital helped fill the people void, opening me up to the colorful lives of local folks. I went in two days a week, bringing flowers, poetry books, magazines and anything else that might lift the patients' spirits.

Though the island was perceived as a somewhat idyllic place, the hospital showed the shadow side with its share of terminal illness, clinical depression and AIDS patients.

One particularly foggy morning on my way to volunteer, I crept along slowly maneuvering my way safely through the "pea soup" fog as the natives would say. At one bend in the road my line of vision was so limited I pulled off to wait it out, allowing the tentacles of sunlight to penetrate the thick haze. I rolled down my window to listen to the early morning sounds when out of nowhere a truck pulled up alongside me. The driver rolled down his window.

"Need some help? Are you stuck?"

"No, no. I'm fine, just waiting for the fog to lift a bit."

"Yeah, she's pretty dense this morning. Be careful and have a good one."

As he pulled away with a wave, I noticed it was the blue Ford with the coffee bumper sticker. I sat perfectly still watching the stranger disappear into the smoky mist wondering what his story was. When slivers of sun finally filtered through the fog, I started up the car and headed toward the hospital.

"Hey, sunshine, back so soon?" said a delighted Virgil Batson, an island native and longtime fisherman who had his leg amputated last week due to diabetic complications.

"Indeed, I am, with lots of poetry filled with images of your beloved sea!"

"You are a gal after my own seafaring heart, Olivia. Read on!" He patted the chair next to his bed and I nestled in for the next hour reading, laughing, talking and listening to Virgil repeat his favorite stories about his days on the high seas. When I drove home, I felt pleasantly charged, and life took on more meaning for me that fall.

Chapter Nine

As fall bristled into winter, Algonquin stood firm in the cold winds that blew across and around her. About this time, we needed to move out of our care-taking situation because the owners were coming for the Christmas holidays. We really needed a more permanent nest and with all the Hanson connections we soon secured a small place in town that one of Dane's childhood friends had purchased as an investment with trust fund money. Moving again threw me into an unexpected tailspin. Packing and unpacking twice in less than six months was creating more upheaval than this orderly type could handle. But eventually the sweet, shingled cottage with federal blue shutters took on a quality we were satisfied with. Family photos, dried flowers hanging from beams, and Dane's sculpture pulled it all together as we hunkered down for the winter.

We used our wood stove as a source of both heat and ambiance. We fired it up as soon as we got home from work and allowed the warmth to take the edge off the day. Dane had finally landed a part-time job at the hospital's outpatient physical therapy unit. My volunteer work paid off and I was now the coordinator of their program, recruiting and training new volunteers from the community.

I was also dancing again with a group of women from exercise class and we were working toward a community performance, so life felt good. Returning from one of my weekly dance rehearsals I stopped at the doorway of Dane's studio. He did not hear me come in, so I watched in total amazement as he handled the band saw with steady precision. Deep appreciation for his abilities turned into lust and I couldn't resist interrupting his artistic focus. I came up behind him and stuck my hands in his pockets. When I received a warm welcome, I began squeezing his finely shaped buttocks. I never even got my jeans entirely off and our animal lust won out over precaution. We ended up on the floor of his studio with sawdust clinging to our half-clothed bodies.

About six weeks after that scrumptious interlude I was stoking the fire, and I realized my period was about ten days overdue. That evening while Dane slept, I sat naked on the edge of our bed stroking my round, soft belly with curiosity *What if there was life in there? Were we up to it?* When Dane arrived home from the hospital the next day, he gave me the customary greeting, a solid, warm wrap-around hug.

"How's my sweetheart?" I stayed smothered in his neck, while he gently kissed all my favorite spots, not responding to his question.

"Everything okay Olivia?" Eventually I pulled away from his comforting embrace. There was moisture forming around my eyes that caught him off-guard.

"I took a home pregnancy test today."

"What for? Are you that late?" He was clearly shaken.

"Almost two weeks. Dane, the test was positive." He grabbed my hand and pulled me down on the futon where he sat unlacing the boots he had worn due to last night's snowfall. Those same boots had so often led to my seduction while he was either dressing or undressing from work. There was something about the rustic leather as it traveled midway up his muscular calf that made me warm and wet inside.

"My god Olivia, I can't believe it! Are we ready for this?"

Perched on the edge of Dane's lap, I sighed a deep one, a breath that filled my whole body.

"Dane, I'm strong, healthy, and in decent shape from my years of dancing. But thirty-one is not considered young in terms of childbearing years so it's time. I think we're ready."

I tried to sound convincing for both of us. But even as the words passed from my lips a dark corner of my mind pulled me in, forcing me to question whether indeed this was true. I had so much negative residue from my childhood that was still with me. *Would I repeat the sins of my own parents with my child? Would Dane be able to provide for us?*

Somehow, I was able to chase my fears and doubts away as I focused on my pregnancy with an uncompromising commitment to stay fit and flexible. I became concerned when I started putting on more weight than the books said was appropriate. My next visit to the doctor cleared that up. We were having twins. Walking back to the car we were both speechless. This was not something either of us had ever considered. Suddenly everything felt chaotic and unmanageable. Our rental was only two bedrooms and Dane had turned one into a studio. He only had a part-time job and I had planned on taking three months off with one child and then finding a suitable childcare situation. Having two mouths to feed, clothe, care and create space for set off panic buttons everywhere in my body and psyche. Dane knew I was on overload, but he too was overwhelmed and unable to comfort me. We were like two breathless swimmers searching for a raft that would keep us afloat.

After dinner that night we came out of our stupor and I initiated a planning process once again. I didn't even give Dane time to take the lead, I was so stressed. It was abundantly clear that we needed a larger place and Dane would need to be working full-time. First, he would pursue additional hours at the hospital and if not, he would try remodeling jobs on the side. His artwork would have to go on hold which was unfortunate because he was getting ready for a one man show that summer. We didn't want to take the chance on his sculpture bringing in the extra money we needed, so he reluctantly postponed the show and put his art on the back burner.

Within a month we found a small, three-bedroom house near town that had potential. Dane and his brother Peter, a structural engineer, who flew in on business, went through the house thoroughly. Though it was old and needed work, the basic foundation was solid. We would need money for the down payment, so our mortgage was manageable. The idea of actually being settled enough to own a home and raise two children pushed me toward my parents for some assistance. My dad came up the following weekend and went with Dane's father to look at the house. Bill was very familiar with the island's real estate values and was willing to meet my father halfway with a down payment. Afterwards they went out for a late breakfast and delighted in their joint effort to invest in their grand children's future. When they shared the news with us, I could barely contain myself as I smothered them both with hugs and kisses, with a mixture of tears. This spontaneous display of emotion was a bit much for my father-in-law, but he tolerated my gratitude with a smile.

After signing the sales agreement, we celebrated with sparkling cider and chocolate. We sat on the edge of our new bay window toasting our good fortune and generous fathers.

"Dane, this is a turning point, honey. We now have a home to bring our children into!" He laughed heartily. He was clearly feeling better than he had in months.

"This place needs some work before we move in you know."

"Oh, I know, I understand. It's just that we finally have some real stability, a home. It's like walking into one of my daydreams, for real!" We drained the bottle of cider, spread out a blanket and christened our pine floor with the scent of our bodies mingling. My new size was a challenge, but we persevered and found another new way of coming together.

Chapter Ten

Adam and Julia came barreling into the world in the heat of early August. After twenty-two hours of back labor they were finally delivered cesarean. It was much more excruciating than our Lamaze teacher ever let on. I was so disappointed after practicing the breathing for all those months and then having to endure surgery instead of pushing them through on my own. But after being on all fours because of the back pain I was ready to be done with it. When they were both pronounced whole and healthy, Dane brushed my hair aside and kissed my sweaty forehead.

"We got the millionaire's package baby, a boy and a girl." He was beaming like a lighthouse. I don't think I had ever seen him quite so proud.

Julia's huge brown eyes drew in everybody that met her. Her eyelashes were long enough to create envy among grown women and her disposition was jovial and energetic. Adam's hair was blond and fuzzy, and he had Dane's blue green eyes. He was alert and observant from the start. I was totally consumed and fulfilled by my two babies. I resigned from my position at the hospital and dropped out of the dance company. Over the next few months my mothering instincts got into the driver's seat and the professional side temporarily moved to the rear. I would strap Julia into my over the shoulder baby holder and put Adam in the stroller, and take them on long walks, stopping to give them a closer look at birds, flowers and trees. Everything was new to them and it was a pace that reawakened me to the sweet, subtle details of life. One cool, late September morning we headed out to the bakery. Over the last couple of weeks I had been craving a warm pumpkin muffin slathered with butter. Approaching the four corners to Colette's Bakery, a truck pulled alongside the curb. As I looked to see if I could cross safely, I realized it was that same blue Ford. The man smiled, slowed down and gallantly waved me on. I passed in front of his truck and got a closer look at his face, it was shaped like a full-moon.

While I sat on the bench enjoying my heated muffin, the image of his smile kept reappearing in my mind. The more I tried to banish him, the more persistent he became. I wasn't accustomed to allowing things to just be, so I continued to wrestle with this reoccurring visitor and found him mildly disturbing all the way home.

From the moment Adam and Julia appeared on the scene our life slowly unraveled. Since I was no longer working outside the home, Dane's paycheck was our only source of income. He tried beefing up his hours to full-time at the hospital, but when one of the staff members went on sick leave, Mrs. Limbaugh, the director, gave the extra hours to someone else. He retreated into his studio that night and I pursued him.

"So, did you talk with uptight Mrs. Limbaugh about why she passed over you?"

He wiped the clay from his fingers onto his apron.

"No, I didn't. She left early today."

"Well what about tomorrow, Dane? Are you going to talk to her then?"

"Olivia, she must have had her reasons."

I was totally exasperated now.

"And don't you want to know what those are?" I demanded.

"Not really, I just want her to know how important it is to consider me next time additional hours need to be filled." I was stunned by his casual reply. He was our sole provider and I was relying on him to be my man, come home from the hunt with food for the family, and his lack of assertiveness was scaring me.

The next evening, I walked with Miranda and the other women in the group, Liza and Beverly. They listened and then unanimously encouraged me to confront Dane. They concurred that he had obligations to deal with and he needed to step up to the plate. I tried to hang on a little bit longer, but his passivity and procrastination continued to the point where I could no longer contain myself. One Saturday we had words when he was surfing through the television channels instead of pursuing job possibilities.

"Dane Hanson, we can't go on living like this. We have two children to feed and clothe, not to mention you and me!" Whenever I used Dane's full name to address him as opposed to a term of endearment, such as "honey" or "babe," I got his attention.

"I know, I know, Olivia. I'm doing the best I can. The hospital just doesn't have the census right now and the remodeling jobs are all out of town."

I shot right back full of fire and smoke. "Then you have to do something else for a while. It's that simple!"

"Nothing is that simple honey, you know that."

"Well, Dane, what I do know is that we have bills to pay and I'm home with these babies while you're supposed to be bringing home the bacon, as they say. And it's not happening!"

I was trembling with anger. It was easier for me to shout rather than break down. My parents had showed me how to get mad not sad. Witnessing my father's anger always giving him the upper hand, while my mother seemed to shrink in his shadow, I decided then I would never be trapped in her helpless, desperate corner.

Dane halfheartedly explored other options, but soon it became clear that I was going to have to work to meet our growing expenses. In a whirlwind of resentment, I began combing through the meager classified section in the local newspaper and contacting people I knew at the hospital. By chance someone was leaving a public relations position at the local historical society and I sent my resume in. It was close enough to what I was doing at the Rockland Counseling Center.

It was a gray, windy November morning as I dressed for my interview. Adam and Julia were sprawled out on their blankets while I put on makeup, which I hadn't done in weeks. I looked over at their tiny fingers wrapped around their rattles and my mind swelled with fear and bitterness. *How can I leave my babies at a time when they are so dependent and delicate, with their senses developing further each day? I'll miss so much being away from them.* I imagined that first step or new word without my being there and I came close to tears. With one last stroke of blush-on against my pale cheekbones, I headed out the door while Miranda, who volunteered to take care of them, distracted the children.

Seated in a burgundy leather chair I took in the surroundings as I waited outside the Executive Director's door. From the soft feeling of the leather, it was old and well utilized. I wondered how many other anxious women had sat here in the last week awaiting their interview, imagining what Chad Whitinger would be like. There was a mild level of activity in the background, *enough to keep me busy.* I listened to Claire, the receptionist's British accent, as she greeted people over the phone. *There is something so refined, regal and commanding about that sound. It somehow makes you sit up straight and cross your legs when you hear it.* And so I did.

"Mr. Whitinger will see you now, Mrs. Hanson."

She nodded in the direction of his office. A tall, slender gentleman with salt and pepper hair stood up from behind his desk as I opened the door. He gave me a firm handshake which I returned in equal strength, something my father had stressed since eighth grade when I got my first summer job as a mother's helper. "Never give a limp fish instead of a strong hand. You need to make real contact," he would say with his usual conviction. I immediately noticed all the pastel paintings hanging on the walls.

"I love your paintings. The impressionists have always been my favorite, especially Chagall." I was admiring "The Embrace" when Mr. Whitinger pointed to a love seat across from his mahogany desk and said, "Thank you. My wife and I have been to the Musee d'Orsay in Paris three times. We can't get enough. Please sit down, Olivia." The interview went well. Despite my insecurities about being back in the working force, I was able to appear very confident. While I sat comfortably on the small antique loveseat, I could see staff members pass by the windows through the double doors. One man who resembled Robert Kennedy paused as he walked by and very obviously peeked in to see who was with Mr. Whitinger. He seemed to be a curious soul with a wonderful twinkle in his eye.

The next day I was on the floor playing with Adam and Julia when the call came.

"Is Olivia Hanson there?"

"This is she." With one finger caught in Julia's tight grip I tried to hold the receiver with my other hand.

"Olivia, this is Chad Whitinger calling to offer you the job in public relations here at the Historical Society." Delight and nervous excitement surged through me as I quickly responded,

"How wonderful. What starting date do you have in mind?"

"I would like you to start after the first of the year. We can set up another meeting to go over all the particulars." I was relieved I would have the holidays to adjust and be with my babies.

"Sounds good. Let me get my appointment book."

When I returned from my second meeting with Chad, I put my well-worn black leather briefcase next to the door and went to check on Julia and Adam. They were sleeping peacefully through the enormous transition in their lives that had now been set into motion. Their tiny fists curled next to stuffed bears and fleece blankies sent me into a disturbing place. I grabbed the maple knob at the head of Adam's crib as I was seized by a moment of overwhelming terror at the thought of being away from them all day. My heart sped up and I suddenly felt weak and dizzy. I made my way over to the futon in his room and sat down. With a deep sigh I pushed the terror away instead of letting it run its natural course. My babies were so precious and vulnerable, and now I had to find someone I could entrust them to. I felt like the soft bunny sprawled across the windowsill. He was splitting down the middle and his stuffing was beginning to fall out.

Chapter Eleven

I began my new job the first week in January. Fortunately, I came down with a severe case of the flu over the holidays which allowed the weaning process to happen out of necessity. I was too sick to nurse and wasn't producing enough milk anyway. My parents were there for Christmas and my mother said it was about time to cut them loose anyway, especially Adam. She felt that it was more than enough time to be at his mother's breast. She was so abrupt and overly simplistic about it, seemingly oblivious to my grief about the transition I was making in my domestic life. But she had never breast fed any of her five children, nor had she worked outside the home. This wasn't the first time our mother daughter relationship was out of balance. When I went to her in sixth grade after I asked Caleb Wilson to go steady on Sadie Hawkins Day and he turned me down for curly, blond Megan O'Keefe, she went back to her own high school heartbreak, and completely glossed over mine.

The morning I started work at the Algonquin Historical Society I wore a red knit two-piece skirt and sweater. My choice was based on comfort topped with a bit of flare. I referred to such apparel as "creamy clothes" that allowed me to move freely and unselfconsciously while wearing them. The red had always been a favorite color choice, bold and vibrant, 'makes a real statement,' my mother always said.

The children were still in that soft, sleepy place when I waved goodbye from the sidewalk on that first day. Marietta, a twenty-four-year-old from Bolzano in northern Italy, had agreed to care for them in our home for six months. I stumbled upon her at the bakery one day. I overheard her describing her plans to open a pre-school when she returned to her homeland in a year or so. Her goals and her warm, friendly personality led me to invite her over. After careful screening and significant time with Adam and Julia under my watchful eye, I hired her for this interim period. This would give me ample time to find a more permanent arrangement while allowing her to save some money over the winter. The island was pretty much shut down from January through March except the basics, like Kronin's Pharmacy, the A & P, and the library.

When I reached the end of the sidewalk, I turned for one last wave. Marietta knelt in front of the storm door with each of them propped up so they could see me. Julia opened and closed her chubby little hand, while Adam looked bewildered and on the verge of tears. I felt my eyes swell and burn, but I knew I had to press on or my runny mascara would give me away to my new colleagues.

When I got to the side door of the building, I looked at my watch and realized I was fifteen minutes early. My nervous anticipation got me there faster than I thought. The door was locked, and I had no key yet, so I began removing my slouch socks and sneakers in exchange for black suede pumps. With one heel on and the other off I heard a truck pull into the parking space alongside me. I turned and almost lost my footing when I saw the blue F150 Ford truck backing into the space. My heart raced as I stripped the other sock off and plunged into my shoe. Stuffing the sneakers into my large canvas bag, I heard the truck door slam. Walking toward me was the moon-faced stranger that had been crossing my path all this time.

"Good Morning, are you here for an appointment?" He looked at me in a warm, focused manner with steady eye contact. He had thin, light brown hair which receded. His eyes were a deep hazel green and his lips were slender and delicate.

"No, actually I start work here today as the new public relations person. My name is Olivia Hanson." He reached for my hand. His was stout, strong, weathered with obvious years of outdoor, hands-on work.

"I'm Samuel Ferrell. I'm in charge of maintaining all the historical properties for the Society. So, they forgot to give you a set of keys, did they? Come up to my office and I'll get you what you need." He had an air of confidence and ease as he unlocked the double white doors. I felt as though I was having an enormous Deja vu. *How could this be happening?* I was less than a foot from the mysterious face I had seen over and over behind the wheel of that blue truck. And now I would be working with him on a day to day basis.

"Have a seat while I put together a proper set of keys to both the front and back doors." I snapped back into the reality of what was happening when I heard his smooth but very clear and strong voice.

"Thanks, I'd appreciate that. I guess Chad overlooked that when we last met."

Samuel chuckled, soft and low.

"That's not surprising," he said still smiling, "Chad is a man of great vision, but the details of everyday office management tend to escape him." I was so caught up in being in such close proximity to this man that I couldn't manage my usual quick, clever retort. I was suddenly transformed into an adolescent school girl, awkward, and feeling utterly transparent. I rubbed my cheeks to see if they had become warm to the touch. My eyes darted to his bulletin board. There was a sign in bold blue letters that read "Rock the Boat" and a color photo of him playing in the sand with a small child. *He's married and a father.*

"So which office are you going to be hanging your hat in?" That much I knew so I was able to muster up a response.

"I believe Chad said I'll be sharing a space with Alicia the book-keeper for the time being. He said things are in flux here and eventually I should be going downstairs somewhere."

Samuel laughed again. "Things are always in flux here in one way or another, but you'll get used to it."

"I suppose I will," I said with a shallow laugh. Luckily, the phone rang, and Samuel's focus clearly shifted to the caller. He gave me a wave as I made my way out toward my new office, two doors down on the other side of the hall. As I entered the space I was about to inhabit as a professional once more, I wondered what would transpire here in this room. New spaces always contained such mystery and possibility before you claimed them as your own.

Time passed and without realizing it, we all adapted to the major transition in our lives. Marietta was doing a beautiful job caring for Adam and Julia, evidenced in their beaming faces when she appeared at the door each morning. I had my painful moments and misgivings when I heard about Adam going from a crawl to a sitting position without me seeing it, but somehow, I was able to balance it out with the other part of me that was being fed professionally. With no additional employment on the immediate horizon Dane threw himself back into his sculpture, preparing for his one-man show that had been postponed the previous summer. Seeing him producing such beautiful pieces helped me feel better about him not working as much as I was, but there was still a silent, smoldering resentment.

After a couple of months at the historical society, I relocated downstairs to the front office. There were double doors leading to Main Street and I loved seeing the island wake-up and begin the day's activities. I engaged in my beloved people watching when things slowed down at my desk. But those moments were short-lived after Chad Whitinger quickly recognized what I was capable of. Soon I was entrenched in public relations activities on a major scale.

One of my first major projects was to write a feature article for the Society's quarterly magazine on the techniques used to restore Saint Celia's, a treasured church from the 1800's. I knew very little about the subject, so I did lots of reading and looking through old photographs at the Society's library. After a while it became clear that I would have to spend more time with Samuel who headed up the restoration project. Up to that point I had maintained a safe distance knowing there was something incredibly magnetic about him. Now and then we had a few casual conversations that were not always work-related, and more than superficial. It was apparent that a friendship could easily develop between us, but I sensed something bigger that kept me away, and I chose not to mention it to Dane.

I did not seek out opportunities to spend time alone with Samuel Ferrell, but the article on the Church of Saint Celia pushed us into collaboration and forced my hand. As our time together increased, we brought the story to life for the lay readers who had no background in historic restoration.

Samuel's ability to focus was something I became acutely aware of each time we met. Whenever we discussed a specific aspect of the process, Samuel would explain it with great clarity and detail, using his hands in minute and grand gestures to illustrate the technique he described. He stayed on track and completed his statement while I followed along struggling to absorb this foreign information and vocabulary. I was struck by his ability to see a topic through so completely, in contrast to my explanations taking detours, twists and turns.

The project on St. Celia started to take up at least one hour of every working day. Without realizing it, I became increasingly comfortable in Samuel's office and genuinely looked forward to our meetings more and more. Something was creeping up on me, like a black cat in the shadows of my heart waiting to lunge forward.

One morning we had to comb through a series of historic photos of the church to use as before and after comparisons for the article. I spread them across Samuel's office floor and we both knelt down, scanning for just the right ones. Somehow being on the floor sparked yet another level of comfort, and the conversation flowed into a more personal direction. Before I knew it, I was asking the kind of bold, pointed questions I'm so famous for.

"So why is a good soul like you single in your late thirties?" By now I knew the baby in the picture was his niece. His response was open and candid in return. He wasn't unnerved at all.

"Just haven't found the right one, though I keep going up to bat and swinging again," he said with that seductive twinkle in his eye, *at least that's how it affected me*. The conversation lingered along those lines, interspersed with commentaries on the photographs, what period they were from, and how they might best illustrate what the finer points of the restoration were all about. When I collected my notes and piled them neatly into a folder on my desk, I knew the friendship had taken a distinct turn.

When Dane returned from work that evening, Adam and Julia had their toys strewn across the old red brick linoleum kitchen floor while I made spinach linguine for dinner. He came in the back door in his hospital whites.

"Hello family, daddy's home," he said in a kind of sing song voice that the children always responded to though suddenly I found it a bit irritating. Julia pulled herself up with the help of one of the kitchen chairs and Adam turned in Dane's direction with an adoring smile. After a playful, prolonged greeting with the kids, Dane made his way over to the stove where I stood over the boiling water, steam misting my face.

"How's my Italian Mama tonight?" Dane said as he ran his hand over my buttock, ending with a pinch.

"Hot, tired and ready for Friday to be here." I wasn't feeling as fun loving and affectionate as he was.

Later that evening when the kids were finally asleep, Dane went down to his studio to work on a sculpture for his show. I showered, put on a long tee-shirt and joined him in his space, knowing we needed to connect. I sat on a stool drying my hair and watching him shape the clay. Here, in this world of transforming objects into art, he was a master. He seemed in control, strong and on top of it in ways that he didn't in the world above. I took him in completely, for it had been a long time since I had admired and appreciated him in this way. For a few moments I became lost in his magic. He was so absorbed in the piece that it took a while for him to even notice my presence.

"It's really coming along, shaping up into something wonderful," I commented.

"Yes, getting closer to where I want her to be."

"And what do you want her to be?"

"To embody much of what the feminine spirit is to me," he responded without looking up.

"You mean the curves and shapeliness?"

"Yes, and much more than that actually, the twists, turns, hidden places and mysterious nature of a woman." I was caught off guard by the relevance of his comment. My own shadow side felt trapped inside wanting to reveal itself.

"Speaking of hidden places Dane, I need to talk to you about something."

"Yes, I've known that for some time now. I was waiting until you felt ready to bring it to me." His ability to sense something was amiss and not demand an explanation astounded me.

"Then why didn't you ask me about it?"

"Because I figured you would come to me when you were ready."

I was stunned by his display of patience and fortitude. If the roles had been reversed, I would have plunged in at the first ripple that something was wrong. This impulsive, relentless quality needing taming but I wasn't there yet.

"So, what is it my lady? What news do you bring me?" His casual, touching manner brought me to the edge of my heart. How could I stray from such a tender, tolerant soul? Yet I was compelled to unzip and expose my feelings to Dane.

"Well, it's kind of complicated," I fumbled at first. Yes, Dane had become my best and dearest friend, and it was this trust and safety that allowed me to spill my guts to him.

"You know how Samuel Ferrell and I have been working on this article about the restoration of the church of Saint Celia."

"Yes, you've mentioned it several times. Tell me more." *Where did he get the patience to wait for the bomb to hit?* His neutral openness was so foreign to me. I walked on.

"Well, we've been spending a great deal of time together and as a result, we've gotten to know each other quite well." Dane wiped the clay on his apron and looked at me. Now he was beginning to show some concern about where the conversation was going.

"Is that a problem, getting to know a colleague?" I took a long, deep breath and paused, wishing the silence could be stretched further.

"Well, I've noticed of late that I look forward to these meetings, perhaps a little more than I should."

"What? Do you have some sort of thing for him? Jesus, is that what you're telling me Olivia?" The intensity in Dane's usually calm voice backed me down a couple of notches. It churned up nervous energy that was very rare for me in Dane's company. I had always been able to tell all without fear of reprisal.

"Well, I don't know if that is what I would call it," I was stumbling now. "But it is some sort of connection beyond collegial." He pounded his fist into the mound of clay, turning toward me; he strained to make eye contact across the room.

"Then get it under control," he said with uncharacteristic anger and strength in his voice. "Do whatever you have to do to clean it up, Olivia!" He was asking me to re-mold the relationship with Samuel the same way he worked with clay. Change the form, that's all. I twitched inside at the thought of this attraction changing the shape of my family configuration.

"Don't worry Dane. I won't let anything happen to us. You are my best friend." I placated him.

"I hope I'm more than just your best friend, Olivia, like your lover and the father of your children too!" I left his studio sobered and determined to reshape my feelings for Samuel into something safe, with clear lines of delineation.

Chapter Twelve

The following month I found myself walking down Main Street with Samuel during our lunch break. The weather was on the cooler side for April and my woolen sweaters were balled up and moth eaten from being stashed in the back of a large steamer trunk. Our basement was damp, and they all had a heavy musty odor that I couldn't seem to get rid of. I was on my way to "Rosie's Attic" to check out their sale on cotton sweaters leftover from their winter inventory. Samuel was on his way to grilled cheese and tomato soup at Kronin's drugstore.

"Hey, Samuel, the manager of Rosie's is attractive, single and available. Want to come and help me pick out a new sweater?" I smiled and winked at him for effect. He nodded and turned in the direction of Rosie's, a store he had done all the woodworking for three years back. He vaguely remembered the manager as being a slender, appealing brunette, but unavailable at that time. He was willing to explore her current status, so I headed toward the back of the shop where the sweaters were cleverly displayed, spilling out from an old hand painted yellow stenciled chest. I assumed Samuel would slide right into polite but interesting conversation with the manager Bonnie Swain. He was so good at that, thinking on his feet. His self-confidence gave him a charming, casual air that women were easily drawn into.

On my way to the chest of sweaters something red and flowing sidetracked me. I stopped and pulled the sleeve of the dress to see the price tag. It was steep, but the lines were exquisite, and the fabric was delicious. Red was always hard to resist, and I could use it for the big fundraising event this summer. Rationalizing to myself as I fingered the silky material, Samuel came up behind me.

"Try it on. It's a beauty" His spontaneous gesture and physical closeness startled me.

"I'm not shopping for a dress. I'm here to get a sweater, but I've always had a weakness for red." While we were playfully debating, Bonnie was perched on her stool behind the counter taking it all in.

"Yes, but look at the price tag. Pretty reasonable for island prices."

Did he know about women's clothing prices too, what else?

"Oh, do you buy women's party dresses often?'

"All I know is, I have great taste," he retorted, "Now try it on! I'll go in half if it fits and you like it." I got swept away by his generous offer and forgot all about why we were there. It was all so pleasurable, the moment, the fabric, the redness of it all. I came out of the dressing room like a Parisian model flaunting my latest to a crowd of cheering spectators.

"It's you, no doubt about it, Olivia!" He played the role perfectly, eyeing me from head to toe, slowing down slightly when he reached my breasts. My nipples were erect and carefully outlined by the smooth red fabric. I thought I saw him brush his hand past the zipper on his pants. Partially enjoying this unexpected erotic moment, I lost myself in what I imagined his hardness to be like.

"It is definitely a great dress, but this was not part of the plan nor my budget!" Even while I said it, I was still taking in my image in the full-length, three-way mirror. It hid all my flaws and made me look slim in all the right places.

"I said I would go half with you and I meant it. Come on, take it off and let's get it!"

He pulled his credit card out of his cloth wallet as I disappeared into the dressing room.

"Samuel, this is a bit much, don't you think?" I said from behind the curtain.

"Consider it a loan, or a very late Christmas gift, whatever works for you," and he winked. The flattery was irresistible and as I removed the gorgeous dress, I gently traced my finger over my nipples, relishing this unexpected moment of titillation. When I emerged, I saw Samuel and Bonnie making small talk at the register. Everything suddenly went flat inside my sweater. I became invisible as I tried to busy myself by rummaging through the trunk of sale sweaters. But try as I might, I was more than a little distracted by their interaction. He paid for the dress and she carefully surrounded it with pale pink tissue paper with gold stars. Bonnie was obviously taken with Samuel, and he seemed to be enjoying their conversation as well. My attempt to mold myself into the role of matchmaker didn't seem to be working as planned.

"Find anything in there?" Samuel interrupted my rapid stream of thoughts, reminding me that I was, after all, here to buy a sweater.

"Not really, nothing in my size or color," I quickly went numb about what just transpired.

My emotional check out was a familiar one, the exit I took after suddenly losing my parents' long sought attention to someone or something else. The painful sensation in the pit of my stomach was so unpleasant I successfully devised a roadblock that kept me from feeling it. Outwardly I appeared cool, detached and very much in control as the *ice queen* emerged. She covered up my devastation or fear, with total bravado.

"Ready to roll lady?" Samuel turned to me, with the neatly packaged red dress. It crinkled ever so slightly inside the tissue paper cradled gently around it.

"Absolutely," extending my hand I took the bag without meeting his eyes. I moved hurriedly toward the door while vaguely hearing them making future plans.

"Hey, nice shopping with you," he called out as he came toward the door.

"Thanks, I'll be paying you back shortly."

"I won't take it if you do. Consider it a gift for the matchmaker in my life." His comment jolted me into reality, and I tried to make a comeback.

"Ah yes, did it work? Did you guys connect at all?"

"We're having lunch tomorrow. I hope she likes grilled cheese and tomato soup." It happened to be one of *my* favorite combos on a cold afternoon.

"Can't think of a more romantic start. Bravo!" My voice trailed off as I headed back to the office with images of Bonnie and Samuel spinning on stools at Kronin's drugstore the following day.

After the red dress episode my contact with Samuel dwindled for the rest of the week, but the following week we had to make a final selection of photos for the magazine. Just before we were scheduled to meet at the library, I overheard a conversation between he and Claire, the receptionist, who always had more than a casual interest in his social life. But Samuel had initiated this one.

"Hey, my truck was filled with the scent of Bonnie's perfume as I drove in this morning."

Claire knew Bonnie and gobbled up this tidbit, prompting him further.

"Oh, did you spend a lot of time in the truck?" She giggled coyly. He gave a vague but enticing response to her probe. He knew just where to stop and still remain a discreet gentleman.

"Enough to leave the scent of a lovely woman!" My heart plummeted and simultaneously seemed to increase in speed. Thoughts of Bonnie and Samuel sitting close together on the old leather seats of the pick-up sent me reeling. *How could this be happening? I was so sure I had it all under control. Now with the arrival of the green-eyed monster I knew for sure I had failed. Some matchmaker!* Lost in the unexpected siege of emotion, I struggled for composure as Samuel came down the hall toward my office. I busied myself, shuffling the papers piled in my in-box from one level to the other. In that moment scanning the black on white was like reading hieroglyphics rather than my native language. I absorbed absolutely nothing, yet my eyes remained glued to the paper like flies on raw meat. My hands groped the surface of my worn green blotter for a pen, so I would appear to *actually* be doing something when he came in.

"Good morning, how are we today?" I did not look up to acknowledge his presence.

"Grinding it out." I tried to sound tough and business like, "Seems like my in-box doubled in size overnight."

"I know that one. I'll be facing much the same when I go upstairs." A moment of silence rang out that I wanted to fill with words of truth, but I braced myself, leaning away from it into the back of my chair. Samuel sensed my sudden coolness and tried to warm me up.

"Need some Java to get you going?" *Did he have to be so accommodating, thoughtful, and gallant?* I continued my pointless paper pushing.

"No thanks, I've had my quota for this morning." He seemed put off and confused but continued on his way. I was unable to concentrate for the rest of the morning. I wished the CD player was working so Sting's compelling melodies would help drown out the voices in my head. I had several articles to proof for the magazine but couldn't focus my editorial eye. The emotional discord was unnerving. I was being visited by the demons of jealousy but not in relation to my husband. *I have to fix it, to make it right.* That conclusion set me in motion and before I had a chance to allow fear to rob me of my courage, I headed up the stairs. When I got to Samuel's office he was on the phone, which gave me an excuse to turn back. But he quickly motioned me to sit down, indicating he would only be a moment. I watched the silver band roll down his wrist and clink sharply as it met the desktop. I listened to the sound of his strong yet gentle voice, which was incredibly inviting over the phone. My eyes scanned the room, pausing at the bulletin board to see if there were any new additions. I remembered when I first saw the photograph of him lifting the baby. I should have caught myself back then when I felt that shred of disappointment, thinking he was married with family. *But no.*

"So, what can I do for you lady?" Samuel swirled around in his chair and looked me in the eye, as always. I took a deep breath and summoned my now waning courage.

"Samuel, we have to talk soon, real soon."

"I'm all ears."

"No, I don't mean here, now. Could we maybe take a walk at lunch to the boatyard?"

"Absolutely! But you sure have aroused my curiosity," he said with a smile spreading across his finely shaped lips, leaning back in his chair with both arms behind his head.

"Okay, thanks, I'll see you down there at twelve-fifteen."

"You got it!" I left without looking back. *What is this pounding of my damn heart, this racing of my mind?* It would be three hours before I could settle down. I comforted myself by imagining that telling Samuel would make it all go away. We will walk among the old stink pots and sailboats, and this angst will fade into laughter and roll out to sea on the wave's foamy edges.

At about noon I could no longer contain myself, nor had I been able to focus since I had spoken with Samuel. I took a quick detour to the bathroom to make sure I didn't look like I felt, a total wreck. After running my hands through my thick and unruly hair, sliding some mauve colored gloss across my lips, I headed out the back door so no one would ask me what I was doing for lunch. I was a woman with a vital mission that needed to be accomplished in the next hour so I could get my life back on track.

The boatyard seemed peaceful with its moorings tethering the boats to shore. I temporarily got lost in their swaying motion and bobbing rhythm. At this time of year boats were pulled into the old green boathouse one by one for annual maintenance, where men with callused, strong hands worked carefully and skillfully on them. I could hear Anita Baker on the radio belting out "Caught up in the Rapture of Your Love" in between the belt sanders and jig saws. I found a bench facing the ocean and tried to center myself though her romantic lyrics wanted to take me elsewhere.

Moments later I heard footsteps on the wooden pier heading toward me. I dared not turn and face whoever was approaching, knowing my complexion was flushed with anticipation and would surely give me away.

"Nice spot, eh?" Samuel came up behind me and put his hand on the back of the bench as he looked out at the water.

"Yes, it's quite a place we live in." Pulling a grape and orange Tootsie Roll Pop from his front pocket, Samuel sat down and offered me one. Once again, I was struck by his attention to detail. Back when we started working on the Saint Celia project, I would satisfy my sweet tooth late in the afternoon with one. I promptly selected the orange and allowed the unwrapping to fill what seemed like an uncomfortable silence.

"So, what's on your mind my friend? You've really got me wondering if I've done something wrong here."

This was it. Nowhere to run or hide now, just the truth, plain and simple. But it felt anything but simple as I readied myself. I faced the vast ocean before me, hoping there was enough space to allow the intense emotions and words to float away, never to be heard or felt again.

"Well Samuel, actually it's about that very word, *friend*." He was obviously puzzled by my remark and leaned forward to try and make eye contact. I faced the water and continued. I could not, would not, be deterred.

"This morning when you came into the office and you were talking to Claire about…" Before I finished my sentence, he reached for the beeper vibrating in his back pocket.

"I'm sorry Olivia, hold that thought while I see what this is about."

This must be a sign. I am not supposed to tell him here, now. There is a better time and place. But when, where? I need to say this and get on with it. I was vaguely aware of his conversation, until I heard him say he'd be there right away. Then I knew this would not unfold as planned.

"Olivia I am so sorry. There is a problem with the smoke alarm at one of the properties and no one can get it reset. I've got to get up there right away. When can we continue this conversation?" *Finish is more like it.* I just wanted to get it over with.

"How about as soon as you get back. Just come down to my office. People are so used to us meeting about the article they won't even notice."

"Sounds good. See you when I finish up. And again, I'm sorry about the timing."

"No problem." That was such a lie; I was so self-absorbed that I was indignant about having to wait.

Samuel never did return to the office that day. I put on my slouch sox and Nikes for the trek home feeling unsettled, fragmented and distracted. I needed to sort it all out on the walk so that I was centered when I got home to my babies. They were always so needy and hungry when I arrived. I would summon up my adult self and carry on. Passing some of the lilac bushes on Tecumseh Lane I took in the soft scent and let it waft through me. Such a clean, sweet smell, just how I wanted my life to be after my talk with Samuel. The unfinished conversation lingered in my mind along with the lilacs as I headed down the lane toward home. Tomorrow was not so very far away.

Dane was working late that night which was a blessing in many ways. I was not in a space to deal with him just yet. Dinner consisted of pasta stars with butter and cheese for Adam and Julia. I would have popcorn once they were tucked in. My appetite was subdued with all the anxiety and I loved the feeling of my clothes beginning to loosen up. The kids had been playing outside most of the day and the heat had exhausted them, so they went down rather quickly. That was another plus because my tolerance was low and my level of discomfort at a record high.

I tried calling Miranda but then remembered she was off island taking a woodworking class. She was always involved in some new creative pursuit. I crawled into bed hoping to be asleep when Dane returned so I just didn't have to face him tonight. When he finally crawled into bed after midnight, he moved into our customary spooning position and even though I was still awake, I pretended to be in a deep sleep.

The next morning, I was geared up and ready to take the plunge for the second time. Like someone about to do the polar bear dip, I was naked and willing as long as I didn't have to stand around shivering for too much longer. I wanted in and out, as quickly as possible. The minutes ticked by and no Samuel. He was never late, unless of course he had a meeting. I tried to casually query Claire about his schedule for the day.

"By any chance do you know if Samuel has a meeting this morning? I've got a last-minute question about an article I'm trying to finish up."

"Yes, he came in early and left with the woman who does the leaded glass window work. They had to do some measurements up at one of the properties." Panic stampeded through my gut like a herd of buffalo. I remembered Marianna Geiger, an attractive redhead with a great sense of humor, and outstanding at her trade. Samuel had commented on that after he hired her to do the work on the old firehouse. Now the two of them were off alone measuring windows. Knowing the thoughtful gentleman that he was, Samuel had probably arrived with two coffees and they were sipping and laughing right now. *He hasn't even given our meeting a second thought. I better get a grip. This man is a handsome, eligible bachelor. Why shouldn't he be engaged in pleasant conversation with a beautiful, talented woman that he's working with?*

Shortly before noon Samuel appeared in my doorway with a grin and two white bags from the deli.

"Will the veggie and cheese on pita get me back into the running?"

The ice queen appeared from out of nowhere.

"Are you sure there isn't someone else you might like to share that with?"

He looked perplexed but his confusion did not deter him.

"Come on Olivia, I want to finish what we started yesterday."

"Me too, let's go." Our walk to the boatyard did not have the same carefree element it had yesterday. The air was laden with curiosity, albeit a bit stale from the delay. It hovered around us like gnats after a warm rain. I felt a pinch of relief when I saw the empty bench facing the sea still vacant, like it too had been waiting for completion. Samuel dusted off the sea gull droppings and passed me a sandwich. I wasn't at all hungry, so I put mine down on the bench. I was more than ready, though I teetered on the edge of my vulnerability before I spoke. My mind quickly reviewed the implications of what I was about to do, and its magnitude swept through me like a heavy summer storm I unexpectedly got trapped in.

"Okay Samuel here goes. I am having feelings that are inappropriate for our friendship."

He was obviously completely caught off guard.

"What feelings? Where are you going with this?"

"Okay, when you were telling Claire about your date with Bonnie, I overheard the conversation."

He interrupted before I could finish. "That's not a problem. If I wanted it to be a secret, I wouldn't have told Claire." He winked to make light of it.

"No, what I'm saying is I, well, felt jealous Samuel." Clearly, he was stunned. Silence filled the salty air and circled around like the seagulls waiting for a handout. Finally, he spoke, looking out at the boats bumping up against the dock.

"Well, if it makes you feel any better, or worse, I thought about you while I was out with her. Didn't plan to, it just sort of happened through the course of the evening."

Wait, hold on here. Is he telling me that this is reciprocated? Flooded with a total contradiction of emotions, one excitement by this possibility, and the other dread and fear about how to handle a situation rapidly growing out of control with disastrous results on the horizon. I sat stunned staring down at the water. There was a layer of oil creating a rainbow effect. I lost myself in the colors, as a feeble attempt into composure. I was once again a schoolgirl with a mad crush on someone who just checked the yes box on a note passed to him in World History class. But all too soon the burden of adult responsibility shattered that scenario and the complexity of what was unraveling took my breath away.

"So now what?" I asked

Samuel spread his bulky arms out across the back of the bench barely brushing my shoulder, and heaved a long sigh, exhaling slowly. Before he had a chance to answer I jumped in.

"Aren't you taking a trip down south to see your family and look at land in the next week or so?"

"Yes, I'll be leaving a week from Thursday, why?"

"It will give us a breather and some perspective on all this. I'm sure we can put it back where it belongs."

He thought for a minute and took a piece of cinnamon gum from his pocket. He was such an oral person. He had smoked since he was fourteen and tried to give it up several times. He knew how strongly I felt about the habit, so he never lit up in my presence. His clothing always had the unmistakable scent of tobacco, but he tried to disguise his breath with gum and mints.

"Time and space, the old-fashioned cure all." He said and punctuated it with another heavy sigh.

"That's what I'm hoping for. We've finished the article, so we won't be meeting alone anymore. That should help." Just the thought of that made me cringe. Samuel rubbed his weathered hand slowly through his thinning hair and gazed out at a passing tugboat, as if it held the key to all this. He seemed slightly disappointed with the outcome of the conversation. But I knew he was an honorable soul. He once told me that though his marriage to Cat hadn't worked out, he desperately believed in their commitment and tried to save it. But she just didn't want to be tied down, so after months of counseling and a trial separation he finally let her go. But as we sat there something gnawed at my insides. A part of me did not want to let this moment go, like Blizzard with his rawhide. I tried to steer my thoughts back toward Bonnie Swain and being a matchmaker, seeing her long, silky hair, the way it sloped down her slender back and slid nicely over her lemon-sized breasts. And she was single, without baggage and complications. She would be perfect for Samuel and I should encourage him in her direction.

"Yes, that will definitely make things easier on us," I got up first, signaling that I was done for now. *Totally overwhelmed was more like it.*

"Thanks for coming Samuel. I feel relieved on some level."

"Thanks for asking and for being so honest, a rare thing. Everyone has their hidden agendas, but few bring them out into the light of day." We walked back down the dock in silence and when we got to the end, I headed to the drugstore for some Tylenol. My temples were throbbing, I needed to compose myself before going back to the office. I ran through it in my mind, fast forwarding the events of the last few months. It all happened so quickly, starting with a stranger waving from a blue truck who I had now revealed my innermost emotions to. When I got to Kronin's I forgot why I was there. Sadly, what I needed you couldn't purchase at the drugstore. I needed space from all this, and Samuel's trip down south next week would be a welcome reprieve and put all this in its proper place. *Then I can get back to where I belong.*

Chapter Thirteen

While preparing one of my simple western omelets that evening I heard Dane whistling "Penny Lane," as he came down the hall. After all he had been through about Samuel recently to still be whistling allowed some of my buried respect to resurface. It wasn't until just then that I realized how covered up it was by my disappointment and frustration with his masculine strength. It hadn't come to the forefront when our family needed it most.

My dad had no patience for people who didn't pull themselves up by the bootstraps when life dealt them a hard blow. He was a man of action and strength, expecting the same from those around him. His standards made me crazy during my adolescence and college years. No sympathy or tolerance for excuses of any kind, and here I was taking on a similar intolerant, demanding posture with Dane. He came up behind me and squeezed me around the waist, one of my favorite gestures of affection. I leaned into him.

"What's cooking sweet one?"

"One of my famous and elaborate western omelets. How's that for a gourmet's delight?"

"Sounds good to me. Where are Adam and Julia? It's too quiet around here."

"They both still have their colds, plus getting to bed later last night with the full moon, they fell asleep twenty minutes ago. I tried to keep them up long enough to see their daddy, but they were beat. Poor rascals."

Dane ran his hand across my buttocks, pausing at my left cheek, gently but firmly rubbing it back and forth.

"Feel like fooling around? It has been awhile."

Suddenly the expression "fool around" seemed like such an adolescent approach to lovemaking, yet Dane had used it since we met, and it hadn't bothered me until now.

"Let me get this omelet finished and I'll meet you in the shower." Dane brought his hand up under my blouse, outlining my nipple.

"Can't wait," he tweaked it gently until it was firm and erect, then headed for the bathroom. I checked Adam and Julia on my way to the bathroom. They were both in a deep medicated sleep, curled up in little bundles of soft flannel. I resonated with warmth and joy whenever I watched them sleep. I dropped my jeans to the floor and tried to brush the day aside with the shower curtain. I joined Dane who was wet, glistening and curved to perfection. The sight of him managed to excite me because it was a sign of physical strength and discipline. This was the part of him that drew me in initially and now I begged for it to carry me through this dangerous passage. But there were so many other things in the way, not to mention the pile of dirty clothes he left in his wake.

He pulled me under the water and moved my hands around his buttocks. It had been almost a month since we had been together, so he became rock hard within seconds. He started to press his lips to mine, but I redirected him to my neck. Kissing felt too intimate and I wasn't there. As he covered my neck with wet kisses his lips became Samuel's. Wanting to quickly dispel him, I pulled Dane inside me. Though I wasn't ready to receive him, the warm water made it moist enough for him to be inside without too much discomfort. I pressed his firm cheeks into me, trying to get the deepest penetration possible, as if pushing him inward would push Samuel out. I began to create my own lubrication from the stimulation of him moving in and out. Momentum built very quickly, and we climaxed within seconds of his entry. My head was flooded with images of Samuel. Horrified, I abruptly broke loose, and leaving Dane startled by my sudden disengagement.

"What's the matter?"

"Oh, I thought I heard Adam waking up. I better go check." I gave him a quick kiss on the cheek and hurried away. As I dried off, I tried to wipe away the sexual images of Samuel. I was flushed with shame and confusion, unable to discipline my mind. It was running away with me.

The next week at work I kept a very safe distance from Samuel, biding my time until he went south to see his family and I could get some relief from all this. It was deeply disturbing that even though we were having minimal contact, my mind kept returning to him, over and over. One sizzling hot evening in July I was out in the backyard rocking Adam on the hammock and Dane was inside getting chicken ready to barbecue. As I put my leg over the side, I swayed it back and forth until I got a nice rhythm going which cooled us both off. Adam was enjoying himself and I loved the sensation of his small, warm body against mine. Before too long my thoughts drifted to Samuel and one of the interludes we had while reviewing photographs for the Saint Celia article. Quickly they moved into a future scene where we were under a blanket somewhere with an ocean view.

"Hey, Olivia where the hell are you? Didn't you see Julia?"

Catapulted from my fantasy I saw Dane, as if in a movie, running at top speed, with chicken flying from the platter, toward our daughter. Her little hand was inches from the red glowing coals inside the hibachi. As he swooped her under his arm he shouted,

"No Julia, hot, no hot!"

I leapt from the hammock, with Adam who was crying from all the commotion, and ran to Julia. Other than being startled by her dad's speed and volume, she was fine.

"What were you doing out here Olivia? Why weren't you watching more closely?" He flashed an angry concerned glare my way. I cloaked the truth.

"I was just rocking with Adam and drifting off. I'm sorry." I reached out to hold Julia, but her head was smothered in Dane's chest. She was not receptive to my touch. *She knows, somehow, she feels it. Caught in the act of fantasizing and my child almost gets seriously injured. This is where it stops! I am too close to the fire and need to back away before we all burn.*

On the morning Samuel was leaving the wind was whistling crisply through the leaves, announcing the arrival of fall. I busied myself on as many projects and loose ends as I could find, surrounded myself with people, or stayed on the phone constantly. At one point he came in to drop a message on my desk that had to do with the Saint Celia project. I didn't even look up, though in my peripheral vision I saw his crimson linen shirt and off-white pants. I rarely saw him out of his work clothes, and he looked stunning. I quickly reprimanded myself for backsliding. *Keep it together girl!*

When he passed through my office on his way to the airport, I made sure I was well occupied, or at least appeared to be. Out of the corner of my eye I saw him trying to say goodbye. I made it as difficult as possible and when his ride came; my heart sped up as he got into the truck, never looking back.

The almost two weeks he was gone held me in a place of both comfort and distraction. I was comforted by not having to be hyper-vigilant about my thoughts and behavior in his presence, yet I was clearly distracted by his absence. I wondered how and where he was. Dane was picking up on my emotional vacillation. When I seemed present, he would try to enter into that window by rubbing, holding, whispering or even singing my favorite song. He took advantage of that space, though those moments were so rare with the children, our jobs, his art, and working on our old house. Perhaps it was the routine of this life that prompted me to wonder how it might be different with Samuel. While he was gone, I tried very hard to stay grounded in my own, but a part of me continued to stray. Even my love for Julia and Adam wasn't enough to keep me present.

My sexual desire for Dane continued to diminish and when he made advances that finally stimulated me, he became Samuel thrusting deeper and deeper inside me. This pattern became so unsettling that I avoided sexual interludes with Dane whenever I could come up with an excuse. He sensed my distance and rejection, yet he tried to make light of it. One evening after the children had finally gone down and we were lying in bed, he rolled over and stroked my hair.

"So, what is it, babe? Do I have doggy breath or what?"

I tried to respond in kind, keeping things light and playful.

"No, actually it's your body odor lad, you need a shower!" I even managed a giggle and a poke.

"Well if that's all it takes, I'll be right back after a quick trip to the bathroom!"

I grabbed his arm as he started to get up. I didn't want to mislead him into thinking a sexual interlude was imminent.

"How about we just cuddle for a while, I'm truly exhausted"

He sat on the edge of the bed and took an unusually deep breath.

"Is this the same as when someone says they have a headache Olivia or is there more to this? Is this about Samuel?" I grabbed his hand and pulled him down into bed next to me.

"No Dane, Samuel is away and besides, he's dating Bonnie Swain now. I played the matchmaker in that one. But working full-time and mothering two toddlers doesn't leave me with a lot of energy these days." Even before the words left my mouth, I felt something turn and twist inside me, it was dark and sinister. I was lying to Dane, my best friend. And there it was. *He's my best friend, more than anything else. He's someone I want to cuddle down with, but that chemistry is gone.* He left the room and slammed the door behind him. I saw the blue funk descending once more.

As I sorted through the office mail the following day, I spotted Samuel's handwriting on an envelope. It was unique and unmistakable, a combination of cursive and printing. The only other person I knew with that style of writing was my mother, who was usually in a hurry when she wrote. The tail end of Samuel's last name snaked across the page, hardly legible. It was addressed to the staff of the Algonquin Historical Society. *How impersonal!* I was taken aback.

Was I really expecting him to write to me? How outlandish have my expectations become here? I quickly tore open the envelope and inside was Van Gogh's *Haystacks* in the soft blue and lavender shades he put together so well. The note was brief, light and superficial, with his usual touch of humor thrown in. He was so good at coming up with a twist on words that usually resulted in laughter. I placed the card in the "common" pile for the rest of the staff, very disappointed about its generic form. *And he knows I open all the mail. There would have been a way to make it more special to me.*

The feeling carried over through the morning. He was gone but still interfering with my concentration and productivity. Later that day I overheard a conversation Claire was having with Chad. Samuel had apparently been calling Bonnie from the road. I really couldn't believe what I was hearing. He had made his month-long dating relationship with her seem so insignificant, and now he is calling her long distance. I felt utterly foolish and betrayed. How could I have believed his feelings were anything close to my own? I had been duped by his focused and attentive ways. *This is just his way in the world with people, especially women, and I thought it was about me. I took it all personally.* I had been lured into his seductive snare and almost allowed it to ruin my marriage. With this perspective, the feelings of shame and humiliation about my naiveté and risking so much, took over. I was determined to throw myself back into life with Dane, Julia and Adam. Being somewhat of an extremist, I would do it to excess.

I called Miranda and said Dane and I were really stressed with work and preparation for his show. She offered to take the children that Friday evening for a couple of hours to give us some time to ourselves. She loved being with Adam and Julia for short periods of time because she didn't have any children of her own. I felt guilty not telling her the truth about this dangerous equation, but I didn't feel safe sharing my feelings with anyone at that point.

To get myself in the mood for the evening, I removed my bra, put on a snug velour top with a short black suede skirt. Candles lit, beer for Dane, wine for me, I waited for him to arrive home from work. When he came whistling through the back door, I beckoned him into my hopefully enticing scene. He was completely caught off guard by my attire. As he removed his white jacket, he asked,

"Where are the children, and to what or whom do I owe the pleasure of this surprise?" I was amazed at his ability to transition so quickly.

"Our wonderful friend Miranda has them for the next two hours; now keep going with that jacket, and then the pants as well!" I raised my glass of wine and the candlelight cast a shadow of my toast across the wall. Without hesitation Dane began peeling off his clothes. I nodded as he unzipped his pants and let them fall to the floor. He sat down while I came over and began slipping off his shoes. He rubbed the top of my head and playfully inquired,

"Olivia, you are unpredictable. I haven't seen this alluring woman around the house in a long time." My response was quick and easy.

"Precisely! And it is about time she reappeared, she's long overdue!" After I pulled his pants all the way off, I handed him his can of beer. I was determined to have a sexual, romantic interlude with my husband with no intrusion. The wine and the silhouettes of our naked bodies against the wall kept me present for only a short while. It all looked so erotic and yet I was having difficulty opening to Dane, moistening, softening to allow him in. As a last resort I stimulated myself, and when I was close to climaxing, I put his fingers right where they needed to be. But images of Samuel crept in and the more I resisted, the less aroused I became. Finally,

I allowed myself to go with the image of Samuel inside me and it quickly carried me to the peak. When I opened my eyes and saw Dane tenderly gazing down at me, tears began to fill the corner of my eyes. *I am in deep trouble, very deep. I am no longer with him during what should be our most connected, sacred moment.* My body shuddered with fear and self-loathing. Dane pulled me closer, but he could not dispel the presence that had entered our sexual interlude once more.

Chapter Fourteen

When Samuel returned from his trip south, he brought everyone on staff a small jug of molasses. Another harsh reminder that I was just like everyone else, and yet I longed to be special, regardless of the impact it had on my world. A few weeks later he asked me if we could take a walk at lunch time. I fended him off using my heavy workload as an excuse not to take lunch that day.

"Too many deadlines coming up for the winter quarterly," I muttered.

"Oh, come on. It won't take long, and the fresh air will revive you." That's all it took. One moment of persuasion and I was reaching for the cashmere sweater on the back of my chair. There was a bit of wind out there. *Does he want to tell me something about the trip? Maybe he couldn't stop thinking of me? Don't be ridiculous, get a hold of yourself girl!*

When we ended up at the same bench, I tried not to appear overly anxious about what he was about to say. He sat alongside me, his thigh against mine.

"Olivia, I need your advice about something." This wasn't exactly what I had in mind as an opening line, but I encouraged him to continue.

"I'm listening, go ahead."

"Well, as you know, thanks to your expert matchmaking I've been seeing Bonnie for a few months now. Even though I'm not sure if it's anything serious for either of us we do have fun together. When I got back from my trip, she informed me she was heading to Costa Rica on an extended buying trip for Rosie's. I was thinking of joining her for a week so I could see where it goes. What do you think?" I didn't even wait to hear the question. His voice became distant as my mind faded away. I was so crushed that he was talking about another woman that I performed my disappearing act and just numbed out. *I'm not the center of his fantasies or his future!* Why had I led myself to this place again? That attentiveness, active listening, and eye contact had created a relationship that did not truly exist, except in my fantasies. *Why have I misinterpreted him so grossly?* I guess his trip south really did work, *at least for him.*

"Oh, that sounds like a plan. What have you got to lose, plus you get to travel to a wonderful place." My response sounded so hollow, but he apparently bought it.

When I got back to the office I was deflated and attempted to turn my thoughts toward the up and coming holidays, using them as a distraction now that I knew the reality of Samuel's feelings. He was leaning toward joining Bonnie in Costa Rica because he had he earned so much comp time this year. I would immerse myself in the rituals I had become so adept at. The magic I attempted to create as a child carried over into adulthood and I had quite an elaborate collection of decorations and recipes. I was determined to make up for the emotional turmoil of the last several months. I would give Dane, Adam and Julia the best Thanksgiving and Christmas ever.

While I was preparing for my family's surprises, Samuel was preparing for Bonnie's departure. He spent more and more time away from the office on extended coffee breaks and lunches. I tried not to notice his whereabouts, yet our conversations down by the boatyard haunted me whenever I replayed them. Hadn't he said he thought of me when he was out with Bonnie in the beginning? Yes, but obviously things have shifted since then. Perhaps Samuel had the good sense to back away knowing I was married with two children.

Chapter Fifteen

On the way home from work the next week I stopped at a roadside stand and picked up a pound of fresh pecans. It was already mid-November and I was determined to fill our home with the sweet smell of pecan pie for Thanksgiving. Our neighbors Frazier and Ken were coming over to share a meal with us and I wanted to prepare a veritable feast. I would make my grandmother's stuffing, requiring a dozen eggs, sausage and bread crumbs made from Italian bread. I desperately wanted to feel like a real family again, connected in every way, including emotionally.

Early Thanksgiving morning the kitchen was filled with the scent of spices and a fourteen-pound turkey bulging at the seams. I loved the feeling of being in my bathrobe, sipping coffee and preparing the counter for my pecan pie crusts. Outside was gray, cold and the trees were barren, their remaining leaves blown away last week. It was the kind of day that lent itself to fleece, Vivaldi and indoor activity. I had been up since four while my family slept peacefully. I adored my alone time and had to rise very early to get it these days. I gathered my supplies for the pecan pies, sifting the flour through my fingers and spreading it onto the wooden carving board to roll out the dough.

My grandmother's blue speckled mixing bowl awaited its ingredients as it had done so many pies before. I surveyed all the baking goodies before me and cradled my coffee mug. I felt warmed by the whole ambiance I was creating for the occasion. As I reached for the measuring cup, I felt a trace of optimism and grounding that hadn't been there for a long while. It was comforting, very comforting.

As the morning wore on, the children awoke, Dane showered, and the sweetness of my pies filled the hallway. While I changed Adam there was a knock on the front door. It seemed a bit unusual for mid-morning on Thanksgiving. We weren't expecting anyone until around two. I fastened Adam's diaper and called out,

"Just a minute," and then I heard a familiar male voice respond. I swooped Adam up into my arms and we headed toward the door. The moon shaped face peering through the palladium window accelerated my heartbeat immediately. As I opened the door Samuel casually greeted me, as if dropping in was a normal occurrence.

"Well good morning, what brings you into town this early on Thanksgiving?" Adam squirmed in my arms while I tried to compose myself.

"I saw Bonnie off on the early boat and I'm out delivering honey to soothe my aching heart. It's also kind of a holiday tradition ever since I started keeping bees three years ago."

I was unaware that Bonnie was leaving before the holidays. This news and Samuel's presence had thrown off the delicate balance I had so carefully created that morning.

"I put honey in my coffee so this will be a real treat. Thanks." I made a quick decision not to invite him across the threshold, since he had already invaded my emotional boundaries.

"Have a nice Thanksgiving. I can smell the goodies from here." He put his hands in his pockets and turned toward the steps. But I just couldn't let him get away that easily. Being abrupt to *any* visitor was not my style, especially when they came bearing gifts.

"So, what are your plans besides grieving the departure of your sweetheart?"

"Not Much. Hal and I are going to share a turkey loaf like two old bachelors. He smiled and gave that infamous wink. Hal was a retired steamboat captain and an old friend of Samuel's.

"Sounds great. Anything scrumptious to go with it, like a frozen pie?"

Adam was curled around my leg by this time, looking up at Samuel curiously. Samuel smiled down at him warmly and tousled his fluffy hair.

"Haven't even thought about dessert, though whatever you're baking in there sure is tempting!" I could hear Dane pushing the shower curtain aside and knew I needed to cut it short.

"My grandmother's pecan pie recipe. Well, I've got another diaper to change. Thanks for the honey and Happy Thanksgiving to you and Hal."

I lifted a reluctant Adam to have something to occupy my hands and appear motherly. As Samuel walked away, Adam opened and closed his chubby hand and said, "Bye, bye."

Just then Dane appeared in the hallway with just a towel wrapped around his waist.

"Happy Thanksgiving little family of mine. Hey, who just walked down the sidewalk, honey?" I kissed him on his wet cheek and headed into Adam's room. I sat him on the changing table, avoiding his question. Dane's curiosity followed me.

"Who was at the door, sweetie?" He playfully nudged up against me with his damp, bare chest that he was in the process of drying.

"Oh, it was Samuel. He stopped by with a jar of honey. He needed something to do after seeing Bonnie off on the boat. Apparently, it's a little Thanksgiving tradition, delivering honey to his friends." I didn't dare look up and continued to diaper Adam's chubby, restless body. Dane's demeanor shifted and he moved away from the changing table, his body stiffening. His voice took on a stern quality.

"And now you are considered a friend, is that it?"

I tightened inside as I lifted Adam and gently put him on the carpet. I wanted to move away from where this conversation was headed. I wanted Thanksgiving to be easy, to flow without tension, just a feeling of abundance. But Dane was unusually persistent as he followed me into the kitchen to check on the pecan pie.

"You didn't answer my question, Olivia. Is this so-called friendship getting out of hand again?" His holiday voice shifted to a level that triggered discomfort for me.

I could hear the shrill voices of my parents from many a Thanksgiving morning. The intense bitterness they each had toward one another's families' sparked conflict whenever one side or the other was coming.

"Charlene, I wanted fresh provolone for the antipasto, damn it! This is a week old."

"I had to shop when I had time. You're never satisfied when your parents are coming. Let them bring it next time!" Back and forth they argued about the food, how much was spent, how long it should be cooked. Their loud caustic exchanges sent us all running for shelter when we should have been gathered together. Instead we turned up our record players, played solitaire or pretended we were pirates out at stormy seas seeking treasure far from the kitchen madness below.

I turned to Dane and put my arms around his neck.

"No, I've got this under control, honey. I really do. Now let's make this our best Thanksgiving ever! Check out these pecan pies, will you?"

One of the things that always struck me about Dane was his extraordinary ability to let go, while I hung on to things long after they lost their original sting. Perhaps the childlike quality he possessed was both a blessing and a curse for a man his age. He returned my embrace and peered into the oven.

"Marvelous, simply marvelous my love! How about a warm piece with coffee for breakfast?"

"Sounds wonderfully decadent!" I encouraged his refreshing playfulness and allowed myself to be drawn into his spontaneity. I tested the bubbling surface of the pies and they were definitely ready to come out. While they were cooling, I opened the honey jar and slid my finger into the thick, golden substance. I held it up toward Dane's mouth so he could lick it off.

"Try this for starters." He licked my finger and then sucked on it before letting go.

The day went along rather smoothly from there. The turkey was done to golden brown perfection. My grandmother Nona's sausage stuffing was just the right consistency of moist yet firm, and it would have made her so proud she would have squeezed both my cheeks with delight

After the meal was consumed Frazier and Ken stayed to help clean up while Dane occupied the children. I sent them off with leftovers and turned to find Adam and his daddy asleep in the arm chair. With my concerns about maintaining a somewhat "girlish figure" I felt the need for some exercise after that highly caloric, rich meal. Julia did not seem the slightest bit tired, so I bundled her up and put her in the stroller. As I filled her cup with apple juice for the ride, I went over and cut two very generous slices of the pecan pie. Carefully wrapping them in layers of saran and tin foil, I placed them in the pack that hung on the back of the stroller. I scribbled off a note to Dane, letting him know we were off for a dose of fresh air and exercise. He wouldn't be at all surprised knowing my constant concerns about weight.

We headed out the door and across the yard. Julia was delighted to be outside and clapped her hands as I strapped her into her seat. It felt good to be out working off the thin slice of pecan pie I allowed myself to indulge in. We traveled down the path, looking at birds and whatever else fascinated Julia along the way. When we came to Bartholomew, I turned right and started down the winding, graveled road. It was then that I allowed myself to admit what this trip was *really* about, besides the great outdoors and my body. In the distance I saw the Ford and Hal's old jeep parked in the driveway and headed toward them like someone being pulled along in a trance. Smoke softly billowed from his chimney and the curtains were pulled aside to allow the subtle November light to enter his space. Speaking gently to Julia as we approached the stone path leading to the cottage, I told her,

"Mommy's friend Samuel lives here. We're going to give him some pie." Julia reached up to be lifted out of the stroller.

"Mama up," she reached toward me with a sweet grin on her face, dimples beaming at either end. Before I got to the door, Samuel opened it and stepped out with an even broader grin than Julia's.

"Well, hello you two! Come on in." I could feel the hot, pink flush climbing up my neck and spreading across my cheeks. I was genuinely touched by the warmth of his welcome.

"I just couldn't bear the thought of you and Hal going without a homemade dessert on Thanksgiving, so I brought the bachelors the last two pieces of pecan pie." Samuel's smile spread further as he leaned down to greet Julia at her level. I noted this sensitivity on his part. *For someone who lives alone and doesn't have children, that is rather astute of him.* In that millisecond he became even more appealing.

"Do you lovely ladies have time to stay awhile?" While I hesitated, Julia had already crossed over the threshold to explore.

"Just for a few minutes. I've got to get her back for a nap." Once inside the door I tried to capture every detail of his living quarters in one quick scan. For a single guy it was incredibly clean, the colors were warm and inviting, and the artwork was tastefully displayed. There were wood carvings on shelves, old black and white photographs of the island, and a stuffed bumble bee on the desk. His home seemed well thought out and inviting. *Just like him.* I knew I needed to get out of there before any more of his essence permeated my rather thin psychic boundaries. Standing in his living room I was aware they were melting away like the butter in my pecan pie recipe. He was getting in, getting past them and I felt powerless to stop it. A giggle from Julia pulled me back.

"Is it okay if I give her a bread stick? I got them at the bakery and there's nothing unhealthy in them." I couldn't believe he was even conscious about something like children's health.

"Sure, that would be great. It will give her something to munch during the ride home." He lifted her up and took the top off the tall glass jar. He let her choose the one she wanted. She didn't grab immediately because she was more intrigued by Samuel making funny faces than the bread sticks. Then she picked two, one for each little hand. As Samuel handed her to me, I felt an intense, warm rush as his body brushed against mine.

"I'm really glad you came over. We're going to enjoy that pecan pie with turkey loaf if I can ever drag Hal away from watching football." I realized I had completely forgotten Hal was even there. I could see his pipe smoke rising toward the ceiling in what must have been Samuel's bedroom. To be socially appropriate I called out, "Happy Thanksgiving, Hal!"

He barely muttered back the same as he was completely absorbed in the game. Samuel walked us to the door and down the path. "Glad I got to meet Julia. She's a real cutie."

"Thanks."

"Takes after her mom." I was taken aback by the compliment. *Doesn't he realize that could be construed as flirtatious?* It was all I could do to properly belt Julia in and point the stroller in the proper direction toward home. I ignored the comment as Samuel stood at the door and waved.

"See you at work. Bye, bye Julia." Julia was too busy munching on her bread stick to wave. I picked up the pace once I got onto the sidewalk and intentionally did not look back. Arriving home, I secretly hoped that Dane and Adam would be just as I left them, sound asleep, our absence unnoticed. We had been gone a little over an hour and a half. As we came in the back door quietly, I heard Adam running down the hallway calling, "Mama, mama!" I met him halfway and swooped him up into my arms.

"Hello little pumpkin, did you have a good nappy?" Adam snuggled into my neck. His rosy face still marked with the design of his blue comforter meant he hadn't been up long. Just then Dane came around the corner and Julia handed him a half-eaten bread stick.

"Hey sweetness, where did you get this?" He looked over in my direction with a curious glance.

"The bakery isn't open today is it, honey?" I swallowed and responded with what I knew had the potential to shift our peaceful Thanksgiving Day, *to rock our little world that I so diligently put together.*

"When Samuel came by with the honey, he mentioned he and Hal were having turkey loaf with no dessert. I thought they needed some pecan pie to go with it." Dane bristled.

"You've been over at Samuel's? I'm really beginning to wonder if you've got this so called 'friendship' under control after all!" I didn't want raised voices around the children. Those loud, blaring Thanksgivings of my childhood still remained such a nasty blur. I quickly tried to smooth things over, dismissing Dane's accusations.

"Honey, it's Thanksgiving. We have so much to be grateful for. Let's not spoil it by arguing about pecan pie. It was just a gesture, nothing more." Even as I said the words, I again felt the deception forming in my gut like a dark mass of tangled threads, pulling tighter and tighter. Dane was not convinced this time. He sensed danger and he lunged back at me.

"Sorry Olivia, but I don't buy that. Months ago, you told me you were attracted to Samuel, and that you would get it under control, that you would not allow it to jeopardize this family unit. You obviously didn't succeed if you have to sneak off while I'm napping on Thanksgiving Day!" I crumbled as I saw the bewildered faces of my innocent children as they witnessed this scene. I was repeating the sins of my parents. Trying to soften the moment I turned to Dane, held out my arms, hoping he would enter. He stood motionless, though his body pulsated with raw emotion.

"Okay, so I might have crossed over some boundaries there. It probably was inappropriate. I promise I won't let this happen again. You know how spontaneous I am, and boundary issues are ongoing for me". My voice trailed off at the end there. Dane didn't even wait for me to finish. He grabbed his jacket and left, slamming the door behind him.

Chapter Sixteen

After the Thanksgiving episode a quiet tension lingered over our household. We stopped talking about it, but a huge, clumsy elephant was sitting prominently in our living room. The silence and omission were a dangerous, uncomfortable place to enter into. Throughout our entire marriage we had always talked, about everything. In some ways it felt like the loss of a best friend to me. Oh, we carried on 'as if' but inside so much had shifted. But it wasn't the loss of my husband and best friend that consumed me as it should have, rather the compelling nature of Samuel stalking me at every turn. It took hold of me and like Ariadne, I followed the thread deeper into the cave.

When Christmas rolled around there was a flurry of activity both on the home and work front. Dane's whole family was coming from all parts of the globe for their annual gathering. The Historical Society was hosting a twilight walking tour, culminating at one of the island's oldest homes, the "Shyler House." Champagne and desserts would be served to honor benefactors for their contributions over the past year. Between preparing for the arrival of Dane's massive family along with the public relations surrounding the event, I was in high gear. Dane maintained his usual leisurely pace, not allowing himself to get flustered. From the moment my eyes opened each morning my mind raced forward into the day ahead, and there was something about this driven state that I loved. I was surging with energy, a mission, a deadline. It was a satisfying high, like a jockey moving toward the finish line at high speed.

The night of the gala affair I was dressing while Julia and Adam went through my jewelry box, exploring necklaces, beads and baubles. They had earrings and bracelets attached and hung from all sorts of places. I stopped and really took in their creative display, which was unusual for me this last month. They were so precious. I lingered in that place and wondered what would happen to all this if I continued down the path I was traveling with Samuel. Quickly I stashed the thought away and slid into my red silk dress. Glancing in the full-length mirror on the door I nodded with approval. *Not bad for a mother of twins who is almost forty!* I brought the children into Dane's studio to let him know I was leaving. He looked up from his sculpture.

"On your way lady? Pretty risky in that red. Quite a statement!" I immediately went over and put my arms around his waist, kissing his neck gently. I did not want to get into it, not now. I was already running late.

"Not to worry handsome. I'll be home by ten. Will you wait up?" He turned to pick Adam up who was just about to squeeze a tube of brown acrylic paint into his mouth. Dane was doing more painting now and he was working on an autumn landscape.

"I'll do my best. Have a good time brown nosing the mucky mucks. And by the by, try to behave yourself." I squeezed the children, ignoring his comment, knowing somewhere I was walking the fine line tonight. I put my black pashmina over my shoulders and headed out the door. I was in the mood to party.

When I pulled into the back of the Shyler House all brightly lit, she glowed like a yellow diamond in the middle of the cluster of pine trees surrounding her. Other staff vehicles were already in the driveway, Samuel's truck among them. I entered the kitchen through the back door and caught his eye almost immediately. He was in conversation with Claire. We exchanged smiles and I went down the hall to get rid of my shawl. I stopped to speak with Chad who was all aflutter with last minutes details. He was fanning out extra cocktail napkins and putting last minute touches on the floral centerpiece. It was a combination of red and white poinsettias, carnations and boughs of evergreen. I noticed candles that needed lighting around the food trays. The presentation was so artistic they deserved further illumination. As I searched through the antique sideboard for matches, I sensed someone behind me.

"Ah, the red dress finally makes an appearance." Without missing a beat, I pulled out the matches and lit the candles and returned his words with a mere smile. I hadn't felt this gorgeous and downright sexy in a long while.

"Yes, and we know red is definitely about making a statement!" He obviously wasn't going to let that comment slide by. He picked up a lit candle and joined me around the table to complete the job.

"And what might that statement be this evening?" I felt the full body flush I had experienced in his presence before. I knew what the statement was and how I felt from the moment I chose the dress weeks ago. It shimmered with sensuality and a touch of coyness with the above knee length.

"Oh, a festive mood with a bit of intensity for good measure!"

I kept moving through the room searching for something else to do now that all the candles were lit. The room was glowing and so was I. Part of me tried to pull the reins in, but I stepped aside and allowed the other part to take the lead, seductively pulling me along.

"What's the intensity about?" He pushed further into my psyche.

"Oh, I think you have an idea." I was being playful and evasive, and it felt great. Our eyes captured the light of the candelabras and met. Neither of us pulled away this time.

"Is everything set in here, Olivia?" Chad's voice broke the silence, but not the spell. I was both relieved and disappointed in the same breath. So many things had layers of meaning now. He took Samuel by the elbow and led him out of the room saying he wanted him to check one of the electrical panels. Some lights were flickering, and he was concerned about blowing a fuse. As Samuel walked away, he looked over his shoulder and winked. This time I winked back without hesitation. Something was surfacing inside me, and I was allowing it to have its way.

The evening was filled with conversation, carols, spiked eggnog and mulled cider. I mingled with the appropriate number of Board members and their spouses, yet somehow wherever I was and whoever I was with, I was aware of Samuel's presence, near or far. Whenever we made eye contact, we held it for a moment. I wondered if the energy between us was as obvious to our guests as it felt to me.

When the last guests were ushered to the door and given their basket of holiday chocolates with a silver ornament of St. Celia's church, I began picking up leftover napkins and nearly empty food trays. As I walked down the hallway with both hands full, Samuel came up and put his arm around my waist.

"Need a hand?"

"I thought you'd never ask." I leaned into him and handed over one of the trays.

"Turned out to be a nice gathering, eh?" He said as he gently took the tray and dropped his hand. My body registered its departure.

"Yes, all that prep time was well worth it. I think they all felt very special and now we can all relax and enjoy the holidays."

"Speaking of holidays, before you leave could you walk out to the truck with me? I have something for you." He was holding the door open with one hand and balancing a tray with the other. I certainly wasn't expecting a gift exchange, along with all the other exchanges that had taken place throughout the evening.

"Okay, just let me get these glasses in the dishwasher and then I'll be all set."

Other staff members began to come into the kitchen with empty platters, congratulating one another. Everyone was pleased and relieved with the outcome. I wondered if the others were sensing what was in the air. I placed the last eggnog cup in the dishwasher, filled the bin with soap powder and closed it up. I could hear the others packing up leftovers in tin foil, wishing each other happy holidays and exchanging hugs. I waved and wished them all a Merry Christmas. Samuel helped Claire to her car with some boxes and I felt a twinge of jealousy as they chatted and laughed. *What is this? Who are these strange and unruly demons and where do they descend from?* When Samuel returned, I was getting my shawl from the brass hook in the hallway. He came up and gallantly assisted me, rubbing his hand down my back and shoulders. *Was it my imagination, or did it linger a bit longer than necessary?* My senses were so heightened at this point I couldn't tell.

"All set?"

"Yes, if you could just give me a hand with these boxes."

"At your service." Another wink and we were out the door, locking it behind us. I went to put the key in my pocket and one of the

boxes lost its place in the stack and toppled to the frosty ground below. We both bent down, and our eyes locked into place. It was like something out of a Rock Hudson and Doris Day film minus the corny music in the background. Neither of us made a move to break the stare. He took hold of my elbow and rubbed his thumb back and forth against it.

"Olivia, there's something in the air tonight and I can't shake it. Nor do I want to. He continued his hold on my arm. I was vibrating beneath my skin, like someone had flicked a switch that I did not want to turn off. After what seemed like a long time, we both got up and walked toward our vehicles. I opened the trunk of my Chevy Vega wagon and made space for the boxes, moving the children's blankets and toys aside. Samuel walked over with the last box, carefully fitting it in amidst the others and slammed the trunk closed.

"Would you like your gift now?"

"I wasn't expecting this and I'm a little embarrassed here. I didn't get you one."

"Not to worry." He put his hand on my back and led me over to the truck.

"Please get in. I'd love to see you open it." I was beginning to be aware of the time and my other life was pushing its way back in.

"All right, but we'll have to be quick. I need to get home." I slid into the front seat consciously trying not to get too close. He handed me a beautifully wrapped box with tiny silver bells hanging from the red ribbon. They jingled slightly as I shook it.

"Here, use my pocket knife to unwrap it if you like."

I was taken aback as I always ripped through paper with no method to my madness. I was so excited to get to the contents I gave little thought to how I got there. And here was Samuel presenting me with his careful, methodical and slow approach, focusing on the process. I accepted the offer and gently sliced through the tape on either end of the rectangular box. When I removed the wrapping and set it on the seat, it created an artificial boundary that neither of us could cross, yet we had already crossed so many without acknowledging them. I lifted the cover off and let out a mixture of a whimper and a sigh. Nestled underneath the pale green tissue paper lay a tiny crystal figurine. It was a woman. I lifted it gently and realized she was in the posture of a dancer in motion.

"How did you know? I didn't think we ever talked about my dancing career."

I was surprised and delighted by his perceptiveness.

"I overheard a conversation with you and one of the museum guides. Then I remembered reading about a performance you were involved in at the hospital awhile back."

I was more than flattered by his interest. He had taken a casual conversation that he wasn't directly involved in and made the connection about the significance of dance in my life.

I remembered back before marriage, and the twins, when I was working out two hours a day in my Lycra jumpsuits of deep purple, crimson or turquoise complete with black leg warmers. I would never forget my field work at the Bent Creek Nursing Home watching ninety-one-year-old Mr. Winston gracefully stretching his aged body upward while tears streamed down his cheeks. Movement had been a central part of my life before my beloved children arrived and bumped it out of center stage. As I cradled the figurine, I was struck by how much my body missed it. He had definitely struck a chord, and it was quivering.

"Once again I'm impressed by your level of sensitivity kind sir. It actually makes me a bit uncomfortable you know." He removed the box and placed it on the dashboard, eliminating my flimsy line of delineation. He got closer and filled it all in with his down vest rubbing against my shoulder. My heart raced with fear, yet I was so drawn to this man. I chose not to back away and he felt my silent consent. Before I knew it, he was removing his gloves and lifting my face into his hands. His tongue entered my mouth with strength and determination. I was swept away with a burning intensity, for how long I don't know. Then, like an exotic, large bird suddenly landing on the windshield in front of me, a flash of Julia and Adam's pudgy, soft innocent faces passed before me. The vision was strong enough to abruptly break Samuel's spell. With my hand on the door handle ready to leap from the truck I said,

"What are we doing? How did we get here?"

I slammed the door and ran toward the security of my car while he sat in the truck shocked by my abrupt exit. The only evidence that remained of the impassioned interlude was the crystal dancer glimmering ever so slightly on his dashboard.

I backed out of the Shyler House driveway moving at an un-characteristically rapid pace gravel flying everywhere. I usually drove at a slightly defensive, slow pace, especially after I had chil-dren. But now I wanted to get away fast and far, from all of it, as if the sheer speed could dispel the entire episode, erase it from time and space. I had only gone a few blocks when I turned down a side street and parked in a rather lopsided manner, my right front tire up over the curb. I shut off the engine and sat in the darkness, my heart pounding furiously as I replayed the evening, pausing at the places I wanted to savor, and fast forwarding through the rest.

When I pulled in the driveway it was close to midnight and the house was dark except for the glow of the Christmas tree lights. Dane had left them on knowing how much I loved seeing them at night. When I was a child I hated going to bed and leaving the

Christmas tree. On rare occasions my mother would allow me to fall asleep under the tree and my dad would carry me off to bed when he turned in for the night.

As I walked through the door, I was startled to find Dane sitting in the blue-checked easy chair sipping on some eggnog.

"Ah, she returns at last!" The eggnog was obviously spiked, and his words slurred together, coated with sarcasm. I was careful not to overreact based on the enormous guilt I was carrying inside.

"Hey sweetie, surprised to see you awake at this hour. How were the babies tonight?" I removed my gloves and shawl to avoid standing there and looking into his eyes that were clearly demanding an explanation of my late arrival.

"They were great. The bathroom looked like a swimming pool when they got through splashing, but after that things were dry and smooth. How did the party turn out? Did some of the high rollers keep you behind?" His voice seemed slightly more relaxed. He patted the arm of the chair, motioning me to come closer. I was relieved by the invitation.

"Olivia, come sit beside me. I have some interesting news." I slid onto the arm of the chair, leaning into his shoulder. I bit the end of my lip hoping it would keep me from revealing anything about tonight. *Could he see it? Feel it?* I tried to stay centered on what *he* was about to reveal.

"Stephan came over tonight after the kids were in bed and we had a really great conversation about some additional employment possibilities for your mixed-up husband."

Stephan was Adam's godfather, short, and stout with a great sense of humor. He was a true entrepreneur and had several small businesses that amounted to a decent income, allowing him to do what he enjoyed most, photography. He and Dane frequently talked

about the "struggling artist" syndrome over dark German beer and blue tortilla chips. I was curious about where this conversation had taken them, so I encouraged Dane to continue.

"Yes, go on, please!"

"Well, the school where Ellie studied yoga also has a Reflexology and Massage component, and they give scholarships with a preference toward students with special needs." Ellie was Stephan's nosy sometimes intrusive, but fun-loving wife, who home schooled her children. For the two of them to support a family of three children they had to be creative about it. Ellie had studied yoga which she taught a couple evenings a week to supplement their income.

"Anyway, I know we've both been frustrated by the lack of full-time employment opportunities at the hospital. Reflexology has some real possibilities for me. It's all hands and my hands are my gift, and it has nothing to do with vision, it's all touch."

My focus on the night's activities dramatically shifted to Dane's totally unexpected news. I urged him onward.

"Keep going, I want to hear more!"

"Well, they have a late winter intensive in February which is a month long."

"And you're considering going?"

"If I can get a scholarship, yes, I want to!" There was conviction and excitement behind his words that I hadn't heard for a long time.

"Stephan said there could still be scholarship money available for someone like me." I clicked right into my fixer mode. It was as natural as brushing my teeth or taking a morning shower.

"What do we do to set this in motion? What's the first step? Who do we have to contact?" I was so excited by Dane initiating this new direction that I fell into his lap and threw my arms around his neck. The Shyler House party and Samuel temporarily faded out as Dane gave one of his hearty laughs,

"Wow, slow down lady, one thing at a time! I have to call tomorrow, get the details, and have them send the paperwork." I had slipped into my role of superwoman with my red cape flying.

"Well you'll be at work tomorrow and I'm off. Let me do it!" I was as eager as a puppy awaiting her evening stroll.

"Okay, okay fine. Go ahead and call. I think I left the number on my dresser."

"Dane, with the holidays right around the corner they'll probably close soon. We need to get on it immediately!" Before I finished my sentence, my mind raced ahead into the future, about how I would manage alone with the children, my job and the household chores for a month. Then something unexpected injected itself into my mind. I imagined Samuel helping me out with all this. *How ridiculous! He's a happy go lucky bachelor. What's he going to do with two toddlers?*

"Olivia, are you with me or what? You seem like you just went to the mainland and back."

"Oh yes, I'm here honey. I'm just so thrilled by this idea that it's carrying me away!"

"Well stay here. I need you to hear more about the details. If it's not too late for me to apply and get the scholarship, the month-long program will allow me to receive a certificate. With the certificate I am eligible for state licensure." I interrupted, a common dynamic in our conversations. I was always running two steps ahead.

"You mean it might be too late?"

"Well the course starts in early February and I'm coming in on the back side, but we'll see." My head spun out with the notion of being on my own for a month and where that might lead. I was terrified and exhilarated by all the prospects. I settled myself down by pursuing my line of questioning, like a district attorney hot on the trail.

"If it all falls into place, what exactly does a certificate allow you to do?"

"I would be able to practice Reflexology in the state of Maine and then work towards national certification which takes longer but allows you to practice anywhere in the country."

"And how long is longer?" I wanted all the answers at once.

"I don't know exactly. But this will give me a chance to get my hands wet so to speak, to see if I would enjoy this kind of work before I put too much into it." I had already been snagged into a future fantasy. Dane had on terry drawstring pants, Birkenstocks and a soft, open velour top as he welcomed clients into his colorful, sun-filled space, with his artwork for sale on the walls. But the reality of his uncertainty yanked me back to reality.

"In other words, this is just a possibility that's out there, and it may or may not work for you," I said already wanting premature guarantees.

"Yes, that's right. I've got to try it before I make some sort of lifetime commitment. I'm not impulsive like you, Olivia. I need time and hands-on experience before I make decisions. You know that better than most." Yes, I knew only too well my style of moving fast, taking the plunge without testing the depth or temperature of the water. *Isn't that just what's happening right now with Samuel Ferrell?* Hasn't my heart taken a dive into this without any serious regard for what lurks beneath the surface? Perhaps Dane's time away would allow me to figure all this out. I hadn't really been on my own since we were married, and then after the twins it had been impossible to get away.

"Yes," I agreed, "I know I move with spontaneous speed, but doesn't the possibility of this intrigue you?" I was amazed at my ability to operate on two tracks, rapidly switching back and forth from Dane's future to fantasies about Samuel in his absence.

"Of course, I'd love to be more independent and do something that isn't going to strain my eyes." My heart always softened whenever Dane referred to his physical limitation. It was a place where I was needed. And that part of me that *needed to be needed* formed so very long ago.

One spring our family was invited to an Easter gathering at the home of the Batsons, one of the most prominent families in the community. My mother insisted we all wear our matching outfits for the occasion. Not just any bonnets, shoes and dresses would do. They had to be nothing short of spectacular. My mother had elegant taste and loved to show off her beautiful children in the right social circles. She marched us all down to Saks Fifth Avenue where we were outfitted in lavender silk dresses with a deep purple thistle pattern. My brother Paul had the equivalent in his blazer and lavender dress shirt. The morning my dad found the charge slip on her dresser he was infuriated. Charge accounts and credit cards were unacceptable, and he never allowed my mother to have them. Out of spite and convenience she secretly set up a few anyway. When the argument ensued, my sisters Tina, Joanne and Sienna retreated to their rooms and ate chocolate bunnies while Paul took his basketball and escaped to the hoop in the backyard. But I was drawn into the center of the fray thinking my mother *needed* me to rescue her. When I succeeded in quieting my father down, I felt pumped and powerful, something I hungered for. They were always so distracted. Dad traveled for weeks at a time, so he rarely made it to a field hockey or baseball game, while my mother raised four daughters too close in age, a son with epilepsy and an absentee flirtatious husband.

Chapter Seventeen

The next couple of days were filled with the final preparations for Christmas. I went through every room in the house making sure it had some holiday decorations in it. Even the bathroom had festive green and red striped slender ribbons dangling from the wrought iron shelf. I carefully placed the wooden elves that my Aunt Louisa had made all along the kitchen windowsill. Despite all that was going on I was able to maintain some sense of magic and anticipation about Christmas. I wanted to pass that on to my children as they grew up. Between decorating, wrapping, baking sugar cookies and gathering information about Dane's possible scholarship I was on circuit overload. Yet the level of activity was once again a high for me as I whirled like a dervish. In the few moments when I wasn't busy with the children, cooking, cleaning, and helping Dane do the paperwork for Muldarah's School of Healing Arts; my mind would slip off to Samuel and the crystal dancer. I wanted to reciprocate somehow but there wasn't enough time to get away to find something special for him, something with meaning.

When I held Samuel in my mind, it was a private world, far, far away from my life as a married woman with two toddlers. The

distance unnerved me, yet I traveled there often, and it took more and more to bring me back to my life, even during my most favorite time of year.

Right before Christmas the weather turned bitter cold and the winds circled around Algonquin, creating a vortex of bitter air that kept people home huddled around fires and wood stoves. The pine trees swayed wildly as they brushed against the roof of our house. One afternoon I made coffee to warm up, and while it was brewing, I looked out at the wildness that mother nature had created in our backyard. The sandbox had small branches from the trees scattered throughout miniature dunes that had been formed by the strength of the wind. I wondered if Samuel was sitting with coffee beside the picture window which spanned the length of his kitchen. *Could he be thinking of me?* I imagined his weathered hand wrapped around a cobalt blue mug he might have gotten at the Saturday flea market. Immersed in my daydream, I barely heard the children pitter patter across the wooden floor in their slipper sox. When I finally did it was not a moment too soon, Adam's tiny palm was less than inches away from the top of the wood stove. I darted across the kitchen shouting as I ran,

"No, No Adam!" Adam was so frightened by my loud voice and rapid movement that he fell backwards onto the floor, crumbling into a mass of tears. I scooped him into my arms as Julia looked on with a horror, sucking the ear of her pink bunny. *Instant Karma! Serves me right!* I sat down in the teak rocking chair and swayed back and forth, trying to comfort both of us while I stroked his wavy hair. I reached over to coax Julia closer. As I established a rhythm, they began to calm down while I silently berated myself. My fantasies about Samuel had encroached on my children's safety for the second time. And both episodes had to do with fire, a kind of heart fire.

This mild flirtation and physical attraction had taken twists and turns down a road I never thought I would travel, ever. With both children cradled in my arms I tried to diminish my self-loathing by pressing the warmth of their heads against my body.

"Hey Olivia, you back there?" Dane came down the hallway.

"Yes, we're in the living room." He entered what looked like a touching family scene with his wife gently rocking his offspring. Julia jumped into his arms still clutching her bunny.

"Adam, hot!" Dane held her close and kissed her forehead while glancing over at me for some confirmation.

"What's she talking about?"

"I was on the phone and they were in here playing. When I got off Adam was dangerously close."

"How could you forget about the stove? And who the hell were you on the phone with that distracted you from your children's safety?" As Dane became a bit more puffed up and more assertive than usual, I felt my defensiveness building.

"It was my sister Tina. She was in a state about something that had happened between her and mom. The usual holiday pathology that goes with my family getting together." *How could I do this so easily, without skipping a beat?* These lies were becoming an extremely disturbing behavior. I needed to pull in the reins and bring my life back to a place of truth and safety. Dane got down on the floor and held both children in his arms. He loved them so dearly and they were his life in so many ways. He had so much pride that he had fathered two healthy, beautiful children. I remembered the night they were born, and he passed out cigars to all his friends.

"Yup, the millionaire's package," he repeated over and over, bursting with pride, "That's what I've got."

So much had gone awry for Dane since his biking accident, keeping him from feeling that masculine version of strength and accomplishment. Coming from the Hanson high achieving clan where they all were extremely successful in their chosen profession made it so hard for him. But when Julia and Adam came along, he had something that allowed his manhood to be visible. His nest was full.

Yet even though his nest was full, and he was an especially attentive father, there was something missing. The missing piece seemed to be drive and determination so characteristic of other members of his family. It was the absence of this piece that slowly led me down this gradual, subtle path of resentment. It was like a snake curled in a dark corner and the day I was forced to leave my babies and go to work it unraveled and began to hiss. In the dark of night, it slithered between the covers in our queen size bed, strangling my passion and respect. He was supposed to be out hunting with the other tribesmen and bringing home the kill for his wife and children. His inability to call forth the warrior had left the door open, and the snake found its way in.

Chapter Eighteen

Christmas Eve day I got up early, and despite all the inner turmoil and frenzy I still sat with my coffee looking at the tree lights. I was briefly able to recapture some of my childish anticipation and excitement. Today I would have a hoard of Hansons over for bagels, donuts, muffins, hot chocolate and coffee. Because we had the smallest house in the family it was decided that breakfast would be our part in the rotating festivities. Holly and Peter's summer house on the island had the most elaborate, well-equipped kitchen complete with a stove in the center. It had been featured in *Better Homes and Gardens* last year. Holly would host the very fancy Christmas Eve dinner of prime rib, her famous scalloped potatoes and assorted greens, with kiwi tarts for dessert. Everyone always raved about her cooking and gravitated to their kitchen whenever there was a family event. I felt inadequate in comparison with our unfinished, simple home. As far as cooking went, it was more of a burden than a pleasure for me, while Holly considered it an art form or a hobby. Her decorative presentation of a meal almost made it too good to eat. However, the Hansons were a hungry, active bunch, and they devoured all kinds of food with gusto and humor. They filled their plates more than once, yet their lean, athletic bodies were no indication of their appetites. When they were satiated, they would run out play a game of touch football or bike ride, burning off all the calories they had just consumed.

As I began to select my favorite baskets and line them with linen napkins, I wondered how Samuel would spend his day. Here I was in the midst of all this activity with children and extended family wondering where he was and who he was with. I felt a strong curiosity pinch my mind until I pushed onward toward the bagels, cream cheese and butter. I placed the muffins on a Teflon pan to warm them and put assorted jams into small pastel ceramic bowls with tiny antique spoons that had belonged to my maternal grandmother. I filled my coiled basket with bagels, one of the finest baskets in my Native American collection. I proudly displayed them on top of the cabinets and shelves, filling others with treasures that might otherwise be lost. As I retrieved the warmed pastries from the oven, Julia's squeaky voice traveled down the hallway into the kitchen. She had awoken to another day and it was always a bittersweet transition for me to move from my briefly coveted solitude into my children's arms, noses and warm bodies. I loved them deeply and fully with all parts of me, but lately I required more and more solitude.

"Mama, mama, Julia up, up!" She impatiently called to me, waiting to be lifted from her crib. I rushed into her room so I might claim a few moments alone with her before Adam woke up. Finding one on one time with them was a daily challenge, and each demanded it in their own way. I reached into her crib and gently lifted her over the safety guard that contained her restless body at night. Her golden-brown strands of wavy hair nestled themselves into my neck as I pulled her close, inhaling the unmistakable morning scent of my daughter. It was clean and refreshing as it filled my nostrils. When she first woke up, she was cuddly and playful, allowing me to hold her on my lap. Those times were so brief because once she was fully awake, she would squirm down onto the floor and begin her day of constant motion and inquiry into every nook and cranny of life. We both coveted those times rocking by the window looking out on the day that unfolded before us. It happened less and less now that I was working full-time, and they awoke at similar times. To further complicate the equation, I had acquired a driving distraction that robbed me of my full presence with the children. I rocked on, willing the warmth of her body cradled into mine to keep me tied to this fleeting moment.

The day came on rapidly once Adam and Dane were up. The usual morning routine of eating, dressing and tidying up the house went into high gear as we prepared for our guests. Before I knew it, the baskets were empty with only crumbs left behind, along with half-filled coffee mugs and juice glasses scattered throughout the kitchen and living room. It amazed me to plan for so long and then have it all culminate in two short hours. I always had difficulty with the aftermath of such long anticipated events, especially Christmas. When it was time to take down the tree and put away the ornaments, I always felt an overwhelming sense of loss and emptiness.

This year while I placed the wooden elves back in their felt lined box, Dane struggled in his studio with the final editing of his essay for the scholarship to Muldarah. I had made some revisions and now he was making his own. He would need to feel comfortable with its contents for the phone interview in a few days.

New Year's Day 1991 the moon was blue. This highly prized phenomenon in the sky hadn't happened in six years. I sat in bed that morning musing over the expression "once in a blue moon" and wondered where it had come from. We spent a quiet New Year's with Stephan and Ellie playing dominoes and drinking sparkling cider. Ellie was a purist when it came to alcohol, so everyone refrained without much of a fuss. I was just as happy to have it that way because the few times she did indulge she became overly curious about my life, asking too many questions, prying further and further. I needed an evening of simple games and light conversation. I wasn't into complicated, strategic games where everyone suddenly turns serious, an edge evolves, and egos line up across the table. That's how it always got with the Hansons. Monopoly turned into a five-hour marathon with everyone hooting and hollering. I would usually excuse myself and go for a walk because I became anxious under the Hanson magnifying glass with its competitive edge. I knew it bothered Dane that I didn't join in, but he never confronted me about it.

After Ellie and Stephan left, we had one more New Year's toast about the possibilities that lay ahead, and then tumbled into bed with a brief cuddle. My head was whirling with the prospect of returning to work in two days. I fell into a restless sleep with fragments of strange dreams strewn across my pillow.

Chapter Nineteen

When I got back to work my "in box" was overflowing. Chad had obviously come in over the holidays, in his very compulsive manner, and left me several notes. There were loose ends and follow-up related to the Shyler House event. It was just what I needed to occupy myself knowing that within moments I would have to come to terms with Samuel all over again. The thought of his face in the doorway made everything shift inside. I could feel my armpits moisten and my stomach rumble. I lifted the pile of papers with Chad's small pink memos stuck to them and began prioritizing. There were bills for the accountant and thank you notes to be written to volunteers who had contributed to the evening's success. I was grateful for the myriad of menial tasks facing me that didn't take much concentration but would keep me busy. I turned on the computer and printer, watching the green lights signal their readiness. Then I heard Samuel's voice in the doorway talking to Claire. I quickly got into the word processing mode and focused on the screen.

"Hey, Happy New Year! I've missed you," he said as he came towards me holding the small box containing the crystal dancer.

Removing his brown, worn leather gloves, he placed her gently on the corner of my desk. Before I could respond to his opening remark he continued,

"You got out of the truck in such haste that you left this behind." The silence hung in my ears as I attempted to reply to both comments. I wanted to be extremely careful about how and what I said, knowing so much was hanging in this delicate balance. I teetered on the edge, like a rock climber determining my next foothold. Shuffling the stack of papers, they crinkled beneath the tiny movements of my fingers. I looked directly into his eyes as I spoke.

"Yes, I did leave in a hurry Samuel. The whole episode caught me way off guard."

"Well, I'm sorry if it was upsetting for you. I don't know what I was thinking except that I wanted to connect with you in the worst way." I knew the conversation could easily travel into an intimate place. We had gone there so quickly before and each time it happened sooner. *This is not the time. The walls have ears and so does our dear, curious colleague Claire!* I decided to take control this time and postpone this conversation.

"Samuel, this is not a good time to get into this." He knew I was right, so he acquiesced.

"Okay, but how about lunch over at the Shyler? There are still some things I need to do up there to secure the building for the rest of the winter."

"All right, I'll meet you up there about twelve-thirty. Remember I only have an hour and I'll have to stop and get something on the way." I had absolutely no appetite just thinking about the meeting, but I feigned normalcy as best I could.

"I'll stop at Kronin's and get two tomato soups with cornbread on my way. Is that okay with you?"

"Great, here's some money," I reached down under my desk to retrieve my woven bag where finding anything was like swimming in a black hole.

"My treat, see you there!" And he was gone before I was even upright.

Once again, I was struck by his thoughtfulness and take-charge attitude about things. I welcomed the feeling of being catered to. With Dane I usually initiated, organized and planned the big events as well as details of our life. Dane was usually open and agreeable, and hardly ever made a fuss about anything I suggested. Yet he was sensitive and caring in his own haphazard way. I leaned back and remembered our first anniversary. Dane hadn't given me a card or gift and that night in bed I was sulking as he undressed. He was hanging his shirt on the closet hook when he suddenly bent down and lifted something rectangular wrapped in wrinkled old newsprint.

"Happy Anniversary baby! Better late than never." It was close to midnight and he had disappeared for a couple of hours after we got home from our celebratory dinner. I wondered what he was up to and now beneath the newsprint I would have my answer. I quickly tore through the wrapping and into the box, gasping when I saw what was inside. It was a wooden sculpture of a tall woman with her arms wrapped around a large basket filled with fruit and flowers. The woman strongly resembled me, and the basket was gorgeous.

"Oh, Dane it's wonderful!" I snuggled up to him and cooed, "Is it me?"

"Well now who else would be holding a basket with such delight?" Dane knew how much I loved being the subject of his artwork.

"I still need to sand a few areas." It was a good long while before he actually got around to the finished product, but I loved it, nevertheless. It sat proudly in our living room receiving inquiries and compliments from everyone who entered our home.

His artistic nature was so unpredictable and timeless, while I was a creature of lists that delighted in checking tasks off as they were completed. When we came together that lazy, passionate summer on Algonquin we were like complimentary colors in a painting, a pale yellow against a deep shade of purple. Now with twins, mortgage payments and demanding jobs, we clashed like bright red and neon orange, rather than our initial soft blending.

When I arrived at the Shyler House I sat in my car under the cluster of pine scrub and wondered how I had ever gotten to this place. What would it take to turn it around so that everyone's lives were right side up again? *How do I put the pieces back together and arrange them in such a way that the puzzle appears complete and undisturbed by all that had transpired?* I didn't see Samuel's truck at first as I rounded the back of the house. Then I spotted it parked under the trees in the far corner of the yard, so it couldn't be seen from the street. I was relieved, feeling terribly self-conscious about this rendezvous. However, it could always be interpreted as a work-related task between two colleagues, innocent and legitimate. I opened the back door to the kitchen and there he was, seated at the small white table with a bag from Kronin's neatly placed in the center. He had two silver spoons sitting on top of red napkins leftover from the party. This attention to detail and ambiance once again struck a chord, *all this for me.*

"Welcome to the Shyler Café," he said with a casual grin as he stood up and pulled out a chair for me. He patted it gently with his hand, drawing me closer. I was aware of the uneasiness that was moving through my body, making me review how far it was to the nearest bathroom. In contrast Samuel seemed self-confident and relaxed. To set up a clandestine meeting with a married woman and be so comfortable, now that says something. *But what?* And yet my willingness had given him more than enough encouragement. I sat crossing my arms to stay warm. There was no heat on, and I was chilled. Keeping my coat on and arms wrapped felt like a kind of shield I could use to protect myself against what might happen.

"Soup was tomato with rice. Hope that's okay with you?"

"Just fine, actually I prefer it with rice, gives it some bulk." I loosened up a notch. He immediately broke his sourdough roll in half and started dunking. I wasn't remotely interested, as my appetite had vanished.

"Come on," he pointed to my bowl, "you haven't got much time."

"Actually, I'm not hungry at the moment."

"Well then, we better get into it." He looked up at me as he curled his tongue to wipe away the remaining soup from the edge of his lower lip.

"Yes, we better." Now I tightened a notch.

"I'm sorry about the night of the party and in another way I'm not at all. I'm very confused, Olivia. I'm incredibly drawn to you on so many levels that I'm having a hard time staying away. I've always considered myself an honorable man and you're a married woman. So, what are we doing here? Are you feeling any of this confusion? It feels like you are, but I need to know for sure. Maybe I'm reading into things." He paused, then said, "Talk to me."

I had so much to say, so much rumbling around inside that needed a place to anchor itself. I was unaccustomed to concealing any intense emotion. It was my nature to unzip and expose, like a child in a onesie sleeper getting ready to change. His inquiry let it rip. This thing had been evolving for months and I hadn't even shared it with Miranda. Our time together had been a bit difficult lately with me holding back so much, not to mention being removed from Dane. In the ten plus years we had been together I never held anything back from him until now. This was my chance to let all that had bubbled up overflow into Samuel's lap.

"Well Samuel to be perfectly honest, I knew something was up, for me at least, from the first day I came to work at the Historical Society. Even before that I had seen you in your blue truck. You used to wave at me as though we had met somewhere before. I never forgot your face after the first time I saw you. When you unlocked the door for me my first day of work, I realized you were that guy and I was startled, seeing you up close." Samuel seemed surprised and flattered hearing this unexpected piece of information. He had no idea our paths had ever crossed before our working relationship began.

"Go on," he encouraged me onward with his total focus. Relief swept over me like a cool mist on a hot, humid day. After all this bottled up energy, I was popping the cork and getting sprayed.

"So, for me, this connection, attraction, or whatever you want to call it, has been there for me since that initial encounter. At first, I was able to keep it at bay and remain within the boundaries of our collegial relationship. Then it crossed over into an easy friendship where I found myself playing the matchmaker, finding you a suitable partner." He nodded, never taking his eyes off me.

"Yes, and I appreciated those gestures. I was touched at the depth of your caring. But Bonnie never held my full attention for long. I found myself thinking about you while I was getting her popcorn at the movies, even on our excursions in Costa Rica. It was extremely uncomfortable."

"Yes, I know the feeling. For me the real turning point was the morning after your second date with her when you came in talking about the scent she left behind in your truck. I actually felt jealous and when I realized that, I was so ashamed." My body shuddered in its raw exposure. I closed my eyes and waited for his reaction. *This is it!* I wasn't ready for what I heard.

"Well, I knew I was in over my head when I started fantasizing that Dane left you to pursue a life of art, and that freed you up to be with me." I was stunned into silence by his declaration pointing toward us being together in the future. Neither of us spoke for what seemed like a long time and our soup grew cold in the bewildering interim. It was hard to say who was more uncomfortable and distressed at this point.

"Samuel, Dane has applied for a scholarship to a healing arts school in New Hampshire. He will know within two weeks whether he got it. If he did, he will be away for a month studying refelexology. When he told me about it, I looked at that time as a way to sort this whole thing out." He shifted uncomfortably in his seat.

"What does Dane know?"

"He's known for months that there was some sort of attraction between us. I shared that with him during the summer. We've never kept anything from each other, though we talk about it less and less now. It's just too threatening on so many levels for both of us." As the words came a wave of fear traveled through my body. It was like a tremor that I tried to disguise as a shiver. Samuel looked down at the wooden floor and shook his head.

"I'm sorry this has created such turmoil for both of you."

"Sorry enough to stop here and walk away from it?' I asked, afraid to hear his response. Maybe we could leave this thing behind like a stray dog or a bad accident, something you just want to put out of your mind.

"I'm afraid not Olivia, at least *I* can't turn my back on this. It's gone too far, and I want to see it through to wherever it is taking us." He spoke in a soft but determined tone, a man grounded in himself and the direction he wanted to head in. This was something I longed for from Dane in these last few years after the twins came along. I needed him to be strong, decisive about his path, and stand up for himself, for us. Instead he was forty and still meandering along, stopping to explore various possibilities that might be a fit, and allowing people to disrespect him in the process.

"Well if Dane does go to Muldarah we will have a long talk before he leaves. He has to know what he may be returning to." I said it out loud, but I still couldn't imagine hurting that gentle, loving man, the one I spooned with late at night, who played guitar at Sunday breakfast delighting our children, even before he had his coffee.

"Do you think that's a good way to send him off to start a new experience?" It was a sensitive caring question.

"No, of course not, but it's honest and I don't want to get any deeper into this deception with him. It will only make it that much harder." The table had been spread with a veritable banquet of emotions, too much for either of us to digest. I rose out of myself and hovered over the scene below at the kitchen table. Here I saw a supposedly contented married woman of almost ten years, close to forty, with two toddlers entertaining the thoughts of exploring a relationship with one of the most eligible bachelors on the island. *They will talk, god how they will talk.* I dropped back down and glanced at my watch.

"Oh Samuel, it's past one o'clock. I've got to get out of here!"

"I'll drive you Olivia," he reached for his soft leather jacket hanging innocently on the edge of the chair.

"No, I don't think it's a good idea for us to leave together." Panic was setting in.

"We're colleagues, aren't we? Couldn't we have been working on something over lunch?"

"Not today." I whipped my coat off the table and rushed toward the back door. When I was at the door, he called with a bit of desperation in his tone, "Olivia, what's next? When do we talk again?"

"I don't know, tomorrow somehow, I guess." My voice trailed off leaving him with the burden of uncertainty.

I returned to the office and closed my door, signaling to my colleagues I was not to be disturbed. Whenever I was working toward a deadline for the quarterly, I sequestered myself and the staff respected my need for solitude. The finished product was a stellar magazine, so they left me alone when my door was closed. But there was no deadline today and I was just perusing possibilities for the spring issue. My eyes lightly scanned pages of material that had been sent for my approval, but I was so tense I found it hard to recall a single sentence I had read. We had crossed a disturbing line at lunch that was hard to put behind me. I rummaged through my top side drawer looking for a Tootsie roll pop and a soothing tape to put on. *Enya* was among the selections, but I suspected her melancholy voice would only take me deeper into a place I needed to rise above. I finally settled on Grover Washington who was jazzy and light. There was no going back and reversing the day's events. We had both put it all out on the kitchen table and now it was like a bad case of emotional indigestion.

Chapter Twenty

Arriving home late that afternoon I found the day's mail stacked on the kitchen table. I sorted through it as I watched Adam and Julia playing in the sandbox Dane had built them last summer. A true labor of love that had brought hours of sheer joy and quiet relief for all of us. Many weekends when we had exhausted Legos, stories and blocks I would bring them to the sandbox with cups, spoons and empty containers of assorted sizes and shapes. They filled them, smoothed the top and spilled the sand onto my bare feet, giggling sweetly, with shovels waving in the air. Marietta now had Adam on her lap and Julia was scooping sand into one of the animal molds and making her favorite "sand cakes." I headed out to greet them when I noticed one of the thicker envelopes was from Muldarah. My impulse was to tear into it, but I knew better than to rob Dane of that moment. It was his acceptance and scholarship in there, hopefully, not mine. As I fought my impulse Julia assisted me.

"Sand cakes for mama, mama!" Her playful tone and small hand waving were more than I could resist so without hesitation I set the envelope down and headed into my daughter's arms. Bundled in her red woolen hooded jacket she looked like a little elf joyfully emerging from the forest. I lifted her into my arms burying my nose in her cheeks, smelling the sweet softness of her skin. I walked toward Adam who was busy unloading sand from his dump truck. It was a contented scene and I realized once again how lucky I was to have found Marietta.

After she left for the day we went inside, and I changed into leggings and a sweatshirt. They made me feel relaxed and nurtured, like a steaming bowl of cream of wheat. I built block towers with Adam and he promptly knocked them down with great gusto and shrieks of delight that bellowed down the hallway. No matter how many times we played this same game, it was as if it were the first for him. *What fine little teachers they are! The simple moments of pleasure they are present for.* I stayed engaged with my children for a while but then my mind began to sneak off. I wondered about the envelope from Muldarah, then about the lunch meeting with Samuel, and the possible ramifications of both.

"Hey everyone, daddy's home." The back door opened, and Dane stomped his feet on the mat, like he was releasing all the aches and pains of his rehab clients. He removed his white hospital jacket and hung it on the hooks lined up by the door. The children rushed toward him as he made his way down the hallway, Adam grabbing his leg and Julia reaching up to pull him down to her level. I watched the scenario unfold that had played itself over and over, but for the children it always seemed brand new.

"Hey sweetheart, any mail for me?" Dane came into the room with a child in each arm.

"Yes, it's here! Open it quick, quick!" I jumped up and brushed a kiss across his cheeks as I had done so many times before that it was automatic now. I relieved him of the little monkeys dangling around his neck in exchange for the manila envelope. Unlike me, he took his time and gently balanced it on the palm of his hand, feeling the weight.

"Not too heavy! When you got stuff back from colleges, light was a bad sign!" He winked and slowly opened the envelope. I put my chin on his shoulder as he pulled the letter out and held it close, scanning back and forth. I leaped ahead and screamed loudly when I came to the part about his acceptance and scholarship. He had been awarded a 'free ride' I grabbed him around the waist and squeezed firmly.

"You did it, babe! You're in, scholarship and all! You're on your way!"

He turned to face me with a grin containing some of what he was feeling. While I was bursting for both of us, he was quietly in-tegrating the news.

"*We* did it, honey. You were there editing and making it happen!"

I was willing to accept some of the credit, but I wanted him to assume the lion's share knowing this would get him off to a better start.

"All I did was some rearranging of a few words here and there. It was your story, your life. Dane, you should feel so proud." And I meant it. The children were watching, sensing the excitement in the room and getting swept up into it. They giggled and clapped their little hands while I pondered the implications of Dane's ab-sence. A month on my own to sort through these chaotic emotions and how they could become orderly again. It was frightening and exhilarating to contemplate time with Samuel, as well as myself, to wade through the murky waters of the heart. I had to get some clar-ity, like a cave diver, I needed to find a portal of entry. I was uneasy in my own skin, leading a life of deception with this kind man I had chosen some ten years ago as he stood before me in faded jeans, soft brown boots and pink oxford shirt.

After the children were bedded down that night, we shared a glass of Blush by candlelight. I wanted to mark the event for him with some kind of ritual, regardless of the outcome.

"Well sweetie, it's really happening isn't it? I've got a lot to get in order in the next three weeks." He gently tapped his crystal glass against mine.

"That makes two of us. I've got to see how much extra time Marietta can give me. Maybe she can stay in the guest room during the week to help me with the morning rush and bedtime routine."

Two nights before Dane was to leave, Marietta agreed to spend the first of many nights with the children while we went off to a bed and breakfast on the edge of town which faced the harbor. When we arrived at "Whispering Pines" I sat on the queen size canopied bed thinking about the month ahead. Dane quickly joined me and pulled me down on top of him. I wasn't ready for such a quick transition into the sexual realm, so I playfully kissed him and moved away.

"How about a shower to help me transition from mother to sex goddess?" Dane was always accommodating when it came to our sexual dynamic. He was ready whenever I made any overtures, willing to go at my pace, sometimes slow and methodical in my approach, kissing and caressing all parts of his body, other times lustful and naughty, furiously unzipping his jeans, thrusting my greedy hand down his pants and squeezing him boldly. As I pulled the shower curtain aside, he climbed into the tepid shower water behind me. He stared for a moment, looking up and down. My body was changing, and this was the first time he really noticed how much.

"Honey, what have you been doing, dieting? Lost your appetite because I'm leaving? You look like you've dropped more than a few pounds." He rubbed his hands along my wet, slick hips and pelvic bone, feeling the lack of flesh that once padded the area. Dane had always loved my body whatever shape it was in, even during my double pregnancy. Being raised in a culture where women were mostly blond, tight, lean and in control of their bodies and appetites, it continually amazed me how much he loved my curves and soft spots. I always felt out of place at the Hanson gatherings where my voluptuous stature stood out among the fair-haired, thin, chosen women of his family.

Since things with Samuel had escalated to such a precarious place my appetite had decreased tremendously only to be matched by a level of increased energy, that seemed constantly on the rise. The results produced a significant weight loss and I adored the bony protrusion at my hips.

"I guess I'm just excited for you and nervous about being on my own with the babies, you know, the whole transition thing." He pulled my slippery body into his and began stroking my pubic area with his fingers, then in and out.

"Don't worry babe, it will be fine. Marietta will be a big help and the month will fly by."

I felt myself swell around his fingers and wanted to go with the feeling. I wanted this last night alone with Dane to be a good one for him to carry into this new experience. I pushed against his touch and felt his hardness. Guiding him into me, I rocked my pelvis back and forth, while he thrusted in return. Lost in our rhythm we quickly reached the summit. It only took seconds before my mind abruptly raced back to Samuel and what lay ahead.

After a few beers over dinner that evening Dane raised the issue of Samuel.

"So, what is a month without me going to mean in terms of your so-called friendship with Mr. Samuel Ferrell?" I swallowed the wine in my mouth, anticipating this moment yet still feeling so unprepared.

"I think the time apart will give me some time to get clear and put all this in its place." Dane shifted in his chair and his demeanor followed along. He leaned over the small wooden table at the tavern and spoke in a low but firm tone.

"Olivia, you need to watch yourself carefully in this one. If you betray me on any level while I am gone, I will know it, I will feel it, and I will cry out in the night. I will howl like the alpha wolf whose territory has been invaded." His response literally took my breath away and I was taken aback by the depth and intensity of what Dane was feeling. All these months I thought I had deceived him with my omissions and casual responses about Samuel, but like an animal that senses danger through its instincts, he knew. Something powerful was out lurking in the darkness and he felt it.

When we returned home the following morning, Dane's last day was swallowed up by the children's needs, packing and last-minute preparations for the trip. Adam and Julia were feeling all the upheaval and were extremely whiny and clingy with both of us. After a late lunch Dane took them both to the sandbox while I cleaned the kitchen and packed some snacks for him to munch on the boat. While filling small zip-lock bags with cashews, raisins and miniature Snickers bars, I watched them play for the last time before his departure. He was such a big chunk of their universe; how would they be without him? While they were all preoccupied with sand castles I went to the phone. While keeping my eye on the sandbox scene, I dialed Samuel's number hardly skipping a beat.

"Hello," he said in a gentle, pleasant tone.

"Samuel, it's Olivia," I was whispering even though I was alone.

"We have to talk. I'm exploding inside," I blurted out words that came from deep inside that were painful to say aloud.

"Me too, but when?" He was right there with me.

"Dane leaves on the early boat and Marietta arrives when the children are napping after lunch. How about one?"

"That's great. Do you want me to pick you up somewhere?"

"No, I'll need the walk to clear my head."

"Okay, I look forward to it. And Olivia," he paused with earnest, "thanks for calling." I hung up thinking about his ability to punctuate a statement in such a polite, warm way. It made me feel welcome in his heart. As I allowed myself to feel the sensation, the back door flew open and in came Julia.

"Mama, come to sandbox," she demanded, as if sensing my preoccupation. She reached her chubby little hand upward and grabbed mine in her usual irresistible fashion. Out we went to join her daddy and brother in the sand. We played for another half an hour building forts, tunnels and then giving Adam the pleasure of flattening them all. To an outsider I'm sure I appeared to be there, yet my mind kept being pulled away by thoughts and fantasies about the next day. Dane would be safely on his way and I would be left alone to face the reality of Samuel.

When the kids were finally tucked in for the night Dane put the finishing touches on his packing while I watched from our bed. I sipped on a cup of warm milk with vanilla and nutmeg, a favorite comfort drink that helped me sleep when I was anxious or wound up. I was amazed at how calm my husband seemed as he prepared for such dramatic changes in his life. There had always been a quiet, solid center inside Dane that I often envied. It was so difficult for me not to engage with and get swept into the vortex of emotion when there was change on the horizon. It succeeded in stealing me away from the present and robbing me of slices of life.

"So how are you feeling about embarking on this adventure, sweetie?" I asked, to disguise the anxiety I felt for all of us.

"I'm going to miss the babies so much. When I kissed them tonight, I couldn't imagine not doing it again for a month. I wonder if there is a way you could come up with them for a weekend." The thought had never even occurred to me which was not a good sign. I sat with that for a moment.

"Olivia, did you hear what I said? What do you think?" I spread my hand across the plum-colored quilt that Dane's Aunt Jacqueline had made for us as a wedding gift. I traced the leaf pattern on it with my index finger. Our wedding day had been filled with such joy and excitement. When I was dancing at the dinner celebration, I overheard Aunt Jacqueline say to my new mother-in-law, "Isn't it grand that Dane has finally found someone who accepts him just as he is?" I saw Audrey Hanson nod, with what seemed like a mixture of pride and relief as she watched her son happily mingling with their guests. He was finally settled with someone, and though that someone might not be who *she* would have chosen, she probably admired my determination and optimism that day.

"Well, honey it would be quite a trek taking them on the boat, renting a car and driving over five hours alone with them."

"What about Marietta? Couldn't she come along?" He persisted.

"I don't know that her work schedule on the weekends will allow for that. I'll talk to her tomorrow when she comes over." The idea of making the trip did not appeal to me at all. I had my mind set on being alone as much as possible, or with Samuel, to get out of the emotional turmoil I was caught up in.

The month that stretched ahead held images of conversations over coffee, perhaps a walk on the beach and maybe even a visit with Samuel and the children. As soon as that scenario passed through my mind I flushed with shame. I secretly hoped and wondered if this month would give us our fill of one other, and upon Dane's return it will have passed over like a brief but memorable summer storm.

Chapter Twenty-one

Dane slipped away before sunrise to catch the early boat. While Stephan waited in the driveway, Dane hugged me tightly. He rubbed my back gently and whispered, "Take care of my babies, and behave yourself!" I squeezed his hands attempting to reassure him.

"Don't worry, we'll be fine. Have a safe journey and call me tonight." As I watched Stephan's yellow jeep pull away, I realized I hadn't told Dane I loved him before he left. This had always been a tradition ever since we had been together. We never parted without saying "I love you." Somewhere I knew I still loved him, and probably always would, yet it was somehow different now, very different.

I did not sleep after he was gone, tossing and turning until light gradually crept through the white sheers on our window. Finally, I got up, brewed some coffee, and curled up in the rocking chair. I sipped and rocked, anticipating my meeting with Samuel in just a matter of hours. When the children got up, I had to explain all over again where their daddy was, and why he wasn't there to greet them. For them it was a Sunday morning and Dane was always there when they woke up, ready to wrestle, make scrambled eggs and play "Raffi" on the guitar. His absence was strongly felt by them both.

After a couple of hours, I was exhausted by the lack of sleep and their demands, so I resorted to a Sesame Street video until Marietta arrived. When she finally got there, I told her I had to meet with a colleague about some work-related issues after the kids were down for their naps. I was distracted as I fed Julia and Adam their lunch of small triangles of whole wheat bread filled with peanut butter and strawberry jam. It was one of their favorites and I was anxious to please them knowing they were struggling without their daddy. When they finished and were off to sleep, I quickly changed into a pair of fitted jeans and a soft, olive cashmere sweater. I felt casual, yet sexy.

"I'm off to meet my co-worker Samuel. We're working on a project that has a very tight deadline. We need to review some things before tomorrow." I made no eye contact with her as I grabbed my knapsack and faded denim jacket.

"I'll be home before the kids wake up, less than two hours from now. Here's his number in case you need me for anything. Thanks so much for being here. It's a big help!" I handed her a torn paper bag with the number scrawled across it and headed out the back door. I saw her watching me cross the backyard at a fast clip while she glanced down at the paper in her hand, probably trying to decipher the numbers.

Walking toward Samuel's my head flooded with several possible scenarios and dialogues that might take place. Envisioning his broad shoulders and weathered hands coming up against my body was one. Words like separation and divorce skirted across my mind as I stayed focused on the bike path where I was walking, not wanting to make eye contact with anyone. On Algonquin it was ever so common for people to stop in the middle of the road and have a conversation regardless of how many cars they were holding up. I didn't want any questions, because I didn't have any answers yet. When I approached Samuel's cottage with its worn gray shingles, spunky red door and shudders, I saw him through the window. He waved and I felt suddenly younger, and lighter, as if floating down the staircase to meet my date for the junior prom, a combination of excitement and uncertainty. He welcomed me with that warm smile and the scent of fresh coffee, and it felt so good to be inside, away from the island's eyes. Removing my jacket, he proceeded to rub the middle of my back as if he had performed this action many times before.

"How about some decaf?"

"Perfect," I responded as if this identical scene had played itself out somewhere before. It all felt vaguely familiar. I watched him reach into the oak cabinets he had probably so finely crafted, lifting down two green mugs.

"How do you like it?"

"Believe it or not, with a fair amount of milk and a teaspoon of honey. But sugar is fine too."

"Ah, but honey is my specialty. Remember I raise bees." Oh yes, I flashed back on that sticky moment when he arrived Thanksgiving Day with a jar and Dane became suspicious and irritated. Samuel reached overhead and took down a glass jar filled with dark golden honey. Carefully removing the lid, he dipped a spiraled wooden implement inside and swirled it around. Each movement was so precise and thoughtful.

"Here, taste this. After a while you won't want to go back to store bought honey, I guarantee." I allowed the honey to spin and circle through my mouth and slide down my tongue. Indeed, the taste was far superior to anything I had purchased at the store. As I enjoyed its distinct flavor, I felt some dribbling down my chin.

Before I could reach up and remove it, Samuel was gently wiping it away. *What is with this man anyway, so attentive and kind, yet rugged and powerful.* I moved away to put a spindle of honey in my coffee and add some milk. While it was warming in the microwave, he sat down at the French country farm table and faced the large picture window. He patted the chair next to him. I willingly joined him as if moving into my proper place in the dream. Part of me could not believe I was here, and another felt so peaceful.

` "Okay lady, where do we begin?" He rubbed my arm from elbow to palm and back.

"Where did we leave off?" I replied with a slight smile born of both nervousness and comfort.

"I think it was somewhere back at what do we do now?" He slid my chair closer and put his hand under my chin, lifting me toward him. I looked away instead of into his eyes.

"Samuel, we are in deep, troubled waters, way over our heads." He tipped his chair back and then dropped it forward onto the hard pine floor. He let out a prolonged sigh.

"I know Olivia, but I don't want to stop now, even though I realize we're heading for the falls." I did not look over at him, there was no need to. I felt all that was necessary in his voice.

"Samuel, I'm so damn scared. I've crossed boundaries with you in ways that I never thought possible when I married Dane." He responded to the sound of fear in my voice by kneading my neck gently. His hands were strong, solid and the edges of his fingers toughened from years of woodworking. My shoulder dropped slightly as I let him enter, wanting him there, touching and comforting me even though he was the source of my discomfort.

"Olivia, I'm not a kid. I've been married once and had other long-term relationships with women. This feels entirely different than anything that I've had or felt before." My shoulders rose and tightened. Something twisted inside me with the mention of other women. I naively wanted our connection to wipe out the others entirely. *How absurd and ridiculous can I be?* I chided myself. *After all, he's almost forty, attractive, eligible and has a past.* How much of a past and how many women, I wasn't sure I wanted to know any of the details now, or ever for that matter.

"Samuel, I've been with Dane almost twelve years. This is the first time I've emotionally strayed from him, yet I feel compelled to go further to see where this is taking me, however scary it may be." He moved closer and pulled me toward him, trying again to lift my face to his.

"Not yet," I struggled, yet wanting to meet his lips, feel his warmth inside me like that night after the Christmas party. He honored my hesitation and took my hand instead, squeezing it, rubbing his thumb firmly into my palm.

"It will happen, you know, and it won't be long," He said with total assurance and a wink. It was this certainty that drew me to this man, and yet disturbed me in equal measure. Like a sudden noise jarring a sleeping puppy, it aroused some kind of nameless fear. It was almost as if my center became unbalanced at the recognition of his confidence.

"Yes, I'm sure it will but I want to be clear about what we are doing here before we connect on that level again. It's too distracting." He grinned and stroked my hair.

"It certainly is, and I want to be distracted again soon!" I made a mental note about Samuel's ability to be lighthearted in the midst of upheaval, a quality I longed to cultivate in myself. Everyone always described me as too intense.

"Come on," he grabbed my hand, "Let's drive out to the beach and walk, give this thing some time and space to move around."

"Sounds good," I said as I pushed my sweater sleeve up to check my watch.

"I need to be home in an hour before the babies wake up." As he opened the door to the truck, he nuzzled my head with his hand.

"I shall have you there, no problem."

We walked the beach in silence as the wind blew through my hair, a sensation I adored. It made me feel as though I could fly, and right about now higher altitude would do me some good. When we headed back to the truck he reached for my hand and held it very tightly.

"So, what's next?" He inquired, anticipating our separation. He stopped and looked directly into my eyes, penetrating all the way down into my soul.

"I think I need some clarity from someone who is not involved here." This response baffled him.

"I don't understand."

"I think I need to talk to a therapist to help me sort through some of this. I need to stand back and look at it with someone who has fresh, objective eyes." Samuel was obviously unaccustomed to needing input about emotional matters, so it seemed new and foreign to him.

"Oh, I see. I usually do that by standing in the center of my circle and looking out in all directions, examining each one." His stance was just as unfamiliar to me. But unlike his casual curiosity about my way, his incredible self-reliance created discomfort at my end. *He really doesn't need anybody, does he?* I always reached outside of myself, asking other people in similar situations about how they would proceed. We had two very different ways of operating in the world.

"I think I'll call Rosemary Shallot, a counselor, and set up something within the next day or so."

"Where does that leave me?" He pushed.

"Traveling around your circle, I guess." I looked at my watch and our time was up.

"I've got to get back; Adam and Julia never nap longer than two hours. I need to be there when they wake up, especially with Dane gone."

"Let me drive you."

"It's not a good idea for us to be seen together outside of work right now. Why don't you let me off on Kezar Road? Walking the rest of the way will help me transition from here to there." I was aware I needed some space to put my mothering hat back on. I was vibrating with an energy that had little to do with mothering. It would be tough to shake it off and put on my green-striped apron to prepare dinner. While Samuel placed his hand across my lap, no words were spoken until he pulled over on Kezar. I opened the door and with one long leg already out, I turned toward him.

"See you tomorrow. And talk to someone you trust." He nodded and smiled slightly, probably puzzled by my suggestion. I turned around only once to see if he was watching. Elated that he was, I gave a final wave and headed for home.

When I got within a few feet of the front door I could already feel Adam and Julia all over me, anticipating their neediness due to Dane's absence. I imagined how uncertain they must be feeling without him there. At the same time, I was attempting to shed the taut, nervous energy leftover from the encounter with Samuel. I was swept away by our conversation, the physical contact and walk by the ocean. A part of me just wanted to lie in the hammock out back and replay every word and touch. But the babies needed me so I would tuck the interlude with Samuel in the back pocket of my mind and call it forth when I was under my soft down comforter that night.

When I opened the back door, I was startled to hear the children's voices coming from the living room. *They woke up early and I wasn't there for them.* Pangs of guilt shot through me like darts. Here they were dealing with their daddy being gone and now I had stretched them to another level by not getting back on time. I hurried down the hallway and found them in the rocker with Marietta.

"Hello babies, mommy's home." I stretched my arms out and surrounded them.

"They just woke up about ten minutes ago," Marietta said rather casually.

"I'm sorry I wasn't here. Usually they sleep longer. But I guess with Dane gone they are a little off."

"Maybe so. They asked for you when they first woke up, then for him. Once we got to rocking, they settled down." I wasn't convinced that all was well. I was so disappointed in myself for not being more sensitive to them. I had such high expectations of myself as a mother and I was usually hypervigilant about anticipating my children's needs.

The remainder of the afternoon was spent sprawled on the living room floor with toys, stories and plastic bowls filled with cheese chunks and cheerios. I believed in light, healthy snacks throughout the day to maintain steady blood sugar levels. Coming from a family where hypoglycemia was prevalent, I was very conscious of those kinds of things.

When the children were finally asleep that evening, I snacked on popcorn and spring water in bed. Just as I allowed the day's events to spill into my mind the phone rang.

"Hello," I picked it up before the second ring so the children would not awaken from their new found sleep.

"Hey, it's me. I'm here among the New Age people." It was Dane's voice, so soft, gentle and reassuring in some ways.

"Hello babe. So, you made it. What's it like?" I tried to return that reassurance.

"Well, the setting is magnificent. It's an old Tudor style building nestled in the foothills, overlooking the lake. My room has a great view. The staff is very welcoming, and the food is delicious, for vegetarian fare. I may come back with a few extra pounds with all those carbs." I feigned more enthusiasm than I felt, though I was genuinely curious about what he was doing and his first impressions. It was just so overpowered by the afternoon with Samuel.

"Sounds wonderful and you could use some extra weight on that typically lean Hanson physique. Tell me about your classmates. Have you met any yet?"

"Only a few but they seem about my age, looking for alternatives to their current situations, like me. Tell me about the kids, I miss them like crazy." Another spear of guilt shot through my body and lodged itself in my gut. I quickly tried to regroup.

"They miss their daddy big time!"

"What about mommy, does she miss me too?"

"Well she's very busy, but when she comes up for air she does." Somehow framing it in the third person made it easier for me to be dishonest. I held my breath and hoped he wouldn't probe further. I hurried the conversation along to prevent the question of Samuel being put before me. "Concentrate on what you are learning up there and don't worry about us, okay?"

"Okay, I'll talk to you in a few days. Squeeze the babies for me."

"I will, bye." I hid in the darkness with the receiver on my shoulder, listening to the dull drone of the dial tone. There had been no "I love you", again. A deep sadness swelled inside, like a fresh bruise coming to the surface after a fall. I allowed the ache to penetrate my psyche just briefly, and then moved farther down under the comforter to finally recount the day's events.

Chapter Twenty-two

When the alarm sounded the next morning, I was truly confused about whether my time by the ocean with Samuel had been a dream. I hit the snooze button hoping I could get back there, but when I wasn't able to return, I finally pulled myself out from under the comforter.

My selection of clothing for work that day was clearly premeditated: red pumps, a cropped jacket, and a short black and white checked skirt. During the beginning of our friendship I overheard comments exchanged between Samuel and Chad regarding legs. We were all on Main Street one morning, waiting to photograph one of the buildings for the quarterly, while women in light, sexy warm weather clothing paraded by the shoot.

"Nothing like a tan, long lean pair of legs, eh?" Chad turned toward Samuel to see if he had caught the tall, brunette that had just flitted by in her short white pleated skirt, probably headed for an early tennis game.

"Absolutely. I'm a leg man from way back." They both laughed and promptly got back to work, taking those long legs in stride.

After I was all together, I dressed and fed Adam and Julia. They were all over me and I wondered just how much of my distraction they could sense. Did they know their delicate lives were shifting in ways they had no control over? Perhaps I was reading too much into it. My overactive imagination was getting the better of me, again. I held each of them for a few extra minutes before Marietta came out of the kitchen with her tea. When I headed out the door they whimpered slightly and waved until I was out of sight.

I hadn't even gotten my sox and sneakers off when Samuel appeared in the doorway.

"I talked to my mother last night. Good suggestion on your part."

I wasn't ready for this level of interaction so quickly, but I slid into it without hesitating. My sneakers off now, I wiggled my toes before putting my suede pumps on, giving them one last waggle of freedom.

"What did she say? Was she helpful?"

"Very. She relayed a story about a man from her past, ending by telling me to follow my heart."

"She sounds like someone I'd like to know better."

"She remembers meeting you last October. You made quite an impression." Naturally that made me feel good all over and I wanted to hear more.

"Oh, that's right. She and your dad came to take you to lunch with Jonlyn." Jonlyn was another woman Samuel had dated who was from South Carolina. She was a petite blond he had met while she was apprenticing with a local architect. It was more and more difficult to think of Samuel with other women, even though they were part of his past. I was slowly learning there had been several of them, each so different from the next.

"Yes, that's right. And she turned to my dad after she met you and told him that I was in love with you but didn't realize it. But because you were married, they dismissed it from their minds. Is that amazing or what?" On the one hand I was stunned by his mother's intuition and keen observation skills, and on the other, I figured my feelings were so strong and obvious that people would have to be unconscious not to pick up on them. I wondered how many people at the office would be caught unawares when we went public.

"In a way I'm surprised, but then again the feelings are so intense that I'm always trying to find ways to conceal them. Your mom sounds like an intuitive woman. Aren't you glad you called her?"

"Yes, it was a very good idea. I feel relieved and supported by her."

My mind circled back to my family and what their reactions might be. Even though Dane's vision and career path had been hard for them, he was from a good family and had attended all the right schools. Samuel was bright and articulate but the fact that he hadn't gone to college would never fly with my parents. My mother always made a habit of telling me whose weddings were in the *New York Times*, where the bride and groom went to college and graduate school. She seemed somewhat wistful about her daughters' choices as she rambled on about the success of total strangers.

"Count your blessing that it went so well Samuel. My family is going to have a real hard time with this."

"What do you mean?" I had to laugh under the strain of it all. It was so complicated, my background and its enduring effects on my life.

"For starters, my parents have very high expectations of their offspring, and their daughter leaving a devoted husband for a happy bachelor is not one of them."

"Hey, who said happy?"

"Speaking of bachelors, what are you doing about your relationship with Bonnie?" I was being bold here, but I had to know where she stood in all this. After all they had been seeing each other for a couple of months.

"It's done. I called her after I talked to my mother. It seemed only fair." I was delighted by the swiftness of his action, but some doubt still lingered in my suspicious mind.

"Just like that, a phone call and it's over?"

"Olivia, it obviously wasn't that serious to begin with or it would have taken a lot more than a phone call." I waded in further, still not satisfied with the brevity of it all.

"Well, how did she take it?"

"Devastated naturally, but she'll survive!" He threw his head back and laughed with great gusto. "No, seriously, she was disappointed, but I think it was more playful and sexual than anything else for both of us." The word sexual stopped me dead in my tracks. *Of course,* they had been lovers, but I just hadn't gone there in my mind. But before I could go any further down the path of destruction I was on, he lunged toward me with a kiss. For a moment we forgot where we were, lost in all that compelled us toward each other. But the old, rusty hinges holding my door in place announced the arrival of an intruder and we were jolted apart.

"Good morning you two. Could I see you in my office for a bit Samuel?" Chad stood in the doorway. The interlude was abruptly concluded, and it was back to business. Samuel shifted gears smoothly as he winked and followed Chad out the door.

"See you at lunch. I'll get us some soup and rolls."

I nodded knowing that I would be somewhat useless the next four hours leading to our break, then alone again; we would flirt and titillate each other in the Shyler House kitchen. It was so adolescent, but I recognized it went well beyond the warm rushes that traveled through me when our bodies overlapped. His strength, tenderness, the way we could talk about anything, all contributed to this dangerous liaison.

Dane's time away passed rapidly as Samuel and I squeezed in more and more time alone together. That initial kiss on my forehead escalated into many more and beyond. Our bodies craved each other but we were restrained by the gatekeepers, also known as our rational minds. One night after the children fell asleep; we lay in my bed completely clothed but tangled up in one another. We had been at it for over an hour and his hardness made me open like a rose in bloom. I wanted him between my lips so badly but would not allow myself to succumb. That ultimate pleasure would be on hold until Dane knew the truth, until some declarations were made. I lifted Samuel's head from my chest where he was fondling my erect nipples gently, but eagerly.

"Hey, look at me. Come back to this room. Remember what we promised."

We had mutually decided that our first time together would not be soiled by sneaking and lies. Dane would have to know the truth before we went forward. He looked up from my breast, his face flushed, his hair ruffled up.

"God, I want you so badly woman. And yes, I remember." He rolled to my side and stroked himself. I had never been with a man who was so easy about giving himself pleasure. I watched him rub and squeeze, almost to the point of climax. He stopped right on the edge.

"I'm going to allow myself the pleasure of waiting on you."

As the month drew to a close, I faced the emotionally daunting task of bringing the news to Dane. I had called him ten days before his course ended to let him know I was coming to pick him up. He was surprised and pleased by my offer but expressed some concerns about my not being very communicative in his absence. My usual style was cards, love notes, and long, sweet phone conversations when we were apart. This time there had been no letters and I was distant and brief on the phone. I limited our conversation to issues related to the children and his tolerance of this emotional distance amazed me. I would be poking and prodding around like a pig hunting for truffles, overflowing with questions, demanding answers. At the very beginning of our courtship he was late picking me up one evening. When he arrived on the back of a purple Harley with a woman driving, I bristled inside and out. When he approached me with his boyish affection, I would have none of it.

"Where were you, and who was that?" I demanded. He seemed perfectly comfortable in the face of my accusatory tone and was not a bit ruffled.

"Oh, that was Cynthia Moffit, an old college friend. She's on island for the weekend and she looked me up. It's been years since I've seen her. Can't believe she drives a Harley!"

"Was she just a friend in college or more than that?" He laughed and poked me playfully in the ribs.

"I detect the presence of the green-eyed monster here. Yes, we dated for a few months. She was in my sculpture class and we ended doing an environmental piece together. When we were out in the field, so to speak, one thing led to another." My curiosity was insatiable, and I kept rooting around for more.

"So why did you stop seeing one another?"

"Don't remember exactly, it was so long ago. Can we go eat now, I'm starving."

All during dinner I dug the details out of him until I was satisfied that Cynthia was no longer a threat. Dane remained ever so patient all throughout the interrogation while dunking his curly fries in a horseradish dip. Over time his calm acceptance during those cross examinations left me more secure, plus he just wasn't a very outgoing kind of guy.

I had a horrendous night before I went to get Dane. Distorted, terrifying dreams invaded my sleep on and off. When I finally got up and turned on the coffee maker the small glowing red digital numerals indicated it was only four-twenty-two. While showering I tried to wash away some of the disturbing images from my mind. I could clearly see Dane's tender face wincing in pain as I delivered his fate. Leaving on the early boat spared me the scene with the children who would want to go along to pick up their long-awaited daddy.

Samuel met me at the end of the street with a thermos of coffee and eyes brimming with warmth and support. When he stopped in the ferry parking lot, he pulled my leg across the seat and placed it on his thigh. I was grateful for the connection as we sat quietly with no words available to either of us. Soon the lights flickered from the ticket office window signaling they were open for business. Dawn was splendidly breaking across the harbor in pale pink and the day was thrust upon us.

"Are you going to be okay?" His concern and focus wrapped around me like a warm cape one last time before my departure.

"No, but I'm ready. It has to happen, and I just want to get it over with." Whenever I was in a school play or had to give a presentation of any kind, I always begged to go first due to my low anxiety threshold. When I took my first swimming test at camp, I persuaded the lifeguard to allow me to go to the head of the line by convincing him I would be sick to my stomach. I didn't win any new friends that afternoon, but at least I got it over with. I sat on a nearby rock like a turtle in the sun, basking in relief while the others nervously waited their turn.

The ferry whistle blew, and I removed my overnight bag and leather knapsack from the cab of the truck. Samuel offered to help but I was already detaching, knowing this was very much a solo journey.

"I'll call you tonight if I can. I have no idea what the set up will be or how things will go."

He squeezed my hand tightly and raised it to his lips. He hadn't shaved yet, so I felt his stubble brush against my wrist.

"I'll be waiting to hear from you, whenever it works. Drive carefully."

As I walked across the ferry parking lot, I wondered how the brilliant sunrise could be so indifferent to my plight while it rose with the same magnificence as always. The passenger ramps were lowered, and I crossed over into a new life. The whistle blew indicating the imminent departure from the safe harbor I had known for so long. Samuel stood leaning against the truck as the ferry pulled away and the backwash splashed against the dock. He gave me a final thumbs up and a hearty wave before getting into his truck. I entered the seating area, quickly looking for a place by the window, knowing the last thing I needed was to run into someone I knew and be forced into superficial conversation. Finding an empty seat with a view, I loosely spread my belongings across the seat, marking my private territory. I looked out as the steamboat pushed further away from shore. With Samuel's truck just out of sight, I turned my thoughts toward what awaited me on the mainland. Images and facial expressions tore through my mind as I envisioned the conversation between me and Dane. I wanted it to all be over and yet I knew I had to walk through the fire to experience any relief.

Chapter Twenty-three

When I disembarked from the boat the early morning fog was gradually being pierced by needles of sunlight and beginning to lift. I decided to walk the six blocks to the rental car agency rather than take the shuttle. Passing a store window, I was caught by the reflection of a slender, tall woman. During the month Dane had been away I had dropped almost twelve pounds and my tall physique was looking svelte rather than voluptuous, as so many had described me. I loved the lightness of this new body. It allowed me to dress in ways that expressed the heightened sensuality I was feeling. As I slid my hand down to my waist, and now obvious hipbone, I wondered what my husband would read into this profound physical change.

Buckling into the red mustang I was able to choose from the lot, I rolled down the window, put my Tootsie roll pops in the cup holder and searched through my collection of cassettes for the long ride ahead. Once I found something suitable, I quickly entered the venue of fantasy about less frantic moments when Samuel, the children and I would be settled into a life. It was reminiscent of many a night on the floor in my room with the music blaring to drown out my parents and their loud bickering. I would spin off into a daydream about someone I had a hidden crush on at school. Now I imagined a glorious wedding, surrounded by friends and family, dancing to "Sting" in Samuel's strong and capable arms. We would honeymoon somewhere hot and exotic where few clothes would be necessary and tropical drinks would be plentiful. But when I reached the sign indicating Muldarah was less than sixty miles away I knew I had to switch gears.

Preparing for Dane's reaction was unthinkable, and I shuddered when I saw rage and anger, as opposed to sadness and devastation. I had such a strong aversion to male anger after growing up with a father that had a short fuse and loud, booming voice. Dane had only lost his temper once in our time together when I pushed harder about getting extra work when the twins were born. We were both exhausted and feeling trapped for different reasons. The conversation escalated and our voices were raised to new heights. Dane lost it completely, picked up the kitchen table and turned it over, dishes breaking as they hit the red brick linoleum floor. I fled from the scene and he slept on the couch after sweeping up the evidence of our turmoil.

When I saw the wooden sign at the entrance of Muldarah my nearly empty stomach churned, and my bowels loosened. I had to get to a bathroom before I found Dane. The mustang followed the curve of the long, winding driveway to the main building. The old Tudor mansion stood atop a hill safely hidden among huge ancient oak and elm trees. To the right and down the embankment, pear trees formed a gentle pattern that contributed to the overall feeling of harmony and peace. In just a few minutes Dane's month in this place of tranquility, health food, yoga, massage and reflexology would change color and dimension completely. I steered toward the "Visitors Always Welcome" sign in the gravel parking lot and turned off the motor. Sitting for a moment I tried to absorb this place where my husband had spent time creating another alternative to provide for his family. Now I was about to announce that family was no longer the same as when he left. A dramatic shift had occurred, like an earthquake, it came without warning. Or did the subtle cracks appear gradually but we didn't feel them under our feet? The ultimate devastation would be anything but subtle.

I grabbed my belongings from the passenger seat and headed for the entrance to the building. As I walked toward the front door people in beige colored caftans walked out smiling, bowing slightly as they passed. They emanated a peace and contentedness that eluded me most of the time, especially now. I wondered if Dane would somehow be better prepared or fortified having spent time in this atmosphere with these sorts of people. Once inside the foyer I saw a pleasant, earthy woman behind a large oak desk which had a vase filled with bright pink stargazer lilies. A sign next to a pile of colorful brochures read "Visitors Welcome-Please Take One."

As I headed in the direction of the restroom a familiar voice called my name. It was Dane, and I was not ready. I needed to empty myself and then be the one to find him first, allowing me to be more prepared. I turned to face him as he moved excitedly toward me. I quickly took him in from head to toe, he was thinner and his hair longer now, brushing against his shoulders. He seemed so fragile and vulnerable with an obvious weight loss. *Can I do this?* As he hugged me and gently rubbed his hand down my back, I was acutely aware of the difference between his touch and Samuel's. Samuel's hands were stout and strong with a tenderness that wrapped all around me. Dane's were those of a true sculpture, long, wiry and defined. I felt their delicacy as they traveled the length of my spine. Suddenly a woman's voice called to him from across the room.

"Oh, is that her Dane? At last she has arrived!" A tall, exotic gypsy like woman in purple tie-dyed bloomers came rushing toward us. Without hesitation she took me in her arms.

"So, you're the wonderful woman who stayed home with two toddlers so Dane could do this. I couldn't wait to meet such a devoted partner." She embraced me again, leaving me speechless with her emphatic greeting. The guilt swept through me like a sand castle caving into a strong wind. I had no idea how to respond, but before I even attempted to, she began to walk away. Over her shoulder she said, "You are both so lucky to have one another. Peace be with you and yours." She pressed her palms together, bowed and fluttered off with an array of colored scarves tied at her waist disappearing down the hall. Dane turned toward me.

"That was Lupita. She and I have been reflexology partners quite a bit, so we've had a chance to talk. She was pretty amazed at what you sacrificed for me to be here." As the words flowed from Dane's mouth, I realized by my reaction to that little scenario that something was definitely missing. There was no green-eyed monster present here, no jealous reaction. In the past, hearing about another woman as a partner, touching in healing and intimate ways, would probably have bothered me. Hearing it now, I felt detached, as if listening to a dear friend. My passion for Dane had slowly ebbed away. Not knowing when it started leaving, I didn't notice until it was gone. Left in its place was warmth, tenderness and compassion, somewhat akin to brotherly love. I pulled out of this sobering recognition to say something that might make sense.

"She seems very nice, and she was obviously quite taken with you!"

"Oh, I don't think it was me she was taken with, as much as the idea of a couple like us."

I couldn't hold up the mask any longer. My impetuous nature and low threshold for emotional ambiguity were getting the best of me, and I needed to tend to my body's demands.

"Can you show me where the bathroom is? I'm bursting from the ride. Then maybe we can take a walk?"

"Of course," He took my hand. "I want to show you around this place."

I wanted to pull away from his touch, but not here among these calm, centered beings. After I came out of the bathroom, we headed up a hill behind the building, leading toward the cluster of fruit trees. When we reached the top, he said, "This is the view from my window. It faces east so I could see the sunrise over the lake almost every morning. It was spectacular." I lowered myself to the ground when my knees began to shake. I sat with my legs crossed trying to disguise the movement in my body.

"Yes, it's lovely. Dane, sit down." I patted the earth between us. My fingers ran back and forth in a nervous pattern. Dane rested his hand on top of mine to make contact and stop the motion.

"What is it Olivia? What is this heavy burden you've carried all the way up here to share with me? Put it down, unload, out with it!" I attempted a deep breath, but my chest was so constricted I barely managed a shallow one. I felt my heart speed up as it led the way to this shattering truth.

"Okay Dane. Before you left, we talked about me sorting out stuff about Samuel, right?"

He shifted his body to face me head on. Looking me in the eye he said in an uneven tone,

"Is that what this is about? What happened while I was gone? Did you sleep with him? What?" In my usual fashion, it all came spilling out, down the hillside, like a brutal flash flood. I immediately let him know we hadn't slept together but that we had spent time together. Dane moved to another level, more aggressive than before.

"So, what's the bottom line here? Are you in love with him or what?"

I swallowed, feeling the raw, dryness inside my mouth.

"Yes, I want to be with him Dane."

He jumped up and towered over me like Thor the Nordic thunder god.

"Have you gone crazy? You're probably having a mid-life crisis or something! It will pass, Olivia!" His movements became like those of an animal that was cornered.

"No, Dane, it's much more than that, unfortunately."

"Olivia, do you realize what you are saying? Samuel's been a bachelor for a long time dating all around the island, and he's never been a father. He knows nothing about raising kids!"

His words caught me off guard but then I remembered how gentle and perceptive he had been with Julia, the bread sticks, his stuffed bumblebee.

"Dane, I'm not some star struck adolescent here, nor is Samuel. I don't know who you've been talking to, but I know him." Dane spun around, grabbed my shoulders and held them tightly, forcing me to meet his eyes.

"Where I get my information about this guy doesn't matter. What matters here is that you are destroying our family to run off with some womanizer!" My body convulsed with that punch. Images of Samuel with other women galloped across my mind while Dane paced back and forth running his fingers through his now long hair. My words could not make it out of my mouth. They were suspended in a place of disbelief and confusion. Everything was out of control and focus. I had to know if Dane's accusations were coming from. I would confront Samuel when I got back. And maybe I would finally have to tell Miranda and my walking girls.

"I've heard things like this happen to women when they are about to reach forty. Olivia we'll get through this!" A touch of levity sailed through the air with his comment, reminding me of birthday cards I'd seen for middle aged women. It would be so much simpler if that's all it was, a silly mid-life Hallmark crisis about wrinkles and a soft belly. A makeover would not cure this one. I lifted my body off the ground to an upright position and walked toward Dane with hesitancy. He movements were sudden, abrupt and unpredictable. In a matter of minutes, the man I had felt the safest with for almost a dozen years frightened me as he raged in pain on the hillside. I had created this monster with just a few words. I reached out and tried to ground him through my touch, but he pushed me away.

"Dane, I know this is all so crazy and makes no sense on some levels. But on others, did we not see it coming as my relationship with Samuel evolved and our passion waned?"

With fire in his eyes he spun around and lunged toward me.

"Is this about sex? Because if it is, you have my permission to get it out of your system. Go ahead, sleep with him and get it over with! But for god sakes Olivia don't break up our family!" He continued to circle around me as his hair flew in all directions like the wild creature he was rapidly becoming. I heard his pleas in the distance but knew I could not turn the tide. I was caught in an undertow and couldn't release myself. I forced myself to continue onward.

"I'm sorry Dane but this isn't about a quickie with Samuel. I wish it were that simple. Sleeping with him will not make it go away."

"Then what Olivia? What is it that you need that I can't give you?"

His vulnerability frightened me on some level and made my heart crack open on another. His desperation had opposing effects on me. The part that was repelled and wanted to shut down was just like my father. Whenever my mother appeared weak or unable to handle something, he would become angry and tell her to shape up. To earn strokes from him we needed to excel, succeed, be strong and stand out.

Going home for Thanksgiving holiday freshman year in college was something everyone looked forward to except me. As the excitement in my dormitory reached its climax the night before, I was filled with a kind of dread. My roommate Eileen was bubbling over about seeing her high school sweetheart while she was home. She quizzed me about my dark mood on the eve of vacation.

"It's my dad. His expectations are so high and my grades this semester are definitely not going to meet them. He'll be on my case the whole time I'm home."

"Well, tell him you're getting adjusted to college life. He'll understand."

No, no he won't, I thought. But it was no use trying to explain him to someone who didn't know my dad. When I arrived home, there was a brief celebratory ambiance in the household and then reality hit that evening as he reviewed my grades.

"Olivia, is this what I'm paying for? You've got two C's here! What are you doing instead of studying?" The excuse about adjusting to life in college did not satisfy him in the least. He dropped my monthly allowance down in order to curtail my recreational activities, and he insisted on receiving weekly reports about my average in each course. I lived to meet his demands and be back in good standing, but never quite made it.

⌒

"Dane it's about needs that I didn't know I even had," though I couldn't articulate any of them just then. My circuits were over-loaded. We stood among the pear trees in a thick, ripe silence for what seemed like an eternity.

"Dane, we need to head back now if we're going to make the late boat. We'll talk more on the way." He looked directly at me and for the first time in this interlude I saw his eyes swell with tears. He said nothing and headed back to gather his things. People pass-ing seemed to pick up on the emotional tone immediately. They did not interfere, but you could sense their compassion. While we loaded up the car a man with deep blue eyes and a salt and pepper pony tail came over to give Dane a farewell embrace. Dane broke in his arms and spilled open. He held him firmly though he had a gentle presence. He asked nothing from Dane in the way of an explanation but was totally present for him. Words seemed unnec-essary around here. When they parted, Dane slid into the passenger seat and put his seat belt in robotic trance. We exited the gates of Muldarah and drove the car north toward Algonquin. The last thing I saw in the rear-view mirror was the pile of rotten pears left behind in the orchard.

Being trapped together for the next four plus hours was like struggling to wake up from a horrendous nightmare, but never suc-ceeding. The drive was a series of long silences and sudden out-bursts. There was no explanation I could offer that would assuage Dane's shock and horror. His whole life was being torn apart and I couldn't put it back together. Not this time. It had become so automatic that it felt strange not to, yet that was also part of our downfall. When we finally pulled into the boat parking area Dane broke the silence.

"Olivia, I can't sit on the boat with you for another hour and a half. My skin is crawling, and I need to see my kids. Take me to the airport!" I was startled by his abrupt decision, but I turned in the direction of the airport. When I pulled up in front, he grabbed his knapsack.

"I'll see you over there. Maybe Marietta can fetch me at the airport."

I grasped for something to say in all this chaos.

"What are you going to tell them?"

"The truth!" He slammed the door and hurried toward the entrance. I was motionless until I heard a light tapping on the window. Of all people, it was Donna Gasperson, a dear friend of Audrey Hanson's that had a party for us shortly after we got married.

"Hello, Olivia. I haven't seen you for so long. Those two toddlers must be keeping you busy. I just saw Dane inside and he looked awfully tired. Is he all right?"

"He's been off at reflexology school for a month. It was a long drive." My composure amazed me. It had come from a long series of lessons taught by my dear mother who was always concerned about what other people thought.

"Oh, I see. Is he planning on starting a new career? What about the physical therapy?" Mrs. Gasperson hammered away in her usual curious fashion.

"He hasn't been able to get full-time work at the hospital so he's testing the waters. I'm sorry, Donna, I really need to get down to the boat." Before I realized what I had said, I saw the confusion pass across her face.

"Oh, you're traveling separately?" Quick on my feet like my father, I bounced right back.

"Oh yes, he wants to get home to Adam and Julia as soon as possible. After a month away sitting on the steamship would be torturous!" My response seemed to satisfy her.

"Well you have a good trip on the boat. It's a bit windy."

"Thanks, see you on island," an automatic phrase that year-round residents exchanged when they crossed paths on the mainland. It was as if we all belonged to the same tribe and would meet again on our homeland after traveling away. I had the sudden painful realization that my Algonquin tribe would soon reject me. I would become an outcast once the news of my liaison with Samuel began to spread. By the time I boarded the ferry the heavy weight of the albatross could be felt around my neck.

Chapter Twenty-four

When I heard the fog horn blowing, I realized I must have slept during most of the return voyage. I was relieved for an instant until I remembered what awaited me on this side of the ocean. I quickly pulled the car mirror toward me and saw the mascara bleeding under my eyes, forming gray, misty shadows. Licking my finger, I tried to rub it away knowing I couldn't go up to the bathroom looking like this. But my bladder refused to cooperate, so I headed up the stairs, avoiding eye contact on the way. It was so unlike me to hide out and shut down. *Who was I becoming?*

"Hello Olivia, what brings you on the night boat?" I turned to face Dane's Uncle Cliff, his father's brother. A former basketball star from Dartmouth, he towered over me.

"Oh, Dane spent the last month at a school in New Hampshire studying reflexology. I went to pick him up yesterday and he flew back earlier. Couldn't wait to see the children." Even with my runny mascara I was still smooth. I had painted the normal domestic scene for a family member that would probably find out in less than twenty-four hours that it was all dissolving.

"Well, that sounds promising since I've heard that the hospital hasn't been able to employ him full-time. And you've got those hungry twins! Well, give him my best." He gave me a hardy pat on the shoulder and headed down the staircase leading to the car deck. I was relieved at the brevity of our exchange. He was someone who could be downright intimidating after a few drinks.

As I drove down the exit ramp, I saw faces and vehicles of friends and neighbors waiting for passengers. It was all so familiar, yet this time I felt like an outsider. I kept my gaze straight ahead, not wanting to be seen, wondering what I would find when I got home. I tried to imagine the bittersweet reunion between Dane and the children.

I pulled in the driveway relieved to see there were lights on in the guest room where Marietta was staying. I turned off the engine and sat in terrified silence for a moment trying to summon the courage to go inside. I picked up my knapsack filled with unread books and cautiously closed the door behind me. I didn't want to disturb the slumber of my beloved children who would have plenty to contend with when the new day dawned.

Walking slowly up the crooked, uneven sidewalk and beneath the archway leading to the front door, I was struck by the sad irony of it all. This funky house had meant so much to us when we bought it only a few short years ago. Yes, it was old and needed attention, but at that time we were energized and excited by all its possibilities. We had convinced ourselves we could transform it into a comfortable living space for our family. It had potential, just as we did when we first began. Now our marriage was disintegrating along with the old wooden gutters, and the paint peeling away from the trim.

I put my stuff down on the armchair and moved slowly toward the guest room. I assumed the open door was an invitation, and I desperately needed one. The curiosity about Dane's homecoming was unbearable.

"Hey Marietta, can I come in?"

"Of course, I've been waiting for you." She was warm and welcoming, just the way I needed her to be.

"How are my babies?"

"Just fantastic now that their daddy's home." Her words slit through my insides like a jagged edge knife.

"How does Dane seem?" My voice lowered and the words came out slowly. I was afraid to hear the answer.

"He's obviously exhausted, drained and terribly weighed down by something." Marietta had never been one to pry or gossip, but under the circumstances, it was time to let her in.

"Marietta, I know you are incredibly discreet, and how fond you are of this family. Because of those two things, I must share what Dane's burden is about, though I won't be surprised if you already know on some level. You are a perceptive one." She sat back and leaned into the pile of pillows on her bed waiting for me to continue.

"While Dane was gone you know I spent a lot of time with my co-worker Samuel Ferrell. I'm sure you've wondered just how long this project could take outside of business hours." She nodded me onward.

"Well, it started out as professional, but it has evolved into something far different. I never imagined this could happen to me, or to my marriage, Marietta," my voice cracked, "I fell in love with Samuel and I am leaving Dane." As I suspected, she was not shocked by the news for she had seen it unfold and knew what was happening. My weight loss, the giddiness when I left to meet Samuel, and the excitement in my eyes when I returned, had all given me away. After all, she too was a woman in love with her own man Carlo, so she knew all the signs. The silence draped the room, laced with my guilt and shame. I stood under the paper lantern that hung from the ceiling and the lighting must have revealed the accumulated stress.

"You better get some sleep Olivia, you look exhausted. I'm sure the children will be in your bed bouncing around bright and early. They missed you too."

"Yes, I'll go check on them right now. Thanks for being here for all of us. I hope I haven't made you too uncomfortable." She was kind but swift with her response.

"Don't worry about me Olivia, just take care of yourself and the children."

As I headed down the hall, I felt weak and unsteady. The floor boards groaned as I walked across them, trying not to make a sound. When I peeked in on Adam and Julia their soft rhythmic breathing strengthened me. Standing over them I let myself tune into their gentle, fragile song. Would anyone be singing tomorrow?

Our household appeared normal upon its waking the next morning, with the familiar aroma of coffee brewing and Blizzard wagging madly to be let out. Adam and Julia giggled and rolled around with Dane while I showered. To an outsider this would appear to be a lovely little family involved in its morning rituals. As the cold water splashed against my face, I tried to imagine my first encounter with Dane since the mainland. He was asleep when I came in last night and I got up long before he stirred.

From the doorway of our bedroom I watched him tumble and play under the comforter with his children. My heart broke open all over again, spilling inside me with the realization of what I was doing. *How could I shift from all this to something utterly unfamiliar?*

The thought of Samuel's arms wrapped themselves around me and I moved into them. There was nowhere else to go but toward this image, so I allowed myself to be drawn in further. Heading into the kitchen with some resolve, his warmth swirled around like the thick, rich honey in my coffee cup.

With my chipped Italian made mug in hand I leaned up against the counter and looked out at Dane's creation. When he made the sandbox over that weekend, he worked well into the second night so Julia and Adam could play in it that Sunday afternoon when they awoke from their naps. They were giddy with delight when they crawled outside in their soggy diapers. They had squirmed out of my arms as soon as they caught sight of it, their pudgy little hands and legs could not get them there fast enough. And now it took on a dreary shade of brown sitting in the cloudy morning light, void of that excitement and joy that had once filled it with tunnels and castles.

I could hear the music of my children's laughter as they played with Dane, but I had no desire to join them in our queen size marital bed where I too once moved easily to that same song. The bed held memories of passion and play, which no longer stirred me. Feeling awkward in my own home, and out of step with my family's rhythm was almost more discomfort than I could bear. Feeling utterly displaced in the midst of everything familiar was an unnerving, out of control place for me. I had to do something to shift my way out of it. As I wandered down the hall lost in a maze of conflicting feelings, I hoped a long, hot shower would temporarily wash it away.

"Mommy, mommy, come play!" My daughter pleaded with me.

"Good morning munchkin, I'm on my way." I quickly allowed myself to engage with her. I walked into the bedroom and Dane was still under the comforter with Adam. When my son heard my voice, he poked his head out from the covers and said,

"Mommy come in tent!" I tried to wiggle out of it.

"Mommy has her coffee and it is very hot. I'll sit in the rocker and watch you." I sat down in the corner of the room and Julia quickly deposited herself neatly in my lap. When her warm, soft body had molded itself comfortably into mine we began our rocking. While stroking her chestnut hair and listening to Adam's growls beneath the covers, I felt momentarily soothed by my children's touch and sound. But my son was relentless.

"Mommy, come, come!" He peeked from beneath the covers and held out his stout little hand toward me. Even in my state of distress I could not resist this impish boy of mine. I put my cup down, Julia slid from my lap and together we dove under the covers. As soon as we entered the soft mauve tent Dane made a quick exit. But before he got away, I saw how dark the circles under his eyes were. The moment of spontaneous play vanished.

Chapter Twenty-five

The fleeting, passionate month with Samuel had turned into a cold, stark reality. Huge decisions had to be made, people had to be informed, and I quickly realized how unprepared I really was for all that was facing me. Our home had a tenuous feeling that first morning and Dane looked disheveled and exhausted when he left for work. I hadn't been sleeping or eating the week prior to his homecoming so I didn't look much better.

The children sensed our discontent and responded with whiny neediness. Dane would probably tell Stephan and Ellie today and there would be nowhere to hide. They both had a network of friends that would know by the time Saint Timothy's Episcopal church bells tolled at noon. Dressing for work was next to impossible because Marietta had left to work the breakfast shift at the cafe. Once again, I bribed Adam and Julia with cheerios and Sesame Street so I could pull myself together. When I got to work Samuel would be there to reassure me that all would be well as we forged our path together. My reality was shaken up like the snowflakes in the New York City winter skyline paperweight on my desk. Everything would settle to the bottom when Samuel and I were in our new life. This thought kept me going as I smoothed my navy-blue woolen skirt and ran a brush through my hair to look presentable for him.

Heading out to work I was raw with the grating anticipation of the day. Dane had probably called Stephan by now, and Samuel and I had set up a time to meet with Chad. We wanted to be the ones to inform him of our relationship before it hit the street. There were board members who rubbed elbows with Dane's parents at cocktail parties and some of them were heavy donors to the Historical Society.

When I got to my office, I found a small envelope on the middle of my chair. The handwriting was unmistakable. From the first time I glanced at his signature sprawled across a memo at a staff meeting, I was intrigued. I wondered what a handwriting analyst would say about the smooth, distinct beginning and the illegible snakelike ending. I ripped open the envelope revealing its golden satin interior.

"I know this is the beginning of a very hard time now that we have shown ourselves. Don't worry, I am with you. Hang in there. I love you, Samuel"

A *womanizer would write this?* I read it at least three times before the door abruptly opened. It was Ellie, with an absolutely horrified expression on her face. I thought I had more time.

"Olivia, can I talk to you for a minute?' It didn't even cross my mind to say no.

"Sure, let's go outside." I followed her out the door like a sleepwalker.

"Is it true what Dane told us this morning? Are you really leaving him for Samuel Ferrell?" It was like an abrupt splash of icy water all over my now ultra-sensitive body.

"Look Ellie, I really don't have time to go into this right now. I am at work. I know this all seems crazy and unexpected. But in all honesty Dane and I have been deteriorating for a while. Samuel was just a catalyst in the whole process."

She bristled and jumped right back into the fire, unwilling to abbreviate the conversation.

"Do you realize what you are doing here, Olivia? This is an almost eleven-year marriage with two toddlers. Then presto, it's over?" I snapped back.

"It's hardly that simple Ellie! I'm surprised you didn't see some of this coming. We've been struggling financially for over a year. I think we reached out and let you guys know we were under some real pressure. Dane is forty and still trying to find himself. Juggling two toddlers, a full-time job, and his exploration, has been exhausting, and incredibly stressful."

For a brief moment, she was actually speechless, which was most unusual for my friend. Before she could regroup, I cut her off.

"Ellie, I realize all this is shocking for you and Stephan. But I've got to get back to work. We'll talk some more."

I amazed myself as I turned and walked back into my office, leaving her behind. I had to protect myself from the onslaught that was only just beginning.

Even though it wasn't yet nine in the morning I already needed something to settle me. I rifled through my drawer and found a rather old, soggy, forgotten Tootsie roll pop. It was a fading raspberry that would have to do. Despite its signs of aging I unwrapped it and stuck it in my mouth. Rolling my tongue around its edges had a soothing effect. I've been an oral person as far back as I can remember. Whenever intense periods of concentration were required for exam preparations in college you would find my desk stockpiled with suckers. Everyone came to me for their sweet oral fix.

I hurried and dialed Miranda's number before something else happened. I didn't want her to hear this on the street from someone else. She would be so hurt, and besides I had to know if she had heard anything about Samuel being the womanizer Dane alluded to. She agreed to meet me for a glass of wine that night right after the kids were down.

I didn't see Samuel until our luncheon rendezvous at the museum. He had been out looking at sites for a new storage facility to house the collections that had long outgrown their current space. It amazed me how well he could stay on track despite all that was happening. As I tapped on the museum door, I wondered if that ability was a male thing, or specific to him. He appeared in the doorway immediately with that inviting smile.

"Greetings how goes the fight?" he said as he pulled me through the door and into him.

"Well Dane has told Stephan and Ellie. She came by to see me. With her knowing it should be all over the island before the end of work today." Still holding me he nestled his nose into my hair. His warm nuzzle gave me a fleeting feeling of protection from what was brewing outside the door.

"Are you scared?"

"Not at the moment. All the craziness makes sense when we're connected like this. But I know that will change." His nose dove deeper into my hair, rubbing through its density. Taking his hands down from face, he surrounded my waist.

"How can we keep some of this? How can each of us maintain some semblance of this connection while dealing with the island's wrath and disapproval," he responded.

Insecurities clouded my mind like a storm forming overhead. In my gut I knew that holding onto any sense of security during the barrage of criticism from friends and family would be extremely challenging for me. Even though my tall stature and graceful gate gave an air of confidence to the viewer, I counted on people's acceptance and approval. Unkind remarks and gossip affected me like hail stones on a delicate rooftop, leaving their dents. What someone said or did not say had the power to ruin more than a day for me. But I sensed that Samuel was quite different in his core, and worse, he probably assumed I was too. He would be shocked by my true fragility, maybe even repulsed.

"Olivia, pull yourself together!" I felt flushed with shame by my father's words as he shouted them for the second time. It was the Monday after a humiliating weekend and he was still insisting I attend the middle school field day, which was after all, voluntary and supposed to be fun. It certainly would not be in my case. I had gone to Jody Samson's slumber party, the most exquisite, popular girl in our grade. Somehow, I was included on her list, and I was beside myself with joy to be among the popular girls. You see I wasn't really one of *them*. While they were busy practicing for cheer leading tryouts, I was in the bleachers watching and writing poetry. I felt too long, cumbersome, and uncoordinated. Besides, I was already five foot seven, wearing a size ten shoe (which my mother repeatedly reminded me was Jackie Kennedy's size), and couldn't do a decent cartwheel. Most of the girls in my grade were rather petite and slim, having no trouble getting their little bodies to perform the most amazing of gymnastic feats.

The night of Jody's party they were all bouncing and prancing about while I stood in the background applauding and feigning interest. But Harriet Braun had something different in mind for me. She had a mean streak, and you could see it in her eyes whenever she spotted someone's Achilles heel. She was not content to let me sit on the sidelines that night, and she kept urging me to get out there and at least *try* a cartwheel. She graciously offered to spot me, there by convincing the others of her sincerity. The girls started chanting my name as they circled around me, taunting in their playful, feminine way. Feeling like I had no choice, I stepped forward and the circle parted like the Red Sea. Harriet skipped alongside me, looking ever so genuine in her supporting role as my assistant.

"Just kick your legs up as high as you can and I'll guide them along," she squealed. Jody had a spacious yard and I was unaware of anything around me that could be damaged in the act of my clumsiness. I took a breath, closed my eyes and hurled my long, gangling body through space, just wanting to get it over with. What I had forgotten was the bamboo torches placed throughout the yard to keep the mosquitoes at bay. Needless to say, Harriet was unable to handle my one hundred and thirty pounds, so I toppled over into the closest torch. It hadn't rained in almost a month and the Samson's Bermuda grass was dry and crackling. The flames took off like runners in a marathon after the gun sounds. I remember the high-pitched screams of the girls and the shrill voices of Jody's parents as they looked with horror from the back porch, where they had been leisurely sipping cocktails, and enjoying their daughter's birthday festivities. Her father grabbed a fire extinguisher from somewhere while Mrs. Samson corralled us like wild ponies toward the front yard. Before Jody's dad could get it out completely, the fire had left its markings on a wicker chair and started to eat away at her little brother's tree house. Everyone was herded inside while the damage was assessed. I knew I had ruined Jody's thirteenth birthday party, and I knew she and her crowd would never let me forget it. I caught the gleam in Harriet's eye as I was frozen out of the inner circle of girls comforting Jody, wishing I had just stood my ground rather than groping for glory and acceptance.

Now I faced Samuel attempting to conceal the sensitivity that my father had not succeeded in destroying. Perhaps his anger and repulsion toward it made it want to stay all that much longer.

"As long as we connect somehow on a daily basis and talk on the phone on the weekends I can probably manage." That was the best I could do, but he didn't seem to be in quite the same place about daily, concrete assurances.

"That may not work all the time, so we have to carry it inside. You know, feel the tonnage of our connection. Tap into it when you need to."

I started feeling a little frightened by his seemingly relaxed, confident treatment of our newly exposed relationship. Right then something slithered inside my belly, like a tiny fish flipping over on its side. But I didn't want to acknowledge it, not with the risks I was taking. This was not the time to question our approaches and focus on differences. I needed to be secure and trust our similarities.

"I think I know what you mean but it's hard in the face of all the Hansons and their history on the island."

He took my face into his rough, tender hands. He leaned down and kissed me gently all over, like droplets from a spring rain showering my face. When he reached my lips, his tongue moved deeply inside me for what seemed like a long time. When we parted I could feel them tingling from the force he had used.

"Now," he said, "put that inside and tuck it away. Then pull it out when you need to remember why we're doing all this."

I rubbed my fingers against my lips hoping to feel the same conviction he exuded as we headed toward the door. Our lunch time escape was once again quickly coming to an end.

"Well, it's back to reality." I said as we reached the entrance to the museum. I zipped up my purple and green "yahoo" jacket. It had earned this name because of its bold colors and wild, undisciplined pattern.

"Hey," he said firmly, "This *is* reality woman!" That reality hit me in the face like the cold, March wind as I crossed over the threshold of the museum to the outside world. Without warning, Peter, Dane's brother who must have been on island for business, drove by. *Perfect timing!* When he glanced up and saw us, he slowed way down and backed up. In an uncharacteristically loud voice said, "What the hell do you two think you're up to?"

He drove away thrashing his fist back and forth out the window. I had never seen him, or anyone else in Dane's family display that kind of anger. The only exception was when Dane's Uncle Cliff was drunk. Then a dark side would emerge, and everyone would scatter quickly. Anybody in the line of fire was fair game for his thunderous voice and foul language. I had been able to avoid being the target all these years. My stomach squirmed with the mere thought of being in that position after he heard the news.

I was bone weary when I got home from work that afternoon but walking on the edge of fear released enough adrenaline into my system to keep me on my feet. Watching the boiling water and rigatoni I wondered what Dane's demeanor would be now that he had told someone in his family. Peter's wife Holly had a reputation for stoking the family fires and dousing it with kerosene.

As Adam and Julia's favorite song by Raffi "Baby Beluga" played in the background, my mind traversed the deep murky waters of possibility. Would Dane be pumped up with family muscle? It was after six when the back door abruptly swung open and hit the wainscoting with a slam. "Daddy's home," Dane shouted in a much louder voice than was customary for him. He looked past me and headed straight for the children. His whole demeanor was exaggerated and boisterous. It was as if he was attempting to be larger than life in order to regain his rightful position in the family. It was so unlike him that he almost appeared like an oversized, animated character. Witnessing a man who was always content to be in the back ground now thrusting himself into center stage was hard to watch.

We exchanged only a few polite and obligatory words over dinner while in the presence of Julia and Adam. After they were asleep, he came into the bedroom while I was getting ready to meet Miranda. He leaned against the door.

"I'm not moving out. If you want to be with another man, then *you* get the hell out!"

He got up and walked out without waiting to see what my reaction might be. He had been well oiled and primed for this one. His comment totally unnerved me to the point where I was temporarily immobilized. I just sat on the edge of our bed wondering where I would go.

I was twenty minutes late meeting Miranda at the tavern. When I sat down, she already had a glass of Blush waiting for me.

"You sounded frantic over the phone this morning. What's up, Olivia?"

"Okay Miranda, this is going to take a while, but please hang in there with me and try to understand. I know I should have told you a lot sooner, but I just couldn't. I was terrified about anyone knowing."

She sat back in the rounded leather booth with her vodka in hand and a very puzzled expression on her finely chiseled face.

"Okay, I'm dying to hear what's going on! Get on with it," she nodded.

When I was finished Miranda was silent for longer than I thought she was capable of. I think she was shocked, disappointed and envious all at once. She longed to have someone in her life again that adored her. Ruben had always been preoccupied with his music and she had always taken a back seat.

When I queried her about Samuel's reputation, she told me he had been the one who did the structural survey on the old house she and Ruben had bought years ago. She said he was very skilled at what he did, and his prices were very fair, given his tremendous expertise. She started to say something else, but I was thrown off by Stephan coming in the door with some friends. I didn't hear the rest of Miranda's comment because I was trying to make myself invisible. All I cared about was that my dear friend finally knew. Though she was concerned about the drastic leap I was making into the unknown, she said she could see why I was ready to take it based on what she knew about my relationship with Dane, and her own dealings with Samuel.

Chapter Twenty-six

Looking for a rental in March on the island was like waiting until you arrived in Disneyworld during spring break to think about where you might stay. There were very few options that were affordable with enough space to accommodate all four of us. After spending one dreary afternoon looking at the slim pickings, Samuel and I parked at the end of a dirt road facing the surf. The beach was deserted, and the waves thundered into shore with a mighty roar. At any other time, I would have been captivated by the ocean's magnificent display, but I was so far from my comfort zone that I hardly noticed. Samuel's antennae were up, and he sensed it immediately. He took my hand in his firm, warm grasp and began stroking my palm with his thumb.

"What is it, Olivia? I feel something brewing."

Once again, I was startled by his heightened awareness. I hesitated to reveal what the day's events, along with Dane's lingering accusations about Samuel's colorful past had brought on for me, but he coaxed it out of me.

"Come on baby, you can tell me. That's what we're about, right?"

"Okay, Samuel. I'm confused."

"About?"

"About all of it," I said while removing his hand from mine and turning toward the window.

"That makes sense. Today was a huge reality check about what we're embarking upon."

"Just seeing those places and trying to envision living there with Julia and Adam brought up so much stuff." He turned my face toward his and said firmly, but still softly,

"Olivia, you're not sure you want to go forward, are you?"

A prolonged silence filled the truck and my body shuddered. If I told him the truth would I lose him? But I owed him that, after all he was about to drastically change *his* life too.

"No, Samuel, I'm not sure." I paused and then went further. "And there is something else."

"Okay, what else is bothering you?"

"Well, when I told Dane about my decision to be with you up at Muldarah, he said you were a womanizer and had been with several women on island. Are you sure you want to be tied down with just one woman and two children?"

There, I had given my insecurity the voice it was begging for. His gaze penetrated all the layers of my fear. In that instant I wanted him to grab me and say I was the one and only, and he was all mine forever. But he remained silent for what seemed like too long. When he had digested my truth, he gave me his thoughtful reply.

"Olivia, I have been a single guy for almost eight years. I enjoy the company of women as friends and otherwise, so yes, I have spent time with different ladies over the years. If Dane or anyone else thinks that makes me a womanizer, so be it. Let them think what they want. All I know is I'm a grown up and I think long and hard before I make a choice like the one I'm making now. I love you and I want you, and Adam and Julia, in my life long term."

I was enthralled and delighted beyond words with his declaration. He continued.

"Olivia, I know what I want, and you need to take some time to sort it all out until you're sure about what you want for yourself, and your children. I can wait so we both know it is the right decision for all of us."

I could scarcely believe his words. This kind man of strong heart was willing to give me some time and space to decide what I needed to do. My disbelief had to do with some very fragile, undiscovered sense of myself that was being revealed one mysterious piece after another. This deep, hidden, dark hole of insecurity that lurked inside was beginning to manifest itself in contrast to Samuel's solid, unwavering confidence.

We drove back toward town without speaking or touching. The sound of the engine was all I could hear, along with the wild thoughts stampeding across my mind. When we got within three blocks of my street, he pulled over. He kept the truck running which signaled there would be no prolonged goodbye. When he turned toward me and touched my shoulder, I wanted desperately for him to pull me closer and insist I give him an answer right then.

"Think long and hard, lady. When you know for sure let me know."

I wanted to lunge into his arms and tell him I was all his, but I knew I had to slow down before I created any more bloodshed. It so unusual for me to hold back and I felt the strain bear down on me. I squeezed his hand and left the truck filled with confusion. As he pulled away from the curb I checked to see if he would look back. He did not.

When I opened the front door, I didn't hear the usual sounds of my children or their father. The silence was a bit unnerving, so I hurried down the hall toward the kitchen. There they were, bundled up and playing happily in the sandbox. I stood at the window and watched without being noticed. They were all focused on a big sand structure. Adam had his hand in a fist as he stood above the mound like a giant letting the sand trickle from the cracks between his fingers. Julia circled slowly, gently patting the sides, shoring it up. Dane sat in the corner admiring his children's handiwork. It all appeared so perfect and yet unreal at the same time. I knew he was torn up from our conversation earlier when I broke the news that I was going out to look for rentals with Samuel.

As I continued to take in the scene I wondered if I should tell Dane that the whole morning had gone badly, and I was confused about this next step. My mind could not wrap itself around the reality of packing up the children's belongings just yet. I knew that if I couldn't see it, I couldn't do it, at least not now. I headed out to join my family.

When I awoke the next morning, I had a pounding in my temples accompanied by an overwhelming impulse to call Samuel, which teased me throughout the day. I felt like I needed to hurry up before he changed his mind about me. But I controlled my desperate fingers from pressing those little white circular buttons on the phone. Dane must have sensed my confusion because he seemed to be seizing the opportunity to draw me back to him. He was especially attentive to the children's whims and needs, somehow wanting to prove how responsible and necessary he was to our family unit. He refused to be idle for even a minute, finishing little projects around the house that I had harped on for so long. Watching from a distance, I appreciated all his efforts with a deep fondness, but nothing more stirred in me. The spark was gone and in its place was a warm feeling of affection, void of any passion. He was like a dear friend who knew me so well, but that wasn't enough to sustain me anymore. I had felt something with Samuel that was more than just chemistry, and somewhere I recognized its capacity to transform me in some way. I moved toward the vision as it spread itself out like a picnic in a grassy field, ready to be devoured.

By the time I got to the office on Monday having not seen or spoken with Samuel for two days and nights, I was frantic. Every few minutes I looked up at my clock with the seascape painted on its face and wondered where he was. The more I waited the more unglued I became. *Where was he? What was he doing that was more important than seeing me?* After about a half an hour past his usual arrival time, my body started to respond, and I made several trips to the bathroom. Even though I needed that second cup of coffee to jump start my morning, I decided not to have it in favor of preserving my insides, and they were grateful. I lingered over my in-box trying to find something that would engage me to the point where I would stop watching the time.

When he finally popped his face in my door mid-morning, I experienced a kind of meltdown. Without hesitation I got up from behind my desk and grabbed his hand, squeezing it tightly. He squeezed back, but not with his usual strength and conviction.

"I missed you," I said quietly.

"Likewise. I've got to go out to the new storage center for the perk test in a minute. Let's meet at our usual spot at noon."

He was much too brief, almost abrupt.

"I wouldn't miss it," my hand lingering. As he let go, I knew I could go forward with this man, however frightening the unknown might be.

The remainder of the morning left me preoccupied because my intentions were still unspoken. It was amazing how panicked I felt about what could happen in the interim. I was holding on for dear life, hoping I would not fall flat on my face as I moved toward this next trapeze.

As noon approached, I opened my desk drawer, pulled out my hand mirror and freshened up my makeup. I wore very little, in fact my mother often commented that I was like a picture without a frame because the traces of eye shadow and lipstick were barely evident. But I was different than she and my three sisters, less formal and looser. Reasonably content with my reflection, I picked up my black sack from under the desk and headed out to our meeting spot. On the way I saw my brother-in-law Peter again, filling up his van at the gas station. He had obviously prolonged his business on island for Dane's sake. He didn't see me, and I slowed down purposely to avoid him. As I watched him smiling broadly at the attendant a powerful strike of sadness hit me. We had always gotten along famously. We playfully bantered back and forth at family dinners, creating laughter during those long, drawn out meals with one too many courses. As in-laws we had a comfortable friendship. I walked toward the museum away from Peter, and the life I knew so well, the anxiety gnawing at my insides like a basement rat.

By the time I tapped lightly on the museum door's tinted window I was back in a state of discomfort and uncertainty. I was vacillating all over the place and it felt sloppy and disorienting. But when Samuel's moon face appeared everything vanished with the same speed it had descended upon me. He turned the brass handle and peeked through the partial opening.

"What's the password?"

"Tomato soup?"

"Ah, yes, enter my castle and share a cup with me," he said in a gallant tone.

I was always overcome with a sense of amazement about his self-assurance, and the fluidity of his one liners. A man who thinks on his feet is so seductive and appealing.

My parents attended my dad's college reunion at Yale with four other couples. During the cocktail hour the first evening Hank Walsh, the class president, approached my father who was telling a story about a recent business trip to the middle east. Hank grabbed his elbow and stopped him midstream to ask whether he could give an impromptu speech at breakfast the next morning about his travels. Without skipping a beat, he accepted.

My mother loved to tell the story of how he got up there and had everybody totally captivated before they even finished their first cup of coffee. He even got a standing ovation. There was nothing my dad couldn't handle with poise and certainty. He was incredibly comfortable with who he was and his accomplishments in life. Other people's opinions did not sway his own. Many people assume because I resemble my father, tall, dark and extroverted, that I possessed those same characteristics. It was not so, but when I recognized the same in Samuel; I was drawn in like moth to flame.

"Ah, my trusty knight," I continued the charade allowing him to kiss my hand.

"Where would you like to dine today, my lady? The upper or lower tier?"

"The lower tier, kind sir," I said demurely, surrendering to his pull down the stairs. While he was unfolding the white paper bag from the drugstore containing our soup and rolls, I could hardly contain the decision that had come to me in the last forty-eight hours. Those two days had flown by, yet it felt like a lifetime as it stretched toward this moment. I placed my lunch in the chair next to me and took Samuel's hands in mine. For a millisecond he averted my gaze, but then quickly returned.

"There is no place else to be except with you," I said with conviction and excitement in my voice.

"Are you absolutely sure Olivia? Have you taken enough time?"

"Yes, enough time to know that if I don't do this, I will forever be living a lie. This is not to say that I am not terrified, because I am, on many levels."

He surrounded me with a reassuring hug, kissing the top of my head over and over. He was gentle at first but when he found his way into my mouth, we got lost in the intensity that the moment held for both of us.

The search for a new home was now truly upon us. Having told Dane that evening about my final decision, hope was gone from our household, replaced by high levels of anger and tension. I begged him to stay at his family's house just long enough for me to find and move into a rental. He was adamant about not leaving, and there were many days I felt I would crack open and my contents would leak all over if I didn't get some relief. On top of the stress level, I was filled with guilt and anxiety about what Julia and Adam were being exposed to because of me.

Then an unexpected window of opportunity presented itself in the midst of all this anguish. Samuel was attending a trustee luncheon meeting of the Historical Society. He was conveniently seated next to Ruth Stilling a woman he had befriended a few years back when they collaborated on an exhibit together. As was the case with many women, young and old, she had found Samuel to be rather charming. Recently she had heard through her weekly bridge grapevine that Samuel and I had become an item. For reasons still unknown to both of us, something happened between the salad and entrée. He relayed it to me the next day at a coffee break we conveniently created for ourselves.

⌒

"Samuel, how are you doing these days with all the changes going on in your personal and professional life?" Ruth said politely but very directly.

As he walked me through the conversation, he emphasized that he was cautious and guarded in his response to her.

"Well, with the new storage building breaking ground I have my hands full."

"Oh, I know that. But I'm more concerned about how you and Olivia are faring."

"Well, thanks for asking. As you can imagine making this kind of decision on a small island surrounded by Hanson history and family is rather confining and difficult. At this point I am worried about Olivia getting some space. She is being bombarded at every corner. Dane is still living at home while we look for a rental."

"I can imagine how difficult it must be for her, especially with two small children. I think I may be able to help with a temporary respite for her until things settle down a bit for all of you."

"What do you mean?"

"Well Alvin and I have a house in the northern part of the state on Eagle Lake. It's hidden in the woods and extremely private. When it gets too crowded here in the summer we usually head there for a week or so at a time. It's a perfect getaway spot for Olivia."

"I don't know what to say, Ruth. That's very generous of you."

"Talk to Olivia and see if the idea appeals to her. If it does have her contact me and we'll discuss the details."

"I will and thank you for your concern."

As he conveyed the conversation, I was very receptive. Amazingly enough I was able to work out the details with Dane and Marietta so I could head up to Eagle Lake for four solid nights. I think Dane wanted the space from me as much as I needed it from him, though he probably wouldn't have taken it. In return for the Stillings' generosity, as well as to keep myself busy, I offered to get the place opened up and ready for the season. I would do light cleaning, change bedding and wash curtains.

Before I left, I managed to have one more strained conversation with Dane, hoping to sway him in the direction of moving out temporarily. It was delicate and focused solely on the children and their needs. Dane had hired a lawyer and said he would review it with him and let me know when I returned.

Chapter Twenty-seven

It was a windy spring day when I left on the early boat headed for Ruth and Alvin's place. I waved to Samuel from the deck with tears curling around my eyelids. I held on to the steel railing as I began my first extended journey alone since I had become a mother. It seemed so long ago that I had intentionally carved out space in my life exclusively for me. Prior to marrying Dane my graduate school life in California was an active and political one. Consequently, I was exposed to many independent, adventurous women, who rock climbed, sea kayaked and ventured forth alone on a regular basis. It was almost intimidating at times. But they did inspire me to take my first solo camping trip.

One weekend I took my drum made by the Zuni Indians and headed for the foothills. I drummed by a small, blazing fire until unfamiliar sounds finally drove me into the cramped back seat of my car. When the sun came up, I emerged delighted and proud having spent the night alone, even if my Volkswagen had been a protective buffer between myself and the possibility of encountering creatures from a Stephen King novel. I had spent the night alone in the woods and felt more comfortable among the ranks of my high-risk comrades.

As I disembarked from the steamship, I felt pangs of exhilaration and trepidation with a whole ocean of distance between me and my cubs. I walked over to the car rental agency and drove away in the blue Mazda that would take me on the next leg of my journey. After pulling into the first convenience store for coffee and an ample supply of my suckers, I began to settle in. By the time I reached the long, winding driveway leading to the Stillings' Eagle Lake home, I was relaxed from the scenic drive and a selection of my favorite cassettes.

I was stunned by the size of their "little getaway" and its spectacular view. It was situated on a wooded lot that backed up to the lake where there was a small bridge at the edge of the yard, leading to a tiny island. There were white birch trees and a weathered Adirondack chair inviting me out for morning coffee and a good book. I was glad Samuel had convinced me to take along his binoculars at the last minute. It wasn't something I would have thought of, but looking across the vast expanse of water, there was much to see on the other side. It was magnificent, yet somewhat isolated. Once it registered just how far any neighbors were, a slight chill ran through me. After my morning ritual out on the small island and the chores were completed, I would be utterly alone with lots of free time, without the usual maternal and domestic obligations to occupy me. Part of that felt good, not having a schedule, a meal to cook, or wash to do. But all that time with no one and nothing to fill it, felt unnerving too. It had been over three years since I had been the mistress of my own schedule.

As soon as I got my duffel bag from the car, I headed straight for the tiny island. Sitting on the slab of rock, I remembered back to a similar place from my younger days. My father's parents lived in western Pennsylvania and we used to gather there for many a holiday feast. The food seemed to go on forever, along with the boring adult conversation, so as they lingered over the figs, demitasse and pastries after the meal, I would head for a large rock in the front yard. It was surrounded by magical white birch trees. It was there I would take my Madame Alexander dolls and create a whole new world for myself. When I look back, it was a time in my life when I clearly needed no one except my imagination to accompany me. *What had become of that girl?*

I took in the panoramic view before me as the sun slipped away. The sky began to take on a crimson glow and the water reflected back its brilliance. I crossed my arms and rocked back and forth in a soothing motion in this newly created solitude. I would be here four nights, able to watch the sun rise and set on my own. It was dark by the time I got back to the house. When I entered the living room, I felt a bit uneasy in the unfamiliar surroundings. As Ruth had said, the furnishings were less elaborate and formal than their Algonquin home, but every bit as tasteful. After a look around I headed upstairs to select my sleeping quarters. I decided on the master bedroom because of its stunning view, and a deck complete with a hot tub under the stars. Before I could sleep, I called Samuel to tell him I had arrived safely. We had decided after that initial call we would have no contact until my return. When I hung up, a sudden rush of panic flooded my mind, but fortunately the long drive and the luxurious king size canopied bed quickly swept me away into sleep.

When I awoke the next morning, I was a bit disoriented at first. It took a moment to put the large armoire and rocking chair with my coral colored sweatshirt slung over the side into context. When it all came together, I lay there enjoying the morning sounds and thinking about Adam and Julia. I wondered how Dane and Marietta were doing with them. The children were probably up and about in their padded onesies looking for a fresh cup of cheerios right about now. I deep pang of longing lodged itself inside me. Not wanting the feeling to linger, I got up and headed for the kitchen. I was delighted to find a supply of Colombian coffee and its maker easily accessible. While it was brewing, I washed up and looked forward to crossing the bridge with mug in hand.

The four days and nights flew by more quickly than I imagined. The most unexpected event occurred on my final day at Eagle Lake. After my final chores for the Stillings were completed, I headed out for one last walk in the woods nearby. As I got farther and deeper into it, something started building inside that wanted out. Before I knew it, a dark, primal sound was heaving forth from deep inside me; a place I didn't know existed until it made its way up and out. It was a cross between moaning and howling. I fell to my knees and let it take over me in ways I didn't realize existed in my emotional repertoire. The guttural sound produced by letting go of Dane, the life we shared, the familiarity, and the pain I was creating for my children, gradually built momentum and rolled into uncontrollable tears and sobbing. When it was over, I lay on the ground exhausted, but somehow knowing it was a fitting conclusion to my stay, and the birch trees seemed to concur.

Chapter Twenty-eight

When I arrived at the Algonquin airport, I looked out the door for a cab. Samuel wasn't meeting me because we decided it was too soon to be seen together. With my duffel bag slung over my shoulder and knapsack on my back I headed out toward the taxi lineup in the front of the terminal.

"Olivia, where are you headed? Do you need a lift?" It was Demi Sorensen from my Lamaze class. She was a fairly easygoing type so even if she had gotten wind of my situation, she probably wouldn't treat me any differently.

"Over near Kezar Road out by the Montessori School."

"I go right past there on my way home," she opened the door.

Our conversation was light and easy. We had the common ground of our children to fall back on. When we got to the corner of Samuel's road I suddenly said, "This is fine, you can pull over here."

I think it seemed odd to Demi that I wanted to get out there, but I made the excuse that I needed some fresh air after such a long drive, and I was walking down to a friend's house. Moving toward Samuel's my heart sped up and my stomach churned. I could see the soft light filtering through his translucent muslin curtains.

The thought of being in physical contact with him after five days sent me reeling, but I was also torn about not seeing my children the minute I stepped foot back on island. It felt like a betrayal of my maternal instincts. No matter which choice I made, neither felt peaceful inside.

When I arrived at the door, I could see Samuel comfortably stretched out on his couch with black sweatpants and a turquoise tee-shirt with *Key West* printed across the front in black lettering. He was deeply engrossed in a phone conversation and I felt like an intruder as I opened the screen door. Just as panic was threatening to overwhelm me, he looked up and welcomed me in as he balanced the phone under his chin.

"Hey baby, I'll be right with you," and he pulled me down beside him. As he was finishing up, I was subtly trying to figure out who it was and why he hadn't hung up immediately. *Didn't he realize what a huge step this was for me to come to him first instead of my babies?* I tried to appear composed and disinterested in his conversation until I realized the voice on the other end belonged to a woman. My insides did a somersault and I plunged head long into a state of anxiety that was beginning to feel vaguely familiar though very un-welcome. The team of horses in my head raced onward. *Who was I fooling thinking I could have this handsome, sensitive, intelligent man all to myself? Am I really going to be able to pull this off?* When he hung up and fully embraced me, I could barely feel him through the protective layer of my numbness that was spreading itself over my body.

"Welcome back, boy have I missed you!" He started to kiss me, but I looked down.

"What's up? What's wrong?"

"Who was that on the phone?" I began my interrogation. "Mimi Dillingham, the woman from the Society for The Preservation of New England Antiquities. Remember she was the one who helped with the restoration."

Trying to mask the green web that was spinning itself around my heart I inquired further.

"Oh, did you call her about some information you were needing?"

"No, she called me to let me know she would be on island next week. She's doing a job for some people I referred to her."

This just wasn't good enough. My catlike curiosity stalked further, attempting to trap the mouse.

"Are you going to see her while she's here?"

Samuel started to hear the edge growing in my voice.

"Not unless it's for business reasons. Do I detect a problem here?"

He started to rub my thigh and gently kiss the back of my neck, an irresistible spot for me that we had recently discovered. I felt the hot blush of shame and embarrassment. It was me who had been caught instead.

"Well, yes I am having a problem Samuel. I'm turning my entire life, and my children's, inside out and upside down. I just got back from four days of dealing with some of the emotional repercussions of that decision, and I thought you would be more attentive and attuned. Instead I find you on the phone with a woman when I arrive."

I was surprised to hear all that come out of my mouth. He too was clearly stunned at the extent of my now blatant insecurity. He became defensive in response to what he considered an over the top reaction.

"Olivia, that was a professional call. If it's a problem I won't see Mimi. Our conversation was business related, nothing more. How was I supposed to know she was going to call ten minutes before you got here?"

I sensed his irritation and it scared me back into a place where I could compose myself and contain the magnitude of what was going on. I backed off and quickly did an emotional cover-up.

"You're right," I said. "It was just uncomfortable for me because I just returned from dealing with a lot and it felt like a rude awakening."

He kissed my forehead, assuming the storm had passed.

"Shall we start over?" He pulled me down on top of his hard, anxious body.

After a restless night I pulled myself out of Samuel's bed at five that morning. His alarm clock was set for six but there was no way I could wait any longer. I wanted to get home to my babies. After turning the coffee maker on I headed into the bathroom. I wanted to wash up, brush my teeth, and at least get some moisturizer on before Samuel laid eyes on me. As I splashed tepid water on my face, he walked in rubbing his sleepy eyes wearing navy polka dot boxers. Without skipping a beat, he lifted the toilet seat and relieved himself. Again, I was taken aback by this man's comfort level. Here I was trying to get presentable before he got a look at me, and he was as uninhibited as a dog doing his morning business on the neighbor's lawn. We were in such different places.

When I proceeded to do my daily stretching routine, I was keenly aware that he was going about his own, without taking much notice of mine, as I spread my legs in the typical dancer's stance. As new as I was, I was not the center of his universe. However, he was clearly disappointed that I didn't want to linger over coffee. Halfway into my first cup I insisted we get moving. My impatient desire to see my children baffled him as he grabbed his keys and denim jacket. When we got into the truck, he turned toward me with a grin.

"Excited, aren't you?"

"Actually, very nervous. I've never been away from them this long. I don't know how they, or Dane, will be when I arrive."

"That's true. A lot could have happened in five days. Let's hope he didn't get too much input from his family and friends."

"Actually, I hadn't thought much about that aspect of my absence. They probably had a field day. I bet my scarlet letter is getting bigger and bolder by the day."

I shuddered at the thought of all the gossip that had circulated around the island by now. When I was up at Eagle Lake, I had been temporarily disconnected from it all. When we were three houses from mine Samuel pulled over and took my hand.

"You going to be okay?"

"I suppose. I'll let you know how it all unfolds tomorrow at work."

It seemed so strange after spending the whole night together to now be going back to my other life.

"I'll be waiting." And he was gone.

As soon as I opened the front door, I knew something was different. It was dark and silent, so the children were obviously still asleep. I wondered if Dane was in the guest room or if he gone back into our room during my absence. Marietta peeked out of our bedroom door.

"Welcome back." She gave me a warm hug which helped my re-entry.

"The babies are still asleep."

"I need to look in on them." I slipped into their rooms and stood over them, watching their chests rise and fall with each new breath.

After getting my fill of their soft noses, fingers and toes I headed back to hear how everything went. Marietta had a cup of tea in hand and some coffee brewing for me. She always seemed to know just what to do to make me feel more comfortable, even under such trying circumstances. What a gift she was, to all of us. When we settled down on the couch, she grabbed the comforter and covered up both sets of our feet.

"Where is Dane?"

"He moved over to his dad's after he put the kids down last night." My insides did a flip flop and tightened against the unexpected news.

"You mean he's gone?"

"Yes, he said you could call him regarding the children." It all sounded so cold and formal.

"Did he tell Adam and Julia?"

"As best he could. He told them he would be back to see them every day." I scrounged for the painful details.

"Did they cry? What did they do?"

"They were upset by what they could understand, but he was very soothing."

I knew she was trying to be kind by not describing the scenario in detail. Nevertheless, my guilt rushed in to pick up the slack. While my children's father was moving out, I was alone in the woods doing primal screaming. *What kind of mother am I? I wasn't there to comfort them.*

"I should have been here!"

"Olivia, for heaven's sake, don't be so hard on yourself. I was here, and after Dane left, they both went off to sleep right away." I would have no part of her comforting.

"It doesn't matter Marietta. I should have been here, and I wasn't!" I left the room in a hurry, knowing I was going to completely breakdown. I didn't want to make her any more uncomfortable than she probably was, though she would never admit it.

When the children awoke, I spent an extra-long time taking turns cuddling and rocking each of them. First one would nestle in for a while, and then having their fill they would slide down my leg and make room for the other. I scrutinized every facial expression and gesture they made, looking for signs of emotional trauma due to my absence and their daddy's departure. But as they munched on their biscuits and sang along with Sesame Street, they seemed relatively normal. I prodded them here and there to see if they would talk about what happened, but I could get very little out of them. They were more interested in watching Oscar and the Cookie Monster.

When I got into the office the next morning the pile of articles on my desk for the quarterly magazine was a welcome sight. I just wanted to be immersed in something that would keep me totally engrossed. I was shocked at the sheer rawness and depth of my reaction to Dane leaving. These last three months living under the same roof with him had been a tremendous strain, yet there was an odd comfort about it all. Maybe it was because we had been through so much the last twelve years and I was so used to having him around, even if I no longer loved him in the same way. A deep caring and attachment remained, and it felt like a limb had been severed. It was far more painful than I imagined. An hour went by and I edited at least three articles. Absorbed in my fourth one, Samuel appeared at the door with a latte in hand.

"Time for a coffee break lady," he said in his playful, carefree manner. Noticing I was pretty involved in what I was doing, he pushed a little.

What's the matter? How were the kids when you saw them this morning?"

"He moved out."

"Dane? Where to?"

"He's at his dad's."

"That must have been a relief for you, baby."

He began rubbing my shoulder which made me want to lash out about how totally off base he was. But I didn't want him to know just how far. That would surely give away my strong remaining connection to Dane.

"Actually, it was a shock. I was less prepared than I thought." I toned it down.

"I can see why. He blind-sided you. But you have been saying how tense it's been living under the same roof."

"Definitely. It's just the way it all happened. I wanted to be there when he told the children."

"I can see that. You wanted to comfort them when he left."

I knew that was only part of it. I also knew that it would have been better for me to witness the actual episode, so it became more real and tangible. Now it seemed like a dream, or a story I was hearing about someone else's life, but not my own.

"How are the kids doing with it?"

"They seem okay, just a bit cranky and out of sorts. With me having been gone for the first time and now Dane, it's a lot for them."

"Yes, but it will all settle down as soon as you get moved into the rental and they establish a new routine there."

He tried to soothe things for me, but I knew it wasn't that simple, neat and tidy. Adam and Julia would have a long road of healing ahead. There would be scars from the wounds now being inflicted. They would no longer be living full-time with their dad and everything was changing in their little world. I felt the cloak of guilt wrap itself tightly around me. I was the cause of all this pain and turmoil in the lives of these three precious people, yet I was compelled to keep moving toward Samuel and the promise of this new life with him. No matter what my rational mind, friends, and family tried to do to dissuade me from this course of action, I could not be deterred. But in the background the voices of fear whispered inside my head.

When I arrived home from work that night everything felt so strange and out of sync. There would be no Dane at the back door around five-thirty accompanied by loud screams and giggles as the children headed down the hallway to greet him, or singalongs while I cooked dinner. This was the first real taste of being without him.

Chapter Twenty-nine

Over the next few weeks Dane would come and go, sometimes announcing his arrival, others not. The lack of routine and unpredictability drove me crazy. But he would not relinquish his spontaneous, unorthodox nature to me. It was like his last stronghold. I tried to convince him that regular, scheduled visits would be much easier on the children. But that rationale did not sway him, and he was fiercely stubborn about what little control he had left. Adam and Julia were always overjoyed to see him, and once they were in his company it was like he had never been gone. Meanwhile I tried to maintain as much structure in their lives as I could manage while the next phase of the transition was unfolding. When I began to bring boxes in to pack their belongings, the children began to react more strongly to leaving their nest. This crooked old house was the only home they had ever known.

I tried to console them by stopping every so often to rock them or read a story. I attempted to make a game out of throwing their toys in the boxes, but none of the distractions worked for long. They were being torn from their nest and it was having a dramatic effect on them both. Keeping it together was stretching me well beyond my comfort zone. I was dropping weight, usually eating only a bowl of popcorn for dinner when the kids were finally in bed. I would turn out the lights and find something distracting on television, zone out and munch away. It would allow me to rest my mind for a while, because the voices of guilt and fear were getting louder and harder to drown out.

As the move got closer and Dane spent more time with his family and friends, his posture of resistance toward me grew stronger. He dug his heels in and demanded Samuel not be in the presence of his children until our divorce was final. This limited my time with Samuel exclusively to the working day or when Julia and Adam were with their father. So, when I was with my children, I couldn't be with the man I loved, and when I was with Samuel, I couldn't be with my children. I wrenched inside as I tore straight down the middle.

I continually wanted Samuel's physical presence and touch to remind me why I was creating all this upheaval in my life. My need to see him, feel him, hear him took on a slightly addictive quality. Finally moving day arrived and Marietta was available to take Adam and Julia for the afternoon. Samuel arrived in his truck and immediately went into motion, loading boxes into the cab. I was relieved to have him there, and the children away from this chapter. Samuel's sense of direction, intent and warm embrace was just the reassurance I needed. Somehow stacking boxes and watching them disappear into the truck gave me a concrete, grounded sense about the future. The dreamlike quality of the last few months shifted into a kind of domestic reality.

When we unlocked the door to forty-four Rumford Lane, I once again silently wondered what kind of moments would be shared here, what words would be exchanged within these walls, what memories would create themselves, and what would our life as a step-family look like?

"Hey, where are you?" Samuel was approaching the doorway with a huge stack of boxes.

"Could you hold that door for me honey? I'm loaded here!"

I opened the old maple door and he stepped through. As he passed by, he planted a light kiss on my nose. It felt good, like a warm welcome home nuzzle from a devoted canine. And he sure looked good behind those boxes; strong, capable, directed, and ready to head the household with me. If only I could hold onto that feeling of well-being and security, though it seemed contingent upon his presence. After the truck was empty, we sat down on the floor, leaning against the sturdiest tower of boxes.

"Well baby, we've done it! We're here in our new home together! How does it feel?"

"So far, so good."

I smiled, looking around the room at what had to be done to make this space a home. It felt great that we were there doing this together. Up to this point so much of our time had been either at work, or behind closed doors, hidden away. Unloading the truck brought an element of normalcy into our relationship, after all the secrecy and deception.

"How long will Marietta have the kids?"

I glanced at my watch. I only had an hour and a half before I had to be back at her place to pick them up.

"Another hour and a half."

"Great! How about I go and get us two lattes to celebrate?"

I so appreciated his thoughtfulness. It made me feel a little pampered and somehow protected.

"Sounds wonderful! Hurry back big guy!"

I bear hugged him and watched him climb into his truck and maneuver his way out of the winding, dirt driveway. Turning inside I scanned the modest furnishing that came with the rental. They were a bit tacky to say the least, and I flashed on my mother's face as she entered the room. With her elegant and classic taste, she would be horrified, but perhaps with some of our artwork and throw rugs I could bring things to an acceptable level.

On the second floor now, I wandered from room to room. In Adam's room I pictured him under his tugboat quilt sleeping soundly, making that sweet, whispering noise with his lips as he gently exhaled. Julia's pale rose colored room brought images of her spinning and swirling in her tutu, giggling wildly as she fell to the floor with giddy dizziness. The sage green master bedroom had a window facing a cluster of pine trees. I could see Samuel and I wrapped in each other's bodies with the wind chimes singing to us through the window. My vivid imagination was such an ally at times like these when it conjured such pleasant images. If only I could maintain that relationship with it. But as time wore on and Samuel hadn't returned, it flipped from friend to foe. He had been gone for over an hour and a trip to town and back should have taken a lot less than that. The image that followed was him talking with Lucy, the attractive freckled-face redhead at the coffee shop. He mentioned they had gone out to dinner once. Now I saw them laughing and talking while she slowly steamed the milk. Caught in the middle of her vivacious smile, Samuel breezed through the front door.

"Hey sweetie, sorry it took so long! What a line!"

I pretended not to be concerned about the delay and took the warm cup from his hand.

"Not only was there a long line, but I ran into the people from New York whose kitchen I did a few years back. Very chatty folks, and they asked if I had time to build a deck off their bedroom." I slowly moved from my fears and fantasies into the conversation.

"And what did you say?" I wondered how he would respond now that he was going from bachelorhood to family life.

"I told them all about you and the kids and how I wouldn't have any free time for quite a while." His response stifled the lurking demons that were groveling for bits of suspicion wherever they could find them.

When I picked up the children at Marietta's she said she couldn't get them to nap. They were whining all the way back to the house while I abruptly moved from my somewhat peaceful interlude with Samuel back to mothering. At the house I gathered up a few remaining miscellaneous items that we needed to spend our first night at Rumford Lane. Adam and Julia were hyper as they ran from one room to the next searching for their belongings. It took every ounce of emotional strength I could muster up to bundle them back up and get them into the car. As I backed out of the driveway for the last time, I looked in the rear-view mirror at my babies. Adam was chewing on what was left of his yellow blankie and Julia was sucking her thumb. *What had I done?*

By the time they were finally settled in for the night it was after eleven and I was ready to drop. I fell into the armchair in what vaguely resembled a living room. Amidst the box towers I scanned the space. It was quiet except for the clock on the kitchen wall, loudly passing time. I would have to get used to that new sound. There was a lot I had to get used to now, being alone with two toddlers among them. Samuel was moving in with us in a month, which seemed like forever when I looked around and thought about everything that had to be done to transform this place.

Eventually I lifted myself up and picked up a broom on route to the kitchen. While I made pizza that night the kids had sprinkled cheerios everywhere. I put on an apron, coiled my mane into a knot and started sweeping them into a pile. Disorder in my living space had always been a problem for me, as it had been for my mother. Everything had to be just so before we could go out and play with our friends, even on the weekends. Whenever I had sleep over dates my mother would always make me come home early to do chores. My friends thought this very odd since we had a housekeeper twice a week.

Spirals of hair fell from my scrunchie as I searched through a box for the dustpan. I entertained the thought of cutting my hair as the heat of summer approached. But what would Samuel think? Perhaps he wouldn't be as attracted to me. Now that I was finally down to a nice trim weight, the long hair really enhanced my looks. But right about now my appearance was that of an exhausted mother of two toddlers, with pizza sauce splattered across my striped apron. As I swept along, I barely noticed the headlights of a vehicle pulling in the driveway, until it was too late. Samuel was back for some reason and I had no time to rearrange myself or even brush my teeth. I probably had the remains of pizza crust wedged in between them.

"Surprise, surprise baby!" He grabbed me from behind.

"What brings you here at this hour?"

"I couldn't stay away." He snuggled in closer, pressing his pelvis into me. Instantly my body responded, and I forgot what I looked like. Before I knew it, we were on the couch, wrapped up in one another's bodies and removing our clothes. He pushed my underpants aside and entered me quickly. As he filled me up, I softly moaned with pleasure, but well aware of my children sleeping one flight up. We climaxed together and he lay on top of me breathing deeply, twisting my hair around his fingers. I ran mine back and forth across his tight buttocks. I loved the feeling of his chest hair brushing against me, in my fingers, all around me. I had never felt this kind of physical intensity with anyone, and it was as frightening as it was glorious.

When he left, I felt better about the move and this new life I was entering. The brief physical connection was like an emotional tranquilizer. But like all tranquilizers, it would wear off by morning.

Adam and Julia both woke up much earlier than usual that first day in our new home. They climbed into bed with me and would have no part of going back to sleep. I got myself up and got the coffee going. While I was dressing Julia for pre-school, Adam headed down the stairs on his own. I hadn't realized how much more complicated it would be to keep track of them in a place with two floors. I was so used to living on one floor where I could locate them just by the sounds they made. There were no worries about stairways and falling. I closed Julia's door and left her standing there half dressed, while I checked on her brother, who had luckily made it to the first floor safely. I carried him back up, hearing Julia crying, not understanding why I had suddenly shut the door and left her alone. As I opened it, Adam spit up all over my favorite yellow linen jacket. I was fast reaching my limit as I grabbed a cloth diaper to wipe it off. Adam knew I was upset, and his little lip began to quiver, which was no surprise. We were all in transition and this was our first morning on our own in unfamiliar surroundings. I felt like joining the shrieking chorus as I pulled up Julia's pants and headed into my room to find something else to wear that wasn't wrinkled or still packed away.

I was unsuccessful with the usual remedy of Sesame Street and we were plumb out of cheerios. I hated resorting to television to pacify them but this morning it was an absolute necessity. My mother used to refer to television as the "idiot box" and as a child my viewing time and choices were extremely limited. *Walt Disney* and *Lassie* were weekly carrots held out in front of us if we did what was expected. But as I got my stuff together for work, I tried to be merciful on myself, allowing "Big Bird" to fill in for me.

By the time I arrived at the office I felt like half the day was already over. While taking off my sneakers, I noticed Samuel's line was lit up. He was already off and running. He certainly was hyper conscientious about his professional life, which continued to amaze me. While I slipped my beige heels on, an attractive blond woman walked in.

"Can I help you?" I said in a cordial, rather businesslike tone.

"Yes, my name is Mimi Dillingham. I'm here to see Samuel Ferrell."

I tried not to appear unnerved by her request. I remembered the name from a memo that crossed my desk referring to SPNEA in Boston. This was the woman Samuel had been on the phone with the night I came in from the lake house. He said he wasn't going to see her when she was on island. My gut tightened and the fear whispered.

"Is he expecting you?" The crucial question.

"Not really, but I was in the area and I thought I'd pop in on him." *Oh, you did, did you?* I silently responded. I looked at Samuel's line and it was no longer occupied. I picked up the receiver and buzzed him. In a cool, detached voice I said,

"Mimi Dillingham is here to see you. Shall I send her up?"

He hesitated for a moment, obviously caught off guard. This reaction was definitely in his favor. At least he hadn't known she was coming and tried to hide it from me. Or did he know and just covered it up because he assumed I would have a hard time? The voices in my head were no longer whispering, they were shouting.

"Yes, I guess so. I had no idea she was coming. I've got a real tight schedule. By the way, good morning."

"She'll be right up." I was abrupt and ignored his greeting. I turned to the lovely, fair-haired Mimi in her short-pleated skirt.

"Go up the stairs, take a left and go down the hall. His office is the first one on the right."

"Thank you, I know the way."

Clearly this woman had no idea of the emotional cyclone she created by her mere presence. As she walked up the stairs I glanced at my watch. How long would I have to endure their meeting? Samuel mentioned a busy schedule so it couldn't be too long, or could it?

I tried to busy myself by catching up on phone calls related to the next issue of the quarterly. I prolonged my conversations to keep myself from continually glancing at my watch. It seemed like forever until I heard their footsteps coming down the stairs. Samuel and Mimi came through my door. She turned to him as she started to zip up her briefcase.

"Thank you for all the information. It was very helpful."

In his boyish, polite way he responded in kind.

"No problem. Happy to help anytime." *Anytime*, that meant they would be seeing each other again. While wrapped in the grips of my fear, Samuel came over and hugged me.

"You okay, honey?"

The million-dollar question asked in such an innocent, unassuming tone. I was unresponsive to his touch and did not meet his eyes. The fear tugged at me, tighter this time.

"I'm fine, I guess."

"What's wrong? Are you upset about Mimi? I had no idea she was coming. She needed some information about lumber companies she could contact."

Still I could not yield to the sense he was making. I wrestled with the demon that had me flat on my back at this point.

"Oh, I'm sure there was a perfectly good reason for her visit. It's just a delicate, scary time for me."

"But baby, I'm with you. What kind of reassurance do you need? I still have a job to do."

I sensed a little agitation in his voice so I threw the demons off and tried to be more open to him, afraid he might just turn on his heels and walk away.

"I know, I know. It's just that there's so much change going on for me right now."

I grabbed his hand and held it.

"There's a lot going on for both of us," he corrected me somewhat firmly as he let go,

"Try not to forget that I'm in the circle too. And I wouldn't be if I wanted to be somewhere else, with someone else, got that?"

He gave me the infamous smile and wink that got me on board his bus in the first place. Once again, the voices were silenced by this momentary reassurance. Like circus lions having finished a piece of raw meat, they lay back licking their chops. I knew they would be back for more, but I went with that seductive wink for now.

Chapter Thirty

Before Samuel moved in life felt chaotic and exhausting. Being alone with the children before work and during the bedtime routine was a real challenge. One night I was getting Julia out of the bathtub and Adam once again ventured down the stairs on his own, only this time he slipped and fell. He wasn't hurt, just frightened which then made three of us, Julia reacting to my reaction. I called Samuel that night and he went out the next morning and bought a safety gate and installed it. As I watched him on his hands and knees wearing a leather tool belt with a hammer at his left hip, I felt so safe and protected. He was so strong, decisive and efficient, not to mention knowledgeable about all household mechanics.

If only I could cultivate that same feeling of safety on an emotional level when I was alone, or in social situations with Samuel that involved other women. Our social life was non-existent at that point because we didn't dare make a public debut on the island yet but being socially isolated never felt good to me. I always found people to be so stimulating, but now that the voices had arrived it was a double-edged sword for me. I wanted the contact, but I feared being around other women now, especially attractive women.

The day finally arrived when Samuel moved in and we began another kind of family. As I watched him carry one box after another out of his truck, I was filled with excitement, anticipation and yes, my new companion, fear. *Would all this work out?* Would he be able to sustain his calm temperament around Adam and Julia? Would he continue to love me when he really found out about my insecurities and habits? And what about the voices, the demons that had begun to prey on my mind? I headed out to his truck to help merge his life with mine, dragging my anxiety behind me. Adam and Julia stood by the window watching him enter their space, essentially without their permission. They seemed curious and surprised all at once. Who was this man and where did he belong in their lives? But when he came back with the last truck load and pulled out a red and yellow seesaw, he was off to a good start. They both danced around him with delight, clapping their hands as he set it up outside the kitchen window. As I turned to put coffee on for us, I thought, perhaps all would be well after all.

I had no idea how rapidly things would shift from those first few days of spontaneity, passion and intensity, to a predictable, structured way of living with Samuel. After the first week, I noticed that Samuel was no longer interested in nocturnal lovemaking. His first two nights we made love on the couch and then the kitchen table, both times were erotic, quick and satisfying. But as we entered the second week of family living, by nine in the evening he was in bed reading a Grisham novel. He would cuddle up to me in an affectionate way, but there were no sexual overtones to his touch. His immersion into reading immediately threw me off center. Part of what had compelled me to turn my life upside down was the chemistry that stirred whenever Samuel was close by. I had assumed, until now, that was totally reciprocated. All those moments when we couldn't have each other in the truck, during lunch at the museum, our hands groping all over one another, and now he lay beside me, snoring no less. I eventually had to leave the room to get some sleep, only to return before Adam and Julia woke up. I didn't want to give them something else to worry about. All that I had fantasized about was quickly deteriorating and after only a month I was questioning what I had done.

I had come from a situation where my sexual desire for Dane had gradually subsided and turned into friendly affection, and now I had a voracious appetite for my new lover who was becoming less and less available. Weekend afternoons during nap time and Wednesday evening when the children were with Dane had become the routine. What a cruel joke! My mother's words, "And now you have made your bed and you must lie in it," echoed through my head. Even though Samuel's body was next to mine, I felt disconnected and separate from him. It was as if he had constructed an invisible fence between us at certain times, and I didn't dare try to climb over it. When I did broach the subject, he seemed somewhat abrupt and defensive, so I let it be.

Things began to feel unsafe and out of control and I longed for intimate conversations with Dane where I could unburden myself of all this craziness and disappointment. He would always listen patiently and absorb them like a sponge over a watery surface. When we had those talks about whatever was bothering me, they always freed me up. I felt totally accepted and loved, in spite of myself. Growing up with my parents had so many conditions. Being thin, attractive and feminine pleased my mother. She glowed like a lightening bug when I went along with current fashion trends, kept my hair long and curled it. My dad wanted motivated, high achievers for children. When I managed to make the honor roll in middle school, he doubled my allowance that week. But with Dane I didn't have to jump through any hoops, he was there cheering me on anyway. It was like being in an oversized rocking chair, curling up, and being just plain comfortable there. Now I was really beginning to miss that. But there was no turning back from this life changing, enormous decision I had made.

But another aspect of my life was slowly becoming more comfortable. When Samuel would come home from work and greet the three of us like we were a *real* family, it was so reassuring. He would lift Adam into the air as he took off his hat, and swirl with Julia as she welcomed him with her latest dance. He really *was* a sweetheart, and he was taking to parenting much faster than most bachelors would. Perhaps that's where some of that passion was being channeled, rather than just toward me.

Chapter Thirty-one

The next weekend the kids were with Dane and we had some spontaneous lovemaking in different parts of the house. I even managed to lure him out into the back of the truck one starry night, and we gave the heavens a glorious show as my naked buttocks lifted skyward. Lying under sleeping bags afterward, I felt satiated and secure because in that moment I was desirable enough to move Samuel out of his comfort zone and routine.

The next morning, he had errands to run and I stayed home to catch up on cleaning. But when he was gone longer than I expected, the gnawing began again. At first, I thought it was just low blood sugar because I hadn't eaten after two cups of strong coffee, but when it returned after my muffin and cheese, I knew they were back. *Hush up, will you!* I tried to drive them away, tell them they weren't welcome. But they were coming more and more now, whenever Samuel wasn't within my grasp or control. I tried blasting them away with some "greased lightening" super bathroom cleaner and a Tina Turner cassette while I scrubbed the toilet bowl. When I was coming up with the second load of laundry Samuel appeared in the doorway. He had a single crimson rose in hand.

"That's for your beautiful bare ass in the moonlight." He pinched my buttock as he handed me the delicate vase. Once again, I was caught off guard. I returned the pinch and put the rose down on the coffee table.

"You are full of surprises," I said.

"May it always be that way."

The next weekend we were forced to make our first public appearance as a known entity. The Historical Society was hosting a cocktail party as a kick off to the fundraising campaign. I selected my attire carefully, wanting the perfect balance of irresistible yet professional. I chose a short black and white silk dress, accentuating my long legs. I had managed to tan them in the backyard over the last few weekends when the kids were gone or napping.

When we entered the room and president of the board, Scott Timkin, started fawning all over me, I saw the first signs of jealously appear on Samuel's face. *What a delicious feeling!*

"Be careful of dirty old men lurking in the hallways," he said as he pulled me aside after I politely extricated myself from Scott. I noticed he used humor to deal with his discomfort rather than letting it become something bigger. This guy had real class, and he had chosen me, despite the fact I came with two toddlers, a package deal.

The evening went along smoothly until a stunning brunette appeared and began to monopolize Samuel's time. As part of my job I was taking photographs for the quarterly, so I launched into my professional mode and hid behind the camera. Mingling among the guests, I moved from inside the house to the patio and garden crowd. After Samuel finished his conversation with the dark-haired mystery woman, he tried to make contact, but I appeared too busy taking pictures.

On the way home I kept my distance, pretending to be preoccupied with getting the film back into their canisters. Eventually he pulled over and turned off the motor.

"So, what's this all about," he said in an exasperated tone.

"I was doing my job. I guess I got carried away. Besides, you were keeping yourself busy." There, I let it out of the cage.

"What's that supposed to mean?" His voice got louder and agitated.

"Well, I didn't see you standing around waiting for me. You were able to amuse yourself just fine."

"Oh, for god's sake Olivia, is this about me talking with Jill Stoddard? I did her kitchen cabinets a few years back and we were catching up on our lives. Was I supposed to walk away because she's an attractive woman?" *He* was feeling the demonic presence.

"No, of course not." On one level I meant it, I really did. But it was so hard for me to maintain that safety within myself.

"Well, I want you to promise me the next time we're in a situation like that you won't shut down and become inaccessible. I tried to reach you and you were like the ice queen."

I nervously took his hand, rubbing his thumb, hoping to smudge the episode from his memory.

"Okay, it's a deal." He squeezed my hand and reached for the ignition.

"Hey Samuel, how about a little nookie here on the side of the road?" I felt daring and relieved that I had narrowly escaped again from him realizing the magnitude of all this. He smiled and brushed my cheek gently.

"I'm exhausted after dealing with all those people and their superficial chatter. Let's take a rain check."

I was absolutely crushed. *How could he resist me?* Scott Timkin
and several of his cronies would have jumped at the chance. And
now Samuel could have me in silk across the front seat of his Ford,
and he had declined, again. What was missing in me?

"Sure, another time." I said in a hollow whisper.

Chapter Thirty-two

When the leaves turned, another repercussion of my choice gradually revealed itself as friends made during my marriage to Dane, like Ellie and Stephan, dropped out of my life. Lines were drawn, judgments made, and it felt like Jody Sampson's slumber party all over again. Now that I was wearing the big, bold, scarlet letter for everyone on island to see and comment on, it was lonely. I spent most of my time with Samuel, the children, or at work. I kept in touch with Miranda and a few women in our walking crowd, but now they all took on another dimension as well.

The most disturbing shift came over coffee one day with Miranda. After Samuel moved in, we hadn't spent much time together since that night at Cold Stream Tavern. I realized I hadn't been anxious to have her over on the weekends when the kids were with Dane, so we finally managed to set up a time for coffee one Saturday. With brioche in hand she asked me a million questions about my new life, and it was liberating to be able to talk about it openly without caution or fear of reprisal. Halfway through the conversation an odd expression came over her face that I hadn't seen before.

"Olivia, before you go any further there's something I need to share with you."

There was something foreboding in her expression. Miranda had always been a bit on the mysterious side, very self-contained. She kept you guessing.

"Well what is it? You're making me nervous."

"Okay, here goes," she inhaled in a way that was quite visible.

"Remember I told you that I met Samuel when he did that structural survey on our house?" I could tell she was leading up to something potentially uncomfortable, but I couldn't imagine what.

"Yes, I remember. What about it?"

"Anyway, we ended up buying it and he did some consulting with us as we restored it. As you know my marriage to Ruben was always a bit unstable, and Samuel's marriage to Cat wasn't going too well at that point either. So, one thing led to another, and after sharing a six pack one hot, sticky summer afternoon we ended up in bed."

My body caved in and I felt like I was going to lose my brioche. I tried to control it to the point where she couldn't see how visceral my reaction really was. I said nothing, so she continued.

"It was just that once. We both had a pretty good buzz on, with the heat and all. After that we sort of pretended it never happened. It was his final day on our job, so it was the last I saw of him, except driving around the island in his truck from time to time"

There was nowhere to go with this, but I felt like leaving immediately. Miranda was someone I had known and trusted all the years of our friendship, but now her initial response over wine at Cold Stream that night began to make sense. She was visibly disturbed, and obviously concerned, but I assumed it was about me leaving Dane with two babies in tow. I'm sure that was part of it, but there was much more to it. She had let me go on and on without revealing her little secret. I vaguely remember her saying something else after she told me how she met him, but I wasn't really listening because I was so preoccupied with avoiding Stephan when he came into the bar. Then my mind leapt to Samuel. He knew Miranda was a close friend so why hadn't he mentioned their interlude to me? Was there some kind of collusion going on here? I tried to compose myself while Miranda reached across the table and grabbed my hand.

"Olivia, I hope this has no bearing on our friendship. That was so many years ago. You two are so in love and clearly very happy so this shouldn't change anything, right?"

She searched my eyes for confirmation.

"You're right; I just don't understand why you waited so long to tell me. You had plenty of opportunities."

"Exactly. It seemed so long ago and therefore pointless. Anyway, your mind was made up no matter what I might have said that night at Cold Stream."

That was a strange comment to make.

"Yes, but given all the years we've been friends, it seems kind of unnatural. I guess I'm just disappointed, that's all."

"Well, Samuel didn't seem to think it was important enough either or he would have told you. So, it's really no biggie."

It was going to be a cold, gray complicated winter.

When Samuel got home and I confronted him, he had the same casual response as Miranda. It was so fleeting, insignificant, and long ago that he saw no reason to bring it up. He insisted he had not intentionally omitted the information. He was adamant that it was a non-issue.

I couldn't seem to get it behind me. Every menstrual cycle that winter brought emotional vacillation about my decision to be with him. I had come here thinking this focused, strong, assertive man was going to keep me safe and secure, and now I was feeling anything but safe. He had slept with my best friend, and I was being devoured by fear and insecurity, like moths all over a thick wool sweater in a dark closet.

Every professional or social function that Samuel participated in became reason for worry. I didn't dare convey the magnitude of it to him for it would surely send him running for the hills. Keeping a lid on it combined with my now fragile and more guarded connection to Miranda, left me few alternatives to deal with this enormous malignancy growing inside. Sometimes after Samuel had fallen asleep with his book on his chest, I would sneak downstairs in the darkness and call my dear friend and roommate from college. Lila was a confident, successful woman with a thriving advertising business that she had built from the ground up. She was a very practical sort of person who rarely expected happiness as a daily requirement. In college she used to say, if it's a good day, great, but I'm not setting myself up for disappointment by expecting it. Her life was solid, predictable and stable. She wouldn't dream of making a drastic change like I had. But since I did, and because she loved me dearly, she was there for support and comfort.

"Olivia, you've got to hurdle this thing," she would say repeatedly with strength and conviction in her voice. "This jealousy and mistrust will bury you. You can't let it, there's too much at stake."

After one of my nocturnal pep talks with her, I would feel a renewed sense of commitment. I was determined not to destroy what I had changed my and my children's lives for. Then things would go along smoothly for a while, with stolen, sweet moments when the kids were gone, and tender bonds building between Samuel, Adam and Julia when they were there.

Despite the fact we were renting, he put up a swing set next to the seesaw and they were delighted. Some evenings while I was cooking dinner he would go out and push one on the swing and balance the see saw with his foot for the other. And then the slightest moment of uncertainty triggered by Samuel getting a phone call from or having a meeting with any female would pull me back down into the whirling green vortex.

Around the holidays we dressed for Rosemary and Stan's wedding. Rosemary was the therapist who helped me navigate the delicate passage from ending my marriage and starting a life with Samuel. She listened attentively while I poured my guts out on her hand-woven rug. Their wedding took place in the old Quaker Meeting House on the bluff overlooking the bay. As we walked toward the festivities I looked up and spotted "Tara's Moveable Feast" van. It was an unmistakable butter yellow covered with hand painted red peppers encircling her name. *Wouldn't you know she'd be doing the food?* Tara was someone Samuel had gone on a blind date with. After that night she fixed a few wonderful meals for him, but it never got off the ground. Samuel didn't elaborate as to why, so my imagination took off with the sighting of those red peppers. Would he have misgivings when he saw her now that he knew some of my flaws? Would she find him more attractive now that he was "taken"? While the whispers scrambled my brain, Samuel came up behind me and put his arm around my waist.

"Come on lady, let's dance." As we entered the beautifully decorated dance floor the lively rhythm of the late Bob Marley propelled us into a fluid motion. Flowers cascaded from baskets and bodies wrapped in pastel sarongs swayed to the beat. Samuel had vacationed in Jamaica three times ('Jaja' as he fondly called it) so he had a real affinity to their music. As we danced, I scanned the room for Tara since she was currently the most threatening woman on the horizon. Most of the others were either older, plainer or taken. When the song was over, she came out of the swinging door of the kitchen with a colorful platter of finger foods arranged in artistic spirals. I watched Samuel carefully to see when he would notice her, and what his reaction would be. I was consumed by the moment and the voices went from soft to harsh. *Watch him, watch him.* At one point the voice inside sounded like my mother's.

We were at the country club for our usual Sunday brunch after church at Saint Bartholomew's. It was one of our more enjoyable weekend family rituals. The entire mood shifted when a perky, frosted hair waitress with a sheer white blouse came to our table to take beverage orders. As always, my father was warm, friendly and far too interested. This time my mother felt he had taken one step too far and she let him have it.

"Frederick, she's young enough to be your daughter!"

"What's wrong with being polite, Charlene? You're always saying manners are of the utmost importance, and I'm simply making up for the fact that yours seem to be missing at the moment!"

He sarcastically cut her to the quick while my sisters and I kept passing the bread basket, and my brother played with his new glittery blue yo-yo.

When Tara finally made her way to our side of the room, I had already managed to finish half my glass of champagne. This took the edge off slightly though not enough to quiet the demons dancing inside. She and Samuel exchanged a few trivial remarks and she moved on to the other guests. He nudged me playfully as if to say, "Now that was easy wasn't it?" If only he knew what that seemingly innocent and brief interaction had created in my mind.

Chapter Thirty-three

By spring Samuel grew restless. He had finished the latest restoration and the new storage facility was nearing completion. He started making comments about outgrowing his job, and life on this tiny island. He wanted more, he wanted bigger and I wasn't at all prepared for this discussion. Yet somewhere I could see his logic about change being good for us. There were times I felt like I was either suffocating or becoming invisible, depending on who was ignoring me that week. But to start all over somewhere else, work in separate places, and meet new people was worse than staying and dealing with what I already knew. He would meet new women and I wouldn't be there to keep a watchful eye over it all. That, along with taking the children farther away from Dane just about immobilized me, so we reached an impasse.

One night after we had put the kids down, we sat on the front porch sipping decaf.

"Olivia, we've got to move forward. I can't stay on this island much longer. What are we going to do to resolve this?" Another bridge to cross.

"Well, I'll need to talk to Dane and prepare him for this somehow."

"Look Olivia, you're not married to Dane anymore, you're with me. You need to stop putting him first!" I took a leap and landed somewhere I wasn't expecting.

"Samuel, I'm not married to you either!"

There was a long pause. The evening air suddenly felt cooler and I rubbed my hands along my forearms. About three months ago Samuel had mentioned an antique wedding band that belonged to his maternal grandmother, but he hadn't brought it up since.

"Then we'll just have to do something about that won't we?"

A month later we married in a private ceremony with Julia, Adam, Marietta as our witness, and the justice of the peace. We dined on hot dogs and coleslaw at Daggie's on the wharf and Samuel was asleep by ten. I lay in bed twisting the antique gold band around my finger feeling somewhat relieved we had formalized our commitment.

About two weeks later I set up a meeting with Dane after dinner one night. We decided on Colburn's Seafood so he could walk there from home. I ordered a white zinfandel while I waited for him to arrive. He arrived in his pink man-tailored shirt and snug, worn Levi's and I was amazed at how attractive he still looked to me.

"Hey Olivia, what's up?''

No warmth there. I patted the seat next to me.

"Join me for a drink before we get started."

"Look Olivia, I know you have some major thing you're going to throw at me so don't soft shoe."

"All right, but can't we just wait until we each have a drink?"

"Sure," he acquiesced.

I took a long sip of my wine attempting to loosen up. Funny, I never felt tense around Dane but the information I was about to dump on him made the butterflies in my belly flutter at high speed. After he finished half of his beer, I took the plunge.

"Samuel and I have been talking about our jobs at the Historical Society. We've gone as far as we can go professionally and financially. There is nowhere for us to go from here on the island so we're considering a move sometime next year."He banged his mug down on the glass tabletop.

"What next, Strega? How much more are you going to take from me?"

Strega. I hadn't heard that word since Juan Otillo; head of the Outpatient Rehab Department of the hospital had called me that. I first met him at the "get acquainted" cocktail party for staff when Dane started working there. He described me as exotic, mysterious and gypsy like. From our initial meeting he referred to me as "Strega", which meant "witch" in Spanish. As we became friends with he and his wife Elena, he boldly flirted with me whenever he got the chance. Before I could say anything else, Dane was up, pulling his chair away from the table.

"Dane, we need to finish this." He was out the door.

I paid the bill and wandered out to the parking lot. I felt like driving to the end of the island and beyond, wishing there was a bridge to the mainland. But I knew Samuel would begin to worry so I eventually headed home. As I pulled in the driveway, winding past the blueberry bushes, I wondered if this man would ever feel completely safe and comfortable.

When I walked into our room Samuel was in bed with an arm around each child and they were all wearing red plastic glasses from the children's doctor kits. My heart immediately warmed up to their cozy little scene. Hope does spring eternal in moments such as these. Perhaps it *would* all come together at some point. My mood swings were amazing and seemingly unpredictable.

That summer and fall brought several other Kodak moments, but none that stayed with me long enough. I would sit on the sun porch sipping coffee and watching Julia and Adam play on the swings and the seesaw. During those picturesque days it all seemed in balance, like a normal sort of family, as we created our own history. Then I would take a spontaneous trip to the bakery for our favorite cobblestone cookies and run into my former sister-in-law Holly. An icy edge formed around her greeting, and I crumbled like the stale donuts heaped in the corner for duck food. As I headed up the hill, pushing both kids in the stroller, it occurred to me that the flavor of my day had gone sour in just one chilly moment. I saw my interactions with the children shift based on that brief interlude at the bakery. *How can I let that happen? I'm snapping at my babies because Holly practically ignored me? I need to get a grip here. Where is my harbor in this lingering storm?*

When the holidays approached, oddly enough, I missed my past with the Hanson tribe. I did love all the activity and fanfare that surrounded their festivities. On Thanksgiving the children were with Dane, so Samuel suggested we do something "grown up." He made reservations at the Popham Inn overlooking the harbor. I had a special dress for the occasion, but part of me dreaded the stillness of it all. Over turkey and sausage stuffing I realized how different Samuel's social needs were from mine. He was totally content and felt no desire to add anyone to our equation, while I felt at a loss with no gatherings planned for the holiday season. We hadn't been invited anywhere.

He dragged his feet when I suggested having Miranda and her new beau Davis for drinks one night. But when Miranda called to say Davis was down with the flu, I was the one dragging my feet. The thought of my dear, attractive friend, who once bedded down with my husband, coming alone brought the choir of voices back. Envisioning the three of us sharing a bottle of her favorite Merlot was unsettling at best.

As I put on my snug, ivory wool dress I examined my profile wishing my soft, round belly were flat and tight like Miranda's. I ran some gel through my unmanageable hair and put on my leather belt from Italy. I had purchased it in the open market with Dane six years ago when my father had rented a villa on the Mediterranean coast and flew us all in for two weeks. Dane and I had taken a side trip to see the art in Florence. We stayed in a sweet bed and breakfast overlooking the Piazza Della Signoria, a square in the heart of the city. I could vividly recall feeling tremendously seduced by all Dane's artistic knowledge. He was like a tour guide who knew the detailed history of paintings and sculpture alike. When he was in control I was totally engaged, and he was so patient with my ignorance. I missed his accepting ways. As I sucked in my abdominal muscles, I also missed that feeling of utter security, perhaps because Dane was somewhat shy and reserved around other women most of the time. I gave myself the once over as I heard Miranda pull in the driveway. Before Samuel even got to the door she was in, obviously still feeling comfortable enough to do so.

I got downstairs in a hurry. Samuel must have been uneasy as well because he was already opening the Merlot. Miranda was by his side in her dazzling green Lycra and black leather. I used to be so quick to compliment her about her attire but this time I held back, so she took the lead.

"Don't we look stunning," she said while kissing me on both cheeks.

"Likewise, my dear." I heard myself say. Samuel came out with the wine and glasses.

"Shall we toast to all this beauty in one room?" That innocent remark stung like a hornet who had found its way in through a punctured screen on the back porch. I nervously jumped in.

"Miranda, tell us all about the Watson house on the cliff that you are photographing? Is it everything they say at the cocktail parties?" In addition to being gorgeous, she was talented as well. Everything she put her mind to turned out successfully. She had started her own photography business and was becoming very well-known on island for her work. I admired her entrepreneurial spirit. She went on to describe the house in great detail, its history, furnishing and structure. Samuel was totally engrossed in their common terrain. I sat back feeling like a spectator, watching Samuel's attention keep Miranda fueled. She was lapping it up, and if I was honest with myself, it was that same focused quality that pulled me into his snare as well.

Miranda went on and on about the cliff house and Samuel remained totally engaged. Eventually he sensed my discomfort and tried to pull me into the conversation but never really succeeded as I faded farther and farther into the background. Miranda tried asking me a few questions about work, but it never really went anywhere because I had already disappeared. After dinner I was relieved when she announced she had to head out because of an early shoot the next day. As I rinsed out the wine glasses after she left, I felt sick inside, feeling so threatened by one of my dearest friends. Surely it wouldn't always be this way. I would get over this once Samuel and I had been married for a while.

Chapter Thirty-four

Christmas with the children was bittersweet. I hadn't realized how attached I was to all the little traditions I had established during my marriage to Dane. It had always been so easy creating a festive space and I loved decorating our home. Now I was starting all over. I stood in the basement surrounded by wads of paper I had tossed out of the box the ornaments were packed in. Dane had told me to take all but what his mother had made by hand when we divided things up. It all looked so out of place here in this rental house with its cheap furniture and tacky wallpaper.

"Hey Olivia, are you down there?" Samuel was home from work.

"Yes, I'm down here sorting through the ornaments."

I wiped the moisture that was forming around my eyes.

"I'll be right down to help."

"That's okay, I'm just about done," a fib, but his antenna was up so he headed down the stairs anyway. He came over and started rubbing my neck.

"Is this hard for you? Bringing up old memories?"

I moved into his hands as they continued to massage my neck. I experienced some relief when I sensed he was tuned into where I was and seemed comfortable with it.

"Yeah, it is. I'd like to put some of the ornaments that Dane and I used in a box and replace them with some new ones that we pick out together."

"Sounds like a plan."

He seemed satisfied, so I didn't take it any further. But my heart swelled with a sadness of Christmases past with Dane.

When the tree went up the next day, I was able to get past it as I watched Samuel handle it all so competently, centering it in the red stand just perfectly.

"Is she looking straight and tall my lady?"

He held the tree at attention, waiting for my approval before he secured it in place. She was a short, stout Princess Pine.

"Perfect, just perfect." Adam and Julia clapped as they continued to rustle through the boxes of decorations, leaving balls of newsprint strewn everywhere.

"Shall we lay everything out before we put it on the tree to see what we've got?" Samuel's orderly Virgo nature was showing its face again. He always needed a deliberate plan. But I knew that the children would just want to get started and put things on randomly, every which way they could reach.

"Let's just let it happen. The kids won't be able to wait."

He sighed and sat back on the couch. "Okay, fine, let it rip." Within thirty minutes the tree was unevenly adorned with most ornaments on the lower half, so I worked on the top. Samuel added a few here and there but it was hard for him to work without some kind of pattern.

On Christmas Eve after assembling two bikes and a train we sat back with our spiked eggnog and took a break. I was amazed at his ability to follow directions and put things together so precisely. While admiring his handiwork and what we had created our first Christmas together, Samuel brought up the move again.

"Olivia, what was your last communication with Dane about our move?"

I was annoyed that he had intruded upon the moment with *that* topic.

"It was when we met a few weeks ago, why?"

"I got the *Historic Preservationist* the other day and there was a real interesting job opening listed in Charleston, South Carolina."

I didn't know a lot about Charleston except what I had read in *Charleston: City of Memory* when I was doing some research for an article in the quarterly. It had a rich history and the restoration was ongoing, which was definitely up Samuel's alley.

"So, what are you saying?"

"I'm saying I want to look into it."

"Well, what are we talking about here in terms of time?"

"The job begins in July with the new fiscal calendar so we're talking six months."

I was abruptly jarred loose from my Christmas festivities into the harsh reality of the next transition. I blurred my eyes and tried to get lost in the glow of the tree lights.

Our going away gift and party from the historical society seemed more obligatory than thoughtful. Dane's expression when we pulled out of his driveway on moving day was dark and morose. The children felt his anguish and held their hands out to him as we backed away. I was on circuit overload between my guilt and fear of what lay ahead. Samuel had a new job and I was heading into the great unknown.

We had traveled to Charleston three times after he accepted the offer to become the project manager for Chalmers Restoration Company, a group involved with several buildings in the "Catfish Row" area. Even though he was going to be paid a decent salary, it wasn't enough for us to live right in the historic district, so we managed to find a rental in Jericho, a town just west of Charleston. It had been on the market for a year and we had talked the owners into renting it to us with the option to buy before the end of the year's lease. It had a wonderful front porch and a park with cypress trees just across the street. The elementary school was within walking distance, and there was a sidewalk all the way there from the house.

A long weekend was all we had to get settled in before Samuel had to go to work. The morning he started his new job I was in the kitchen fidgeting with the microwave.

"So how does your man look for his first day on the job?" *Too damn good* is what I thought. He had on his snug jeans and my favorite crimson linen shirt, rolled up at the cuffs. I tried to casually inquire about how many women worked for Chalmers, but Samuel was catching on fast. He quickly let me know there was a plain, elderly receptionist and a married woman who did drafting. Since he said little about her appearance, I assumed she was at least mildly attractive.

"You look great," I said while fingering his collar not wanting to let him out of my sight. He disappeared with a wave while I wondered how I would be able to manage having him in a whole new life, *how I would manage myself, that is*. The voices had followed me down south and they were howling like hurricane wind now that I was alone and could hear them. Even though unpacking and playing at the park with Adam and Julia was distracting, it was not consuming enough to drown them out. When Samuel arrived home later than he expected, the ice queen had already emerged. I could not hold her back as she damaged fragile things in her path. Warm and enthusiastic about his day, I quickly interrupted and relayed mine.

"I unpacked what I could, but the kids were so restless with all the change that I had to get them to the park."

"Well, that makes sense. Did you meet anyone? How did they like it?"

He was trying to get in, but I wouldn't let him. After a few minutes more of attempting to reach me, he greeted the kids and took a shower. In bed that night I tried to thaw out, so I cuddled up next to him.

"Tell me about the people you are working with." He leaned up on his elbow and looked right through me.

"Olivia, you don't want to know about how I spent my day, what I did or where I went. All you want to know is if I'm working with any attractive women. Well, since you've asked, Valerie, the person who does the drafting is nice looking. There, are you satisfied?"

He turned away and opened his book. I wanted to pump him for more details but didn't dare. *Was she tall, thin, blond, curvaceous? How smart do you have to be to do drafting?*

"No, I want to know how it went, really I do."

"Olivia, I'm tired now. I was up for talking when I first got home but you were somewhere else. I'll tell you about it in the morning."

I had blown it big time and tried to make amends, but he was rock solid in his posture.

"I love you," I said.

"I love you too, but you need to get that inside here," he rubbed my heart and kissed my forehead. While he slept, I lay awake wondering what Valerie looked like and how solid her marriage was.

It didn't take long for me to land a public relations position with a local museum. Finding the perfect day camp for Adam and Julia was more difficult because I was so particular about their care, which was only amplified by my guilt. We finally settled on Hugenot Haven which was family owned and run. They were located on a farm with a small pond, pigs, ponies and goats. The kids loved it from the first day, so I was relieved and content. Being out in the world again allowed me to feel more in control of my life, just not in control of Samuel. The more he glowed about his work and the people he interfaced with, the more I squirmed.

Within a month a few of his co-workers invited him on a sea kayaking expedition. He loved going out in his canoe back on Algonquin, so he warmed right up to the idea. Not only was he enjoying these people as colleagues, but he was going to start hanging out with them in his spare time. He was very solicitous when he raised the issue. In his favor, he was very conscientious about being with us on the weekends, and always called whenever he was running late at work.

"How would you feel if I spent Saturday learning how to sea kayak with some folks from my office?" In my mind the question was which folks, not how long and what the activity was.

"Whose going?" A simple enough question, or so I thought.

"Here we go again, Olivia. Yes, Valerie is going, but so are Ben and Duff."

He could read me loud and clear now. There were less and less places to hide. Maybe *he* could hear the voices too.

"Will Bill, Valerie's husband, be going too?'

"You know I really don't know. Would you like me to find out before you grant me permission?" Sarcasm permeated his tone.

"I was just wondering, I mean three guys and one woman. Would she really be comfortable?"

"Olivia, we're all colleagues here. Why do you have to let your fears and suspicions ruin everything! I'll let them know I'm not going so you can relax!"

"No," I pleaded, "You go ahead. It just takes me time to adjust when I'm not included."

"Well if we didn't have two toddlers to deal with, you'd be more than welcome." I heard him tell Ben that he couldn't make it because we had other plans. When he came back into the room, he seemed like someone being freed up from a time out.

"Okay, nothing to worry about my sweet." I tried to say something, but he walked away. As he went out to the porch, he mumbled something about there being other opportunities.

There were other opportunities, and finally he seized one. It was a lazy Sunday morning when we usually made love before the kids woke up, but Samuel was up early and raring to go. I was a little iced over but doing my best to melt my way through it. Part of me really *did* want him to go off and enjoy himself, the other part clutching like a drowning swimmer offshore. I pretended to be occupied with the children while he gathered his croakies, sunglasses and water bottle for the trip.

"Well, I'm off." He bent down and pulled me up toward him. He squeezed extra tight and kissed me quickly. I wanted something more prolonged, but he wasn't there. Samuel was always on time, usually a bit early for things, and when it was a new activity with new people, he was extra punctual.

"Have a good time," I said as he dropped his arms from my waist and was gone with a brilliant smile to match the glorious day he walked out into.

To keep myself busy I planned a short hike and picnic with the kids. Each one had an empty zip lock bag to collect goodies for our scavenger hunt. I wrote down simple words and objects for them to locate on the trail. As I watched the red glow on the back of Adam's black leather Reeboks, I wondered what Samuel was doing just then. Was Valerie showing her competence on the water, becoming more attractive with every stroke? Were they having a deep and meaningful conversation yet? With Samuel's engaging presence and focus that didn't take long. I should know.

Slowly and carefully, Samuel became more involved in the kayaking expeditions. He looked forward to what became their monthly trip out to sea. The group continued to consist of Valerie and the guys. And yes, she had turned out to be rather adept with an oar. Even though Samuel tried to play it down, I knew he was quietly impressed. Whenever he so much as mentioned her name in any context, the voices flared up and a huge knot tied itself inside my gut. I could not tolerate his admiration or focus on any other woman. Each week before his kayaking trip the tightness began to form, and the voices began to whisper. How close is he really getting to Valerie? Is he more attracted to her than he admits? Are they spending time alone, away from the others? And on and on they went. Whenever I would fish for answers Samuel would become visibly irritated. But when he came home one evening and mentioned a possible overnight trip, I lost it big time.

"Oh, I see, you're going to spend the night camping under the stars with Valerie and the gang?' I was treading on thin ice.

"Okay Olivia, I can't take these ugly accusations anymore. I've had it. I've been a great husband and stepfather to your children. I've never done anything to make you mistrust me!"

His voice was getting louder, and I didn't want the kids to hear him.

"Samuel, calm down, please lower your voice." I tried to quiet him, but he came back that much stronger.

"Hey, let your kids hear this! Maybe they need to know their mom is troubled. You've got a real problem Olivia and you better take care of it or I'm history!"

I was speechless. While I was searching the caverns of my mind for a response, he walked out and slammed the door. I was momentarily paralyzed, my feet felt like lead boots. I could barely put one foot in front of the other, but I knew I had to get to Julia and Adam. They heard all this and were probably confused and upset. When I got to the living room where they were busily stacking Legos, Samuel was backing out of the driveway without so much as a glance homeward. This was a first.

I managed to get hot dogs together for dinner, making enough for all four of us hoping Samuel would be back by then. But he wasn't, and as I bathed Julia, Adam sat next to me and asked, "Where's Sammy?" They loved to call him that. Samuel was too formal for their little mouths.

"Oh, he went out for a while. He needed to be alone." Then Julia piped in.

"Is Sammy mad at you mommy? His voice was mean and loud."

"Yeah, and he slammed the door hard too!" said Adam.

"Well, I said something that he wasn't happy about."

They pressed me for more, but I changed the subject and got them interested in the new fleet of blue tugboats making their way through the bubbles. The guilt was unbearable as I thought about how little Dane and I had argued, except about his lack of assertiveness and procrastination, which looked pretty minimal at the moment compared to the gnawing insecurity about Samuel. That familiar, comfortable rocking chair sure was looking good right about now. No matter where Dane went or who he met I was never afraid that he would stray. But then again, he never went very far without me.

When Samuel returned after ten, I was lying in the fetal position begging for sleep to take me into her fold. He didn't say anything until he stripped down to his boxers and sat down on the edge of the bed. His face was tense and serious.

"Olivia, I've done a lot of thinking tonight." I interrupted.

"Where did you go?" The voices answered for him, *he probably went to a bar and ended up pouring out the story of his irrational, jealous wife to some willing, attractive listener. They would meet again when things got rough.* I had to know.

"I got take-out from Goldlake deli and went to the inlet. I took a long walk."

Wrong again, I yelled back silently at them.

"Anyway, I realize how much I changed my life to be with you and these kids. I did that because I love you and somehow no matter what I do, I can't convince you of that. Maybe it's your old man and his flirtations or whatever, but I know that I can't live this way, with all your suspicions."

My bowels began to loosen, my insides felt like they were tearing apart at their fragile seams.

"So, are you, leaving?"

"No, I'm not leaving yet, but I want you to get some help. You need to talk to somebody and get this stuff figured out; otherwise it will destroy what we have. It's already begun."

I had become the Goddess Hera even though I doubted Samuel was really being unfaithful like her Zeus, but I couldn't be absolutely certain.

Chapter Thirty-five

I had forged a friendship with Carla, manager of the museum gift shop, so when I confided in her about what was happening with me and Samuel, she scribbled the name Sandra Williston across her pink message pad and handed it to me. She was a therapist Carla's sister had seen about her agoraphobia. Her sister was now a successful traveling salesperson for a sportswear company, and before working with Sandra she was unable to leave her apartment except for absolute necessities.

As I headed back to my office staring down at the pink slip I wondered if I had a phobia, and if it was indeed curable. My choice to be with Samuel had brought on demons that were having a field day, dancing their way into my life and destroying a once fairly sane, secure woman, or so I thought. I closed my office door and dialed Sandra Williston's number. Expecting an answering machine, I was startled by a real voice at the other end of the phone. We scheduled an appointment for the following Wednesday during my lunch break. She was conveniently located four blocks from the office on Bull Street. In the interim she would send me some intake forms to fill out and review.

That evening I was like an eager school girl with her honor roll report card, while waiting to tell Samuel that I had made plans to see someone. He was less enthusiastic than I had hoped and obviously still exhausted from our encounter about the kayaking overnight.

It turned out that Sandra used a form of therapy called EMDR (Eye Movement Desensitization and Reprocessing) which involved bringing up past issues that seemed to be the origin of your trigger. Then you would proceed to immerse yourself in the memory while doing some back and forth eye movements. After reading her materials I felt a flood of optimism. *Maybe this is it! This will rid me of the demons. I'll be free at last!*

After four sessions Samuel could see that I was genuine about my commitment to change and he started to warm up again. He became thoughtful and attentive once more, and I began to feel optimistic about our life again. The kids were flourishing in school and we were preparing for their trip north to see Dane for Thanksgiving. It would be challenging traveling with them during the holidays. But I had brought this on by moving down here so I had to "deal with it", as Dane said very coldly over the phone one night. He showed no mercy, and why should he?

On the flight back from bringing the children to Algonquin, I put headphones on and fantasized about various spontaneous, erotic episodes with Samuel now that we had the house to ourselves. Driving home from the airport I rubbed my hand up and down inside his right thigh. He smiled and said, "There's plenty of time for that. The kids will be gone for a week." Again, his passion wasn't running as high as mine. We got take-out Chinese food at the Pagoda House. Over dinner he told me what a horrendous two days at work he had while I was gone. The tiles had arrived broken from the distributor and it was going to set the already late job back farther. I knew this was his subtle way of telling me that we weren't going to be having hot sex that night.

The next day we slept in and cuddled. I was too fragile from being put off the night before to make any overtures, so I just waited to see what his game plan was. How strange to pass the baton once more.

"I heard about this great coffee shop and book store down on Meeting Street. Why don't we have lunch and check it out. Then we can come home and have some afternoon delight."

"Sounds like a plan. Are you looking for anything special?"

"Well, Ben told me they have a really good section on Native American stuff." Samuel was one-quarter Lakota and had been expressing an interest in knowing more about his roots.

"Oh, is Ben interested in that stuff too?"

"Yeah, sort of. When we were kayaking last month, we talked about it briefly."

Did Valerie have an interest too? There have been blondes who have been known to have some Native American blood. He grabbed me before I went any further, pulling me under the covers.

"What's this?" I was getting a mixed message.

"You look so damn good in those black panties that I can't wait until this afternoon."

Throw me a bone and I'll gnaw happily until all the juices are gone, and then some. When Samuel wanted me, I was so full it was hard to believe I ever needed any other kind of sustenance. But at the coffee shop I managed a grand latte and a soft peanut butter cookie while we shared a rare uninterrupted, lengthy conversation, near to impossible when Julia and Adam were with us.

Samuel ended up in the spirituality section while I perused the self-help area. I looked for titles that had anything to do with jealousy, insecurity or related topics, but it seemed I was the only flawed soul walking around with green eyes. Shakespeare knew way back when he wrote *Macbeth,* so why was it so hard to find something current? Sometimes I rubbed my fingers against my skin expecting to find some stubby old warts, revealing my sickness to the outside world.

When we got home instead of having afternoon delight Samuel was completely absorbed in his new book, *The Way of the Shaman* by Michael Harner, an anthropologist who had traveled to South America and worked with indigenous tribes. He had spotted it while searching for materials on the Lakota tribe. I curled up in the sunniest spot I could find, feeling a real longing for my babies. I wondered where this book would take Samuel. What was this sudden interest in tribal culture and how did I fit into this new picture? *All about me.*

While the kids were gone, we saw some great movies and had hot sex, usually in the afternoon based on Samuel's rhythm. When they returned, I couldn't wait to hold them and hear about their adventures, since Dane was very vague when we met to exchange the children at the airport. He was not up for any extended conversation, just the basics. He briefly mentioned someone named Sarah the children had met. It was hard to watch him walk away toward the shuttle terminal while the children cried softly into my down jacket. It was hard not knowing more about his life, this new woman he spent time with, how his artwork was progressing.

I stayed with both Julia and Adam until they fell asleep. I was amazed and disturbed when I walked into our bedroom to find Samuel already engrossed in Harner's book. He was great when we picked up the kids, and then played hide and seek with them after dinner. But when they were ready for bed he drifted away easily into his own space. I had such a deep need to reconnect that I couldn't part with them until they were in slumber's arms.

"So how is the book?" There was an edge to my voice.

"It's fascinating. I'm almost done." I plunged ahead, always ahead.

"So, what's next?"

"He has a staff that does workshops all over the country. Maybe I'll find one near here someday."

Here we go. He was just slowing down with the kayaking and now he was on to something else before I could barely catch my breath.

"Can I read it when you're done?"

"Of course, I'd love it if you did!" I lay down next to him and rubbed my now bare chest against his. He tousled my hair, kissed me gently on the forehead and returned to his book.

In the months leading to spring we had a flurry of wonderful weekends with a balance of family and alone time. Even though our lovemaking had become predictable it was satisfying, and our timing was impeccable. The kayaking had lost some of its original appeal for Samuel and he was going less and less. I took that as a sign of his domestic contentment.

My sessions with Sandra were now monthly instead of weekly. She had strongly encouraged me to develop my own interests outside of Samuel and the children. Though I didn't have much spare time, I did start playing with clay. I loved the sensation of the cold, moist terra cotta sliding through my fingers. I wasn't interested in being restricted to a potter's wheel, so I made my own small, primitive figurines. Samuel loved them and took two for his desktop at work. I secretly hoped Valerie would see them and realize that I was a creative, interesting sort of woman too.

A month before my birthday with both kids at soccer practice, I had time to have coffee and go through the mail. After a day of working on a lay out for the museum brochure I craved mindless activity. Catalogs like *Coldwater Creek* or *Sundance* were great for that. Alas, not one in the batch, but there was a rather thick, glossy brochure in the stack. It was from a Shamanic Institute in California advertising their annual workshops. I tore it apart and looked at the listing. My eyes rapidly scanned the dates and places. There was a workshop in South Carolina the weekend of my birthday. *He wouldn't, would he?* I wanted to shred it with my paper cutter and pretend it never arrived. Instead, I dialed Sandra's number and moved my next appointment up by two weeks.

Before I left to pick the kids from up soccer practice, I strategically placed the brochure on Samuel's dresser in a prominent place. I wanted him to see it right away and get it over with. If he was going to pursue this I wanted to know as soon as possible. And if he was headed in that direction, maybe I needed to rethink all this. If he was going to continue to do all these esoteric and adventurous things, that might involve other women, maybe I should just cut him loose now before I became absolutely crazy. *They were back and heckling me.*

I got to Sandra's office early and I was wildly jotting down notes in my journal when she opened the door. I was ready to burst and started talking before I sat down. Samuel very much wanted to attend the April workshop, but he wanted me to get more comfortable with the idea before he made a final decision. He encouraged me to work with Sandra around the issue. By now I had read enough in Harner's book to know there would probably be some hands-on exercises in the workshop. The spiritual healing techniques involved a certain physical closeness between members of the group. I was beside myself with all the "touchy feely" possibilities. There would be a room full of not just beautiful women, but they would be spiritual seekers as well, the 'whole enchilada,' you might say.

That session went over by fifteen minutes because Sandra felt the need to press onward. She had struck a chord and I was raw and bleeding. We went into places in my past that were painful to look at. Nobody was actually at fault, just playing their part in the emotional drama you might say. There was my father's physical absence due to his international travels, and my mother's emotional absence due to my brother's epilepsy. Add to that her preoccupation with dad's womanizing, lack of emotional boundaries, and you leave a wound on a child's sensitive soul. Sandra knew we had opened Pandora's box and she let the green-eyed demons fly. Their crackling, hideous voices filled the room as their wings beat the air. I wanted to plug my ears and cover my eyes as the images bombarded me, and the fluttering of their scaly wings almost drowned out the sound of my own breathing.

When the kids were asleep that night Samuel curled up next to me with a bowl of buttered popcorn and asked about the session. He wanted to know everything, in detail. It was then that I broke down completely. I guess his eager presence allowed the floodgates to open wide and everything just gushed forth. Usually he would have been reading at that hour, but he rocked me until there was no more left. He didn't open his book the entire evening.

His tender display of affection and unwavering attention that night shored me up to the point where I felt ready to send him on his way. It took little prompting for him to send in his deposit for the workshop. As we got closer to the date, which fell on my fortieth birthday, Sandra convinced me to create my own celebration. I became very intentional about it, to the point where I made plans for both Adam and Julia to spend the night out at friends. I had never been alone overnight in our home, we had purchased it by then, and it was high time. I invited a few women from the office over for a pot luck and ordered a white cake, with lavender sugar roses. I would give each of my guests a thick slab of clay and while listening to light jazz we would create whatever the terra cotta muses had in mind.

Samuel was delighted and surprised by all my plans, and probably somewhat relieved. It allowed him to miss my birthday with a little less guilt and go forward with a lighter heart. But he was incredibly thoughtful leading up to the day of his departure, leaving me sweet notes, a rose at my bedside and chocolate kisses under my pillow. It was feeling good, it really was.

On the morning of the workshop Samuel tiptoed around not wanting to wake me too early. Since he needed lots of prep time on a routine day, that morning he needed even more. But as soon as the alarm pierced the silence, I couldn't get back to sleep. As he methodically placed his notebook, pens and chiclets in his knapsack, my stomach turned an unexpected flip flop. I thought I was so prepared, so ready for this, and now I was caving into the demons again. Images of long, curly-haired, earthy women with their Birkenstocks and handwoven sweaters sitting in a circle zipped open my mind. Each one of them would be more naturally sensual than the next. I could see Samuel warmly introducing himself and focusing carefully on each one as they said their names. He would listen intently, giving lots of eye contact and they would swoon.

"Hey, you're awake."

"Yes, I heard the alarm and couldn't get back to sleep." He came right over, sensing my need for attention on this delicate morning of mornings. He looked so handsome in his creamy black, terry shirt. *Damn it, couldn't he wear something less appealing?* Black was always so alluring, and it was a snug fit which really accentuated those broad shoulders, part of his Lakota heritage. His kiss fell on unresponsive lips. The ice queen had returned numbing me to any sensation, good or bad. He felt the chill immediately.

"Olivia, don't do this."

"Do what?" Playing dumb felt clever, when it was actually more on the cruel side.

"Don't pull away from me now. This is when we need to stay connected more than ever. Don't you realize that?"

"It's hard for me right now, that's all."

"It's hard for both of us." *There he goes with his equalizing.*

"You're the one who's going!" He still didn't recognize that we weren't on a level playing field. *I* was the one being left behind.

"I'm going because you encouraged me to, and now you're punishing me."

The air in the room felt cold enough to see my breath. I had nothing to counter him with. I had told him to go, enthusiastically at times, and now I was frozen like a raspberry popsicle that wasn't going to thaw in time for his departure. I managed a kiss, but he knew I wasn't there fully. After the front door closed, I pulled the covers over my head and cried until Adam came in wanting his cinnamon and sugar on toast.

Chapter Thirty-six

My birthday celebration was magical, and it wasn't until my last guest departed that I noticed the time. When Carla hugged me at the door, I realized it was after ten and I hadn't heard from Samuel yet. Perhaps he was having dinner with one of those earthy women who is part Hopi Indian and loves to kayak. I stacked the paper plates, cups and napkins, determined not to turn on the television to distract me from the demons. I was bigger than that. While trying to settle into yet another one of my many self-help books, the phone rang. I picked it up just after the third ring, not wanting to appear overly anxious.

"Hey baby, how was the birthday party?" It was so great to hear his voice that I almost forgot I was scared.

"It was glorious, and we made all sorts of whimsical clay creatures. How is the workshop? How many people are there?" Translated that meant, are you having fun without me, and are there any attractive women?

"It's amazing. I'm learning so much," he said with subdued enthusiasm, "It's a small group, there are only six of us."

Oh, now that's an intimate little gathering isn't it? "Are they around your age, men and women?" He paused for what seemed like too long.

"There's one other guy and four women. The guy is probably a little older. Two other women seem to be in their mid-sixties, one seems younger and the other is about our age." I knew enough to stop there. I wanted to get some sleep that night so I stayed away from anything that would feed the hungry, green demons lurking about our bedroom.

When I finally slipped under the duvet that night, I wondered how Charleston went from being about restoration to the very dismantling of my psyche. But I also experienced a new sense of creative pride about my birthday celebration sans Samuel, along with a deliberate night alone in the house. I had forced my own hand by sending my lover and children on their way while I orchestrated my own coping devices. Just being able to fall asleep that night felt like a triumph.

It soon became abundantly clear that this was not an isolated event for Samuel. He started reading more books about Shamanism and surfing the web for additional information. He was into it but trying to play it down for my benefit. Whenever I came into the den where he was wandering through a site he would quickly log off. My fear was constraining him, keeping him from his other passion. When he got an e-mail from a female participant casually informing him of the next workshop, my sessions with Sandra doubled.

The talking felt like it was taking me in circles, always sending me back to the same place. I now knew the origin of my wound, but how did I heal it? I was truly disgusted with myself. Whenever Samuel and I were at a soccer match of Adam or Julia's I was on the lookout for the next woman that would catch his eye. One night we went to a square dance in the park with the children. They were chasing fireflies and we were dancing to a great local blue grass band, the Night Crawlers. Then I caught a glimpse of Samuel's next partner, dark hair down to her waist, resembling Demi Moore, who was one of his absolute favorites. As he took her hand, I froze up. and lost track of my children, time, everything. All I could see was his arm around her svelte waist as he spun her briefly and moved on to his next partner. When we finally reconnected ice had formed around my edges. By now Samuel knew the signs and he was in no mood for my craziness, as he sometimes referred to it in his less patient moments. We got in the car and his voice was not only loud but laced with anger.

"Olivia, whose idea was it to come here anyway? You bring me into situations and then you punish me for things beyond my control. Was I supposed to skip over her because she was an attractive woman?"

By now the kids were old enough to understand some of what he was talking about and I was mortified.

"Samuel later, please."

"No Olivia, I think Adam and Julia need to know their mom has a real issue."

"Mom, was Sammy dancing with a pretty woman?" Julia said innocently.

Shadows of my youth cast themselves over us. I felt like a fish trapped in a net struggling to get free without an opening large enough to escape through.

"Yes, but that's what you do in square dancing honey, you change partners." I tried to reassure her, but Samuel was too activated to let it go that easily.

"Your mom doesn't like it if I even look at a pretty woman, never mind dance with one!"

"Mom, did you get jealous?"

It was all going too far, boundaries had been crossed and the fish went limp inside the net.

"Yes, I guess I did. I know it was silly, but I did."

I then suggested we stop for ice cream, hoping to sweeten the moment, but it was near impossible to get rid of the smell of that dead fish.

Back in the privacy of our room I felt the shame boil over me, scalding my heart. Now my children knew about my emotional shortcomings. Their mother had a real problem and their stepdad had shoved it in their faces and down their throats. He couldn't control himself long enough to allow me to remain unblemished in their eyes just awhile longer. At eight and nine I still had some time before their adolescent arrogance would knock me from my coveted pedestal. But I was too embarrassed and horrified to confront him about it that night. I went and slept in the guest room.

The next morning, he woke me with coffee and invited me back to our bed. We sipped in silence trying to make sense of how we ended up in this place. Samuel spoke first.

"Olivia you've been seeing Sandra for over a year. She's helped a lot but obviously not enough. What's next for us?"

The voices of panic rushed in.

"I don't know, but I'm frightened by what my children heard last night." He took my coffee cup from me and held my hands.

"Olivia, you're not perfect No one is. They love you anyway."

"Yes, but they didn't need to have that information. They're too young. That's what happened to me with my mom. I knew too much too soon. I was so overburdened at such a young age."

When my dad was on a business trip in the far east my brother Paul had one of his worst seizures. I was the one my mother woke up to help her before the ambulance arrived. I was the one who watched the fear grow in her eyes while we held down his convulsing body and cushioned his head from injury. The expression of terror and helplessness on her face haunted me for days. She suddenly became so vulnerable and imperfect. Now Adam and Julia had seen it in my eyes as I shuddered with humiliation on the way home from a Saturday night square dance on the green.

Our conversation ended without its usual resolution. It always seemed like whenever Samuel and I had put our heads together about anything, we always came up with at least one option. This time we came up empty. Therapy had been helpful in creating a map, then backtracking to where it all began, but it didn't make it go away. Soon Samuel would be going away if I didn't figure this out. My life became a pressure cooker filling with steam ready to explode.

On a rainy Saturday morning while everyone else slept in, I thumbed through *Visions,* a New Age publication, where I happened upon an article about life coaches. There were people out there trained to coach you through anything from writer's block to finding your ideal mate. Surely there must be someone among them who knew how to deal with my horrendous brand of fear.

I set to work on designing my own classified ads geared toward the more psychological and spiritual publications. I also put together brightly colored index cards to hang on bulletin boards in suitable locations: progressive bookstores, Unitarian churches and the like. Convinced I would find a coach who could extract me from this green, sticky substance that was pulling me under like quicksand, I propelled myself into action. I was so good at that.

Samuel was surprised and maybe subtly amused by my latest tactic, but nevertheless supportive. He seemed to appreciate my efforts in all their desperate glory. When I brought my ads in and hung my cards in various locations, I tried to be as nonchalant and inconspicuous as possible. Leaving the last newspaper office, I wondered what they were thinking. *What is a tall, attractive, shapely woman like her suffering from a malady like jealousy for? Is she married to someone famous or drop dead gorgeous?* And then I went to a place I hadn't visited for a long time. Was Samuel in all his warmth and focused nature being flirtatious after all? In some ways he was so much like my dad it was uncanny. So why did I run towards the flame instead of away when I had been in such a secure place with Dane? Dane was nothing like Frederick and that was so obvious from the start.

My parents had us to the golf club for the annual fourth of July celebration a few months after Dane and I were married, and I watched my dad work the crowd. My sister Tina brought her new man Todd, who was graduating from engineering school, and he and dad hit it off immediately. Dane hung in the background knowing full well my dad was not at all familiar with the latest trends in physical therapy, nor was he a great fan of Henry Moore's sculpture. So, while my father introduced Todd to friends, gravitating mostly to the women, Dane sat back with his rum and coke. Even with his physical challenges from the biking accident, he didn't seem to need his ego massaged like other men, such as my father. He had no desire to move into center stage and sat perfectly content watching from the sidelines.

Wherever I went somewhere with Samuel he always reached out to other people and they were drawn in by him. Children in restaurants played hide and seek behind their napkins while Julia's playmates laughed heartily at his dinner table antics and loved hearing his high school bully stories. Whenever my friends called, they always spent at least five minutes talking to him before I got on. He never did anything to abbreviate those conversations with them either because he found most of them more interesting than his male friends.

The phone calls came in steadily after my coaching request got out there, but they were not at all what I expected or needed. The callers were wrestling with their own demons and wondered if I had found that magical person who was going to wave it all away, the wizard of insecurity come to the rescue. While it was comforting to know that I was not alone in the desert, it did not quench my thirst nor turn down the heat. I politely took their names and numbers telling them I would get back in touch as soon as the wizard appeared in all her purple velvet glory. I did secretly harbor a vision of a statuesque, white-haired woman wrapped from head to toe in a royal purple hooded cape. One of the callers suggested I try dealing with fear in another venue, like a high ropes course, which might help. So, the next time Julia and Adam went to Dane's we planned a trip to a nearby outdoor center that had a ropes course. Samuel was all for it, the more physically challenging the better. He brought his old Pentax camera to document my success. When the photos were developed, he promptly made them into a collage and framed it. In the center was a close up of me perched on the edge of a tree, ready to take the "Leap of Faith," with a group of adolescent boys stymied by a woman my age attempting such a feat.

My self-esteem rocketed higher than I had ever known before, blazing like a comet across the sky. Now I understood what Outward Bound was all about, and why people raved on and on when they returned from their experience. On the drive home I was chirping like a bird having just left the nest and tested my wings. Indeed, they had worked, and I was soaring high above all the petty fear, and the demons were nowhere in sight. Samuel was delighted and cheered me on, saying little about his own accomplishments that day. He gave me center stage and held the spotlight on me well into the evening. As we sat with wine in hand, he toasted me.

"You are one hot mama, girl!"

"You're not bad yourself, Mr. Stud!" We clinked our glasses, reveled in our newly met challenge, celebrating further by wrapping our worn-out bodies all over each other.

It was just one short week before the spell was broken. Samuel had read a brochure about rock climbing while we were at the outdoor center and he was interested in trying it. Another hands-on activity where your very life depended on your partner's steadiness and undivided attention. There was no end to his appetite for adventure. As he looked at the schedule of summer classes I tried not to jump in but could not contain myself.

"Do you do this on purpose?"

"Do what, honey?" He was oblivious for the moment.

"Do all these things that involve being with another person, possibly a woman, and having physical contact?"

"Oh, you're back on that track again, eh?' His tolerance level had reached a very low point.

"Well, it seems like all your interests revolve around being paired up with someone and having to touch them, from healing touch to clipping in caribiners."

"Look Olivia, I can't help it if the things I'm interested in involve partners, some of them possibly women. I'm going for the activity, not the women. How many god damn times do I have to say it?" He threw the catalog across the room, grabbed me by the shoulders and pushed me into the chair.

"Woman, if you don't get a hold of this thing that's strangling you, it will suffocate us! Do you get that?" *At least the kids weren't here to witness this one.*

"I'm going out and I don't know when I'll be back!"

"Samuel, please, I'll do more, I can lick this." I was groveling, but he was gone before the words even fell from my lips.

Chapter Thirty-seven

I stayed up most of the night eating popcorn and watching romantic movies like "One Fine Day." I only wanted happy endings. By three in the morning it was clear he wasn't coming home. Sitting in the darkness wrapped in the cocoon of our comforter my stomach churned. Instead of continuing to distract myself with another movie or Belva Plain's latest novel, I did something entirely different. I stayed with it. I actually sat still in the darkness letting the fear surround me. I didn't dart, dodge or run, I just sat there. At one point I got up, lit a candle from the bathroom, and placed it on my dresser. Watching the flame, thoughts of Samuel in a bar talking with a sexy female bartender with a raspy voice, stirred me and passed, followed by a lively parade of vivid fantasies, one more erotic than the next. He had gone from the bar to a motel and was doing her from behind in her white lace panties. He thrusted in and out, she moaning as he penetrated her deeper and deeper. After they climaxed it was silent except for the rain outside their cheap motel window, pelting against the windshield of the blue Ford truck.

The next morning, I awoke early and wandered through the house like a sleepwalker, awake in a very bad dream. I checked the answering machine while the coffee brewed, hoping I had slept through his call. This was highly unlikely since I was the lightest of sleepers. They say most mothers are, always listening for those babies. I saw the red light blinking a number one and my hopes soared as I hit the "play" button.

"This is Dr. Aiken's office calling. Adam has an appointment for a dental cleaning on May 19th at 3:30 p.m. Please call if he cannot make this appointment. Thank you."

I must have been in a deeper than usual sleep if the abrasive, robotic voice blaring from the speaker didn't wake me. I deleted it and walked toward the kitchen calendar to make sure the appointment had been recorded there. I was going through all the motions; meanwhile my marriage had hit a total roadblock.

When the phone rang again, I was less optimistic. It turned out to be another caller from one of my ads. It was a younger woman from a neighboring town who asked to meet halfway for coffee. No, she wasn't a coach, but she had worked extensively with fear and felt she had something to offer. She suggested mid-morning and quite frankly I didn't want to ramble around the house waiting for Samuel's return, so I agreed.

Maxine, who called herself Max, was a spunky redhead with lots of energy. She wore overalls, olive suede clogs and had a tiny gold ring pierced on the edge of her left eyebrow. We exchanged a few minor details about our lives and then she plunged right in.

"So, why are you so uptight about your old man fooling around on you?"

She certainly had a way with words.

"Because he's warm, attractive, friendly, focused and women of all ages eat it up. He even has older women bring him boxes of Godiva on his job sites, supposedly out of gratitude for all his exquisite management." This peaked her curiosity.

"So, what do you care if an old lady thanks him with chocolate. I bet he shares it with you anyway!" She grinned, and I resented this little spitfire with the tattooed wrist making light of my very deep, sore wound.

"Are you here to help, or minimize and invalidate?" *I was puffed up now.*

"I'm sorry, laughing helps, you know, try to lighten up."

"I'm sure it does but I'd like to know what you think you have to offer me."

"Okay, here's my story. I had a real fear around intimacy. I was fine sleeping around, but the minute someone wanted a real piece of me, I just ran like hell."

I had noticed what could be an engagement ring on the appropriate finger as soon as we sat down. Perhaps she had conquered it.

"So, what did you do about it?"

"I did all the traditional stuff: drugs, therapy, obsessive running. None of it worked until I tried firewalking."

"Firewalking, what's that?"

"Just what it says, walking on fire. You name your fear and then you face it, both literally and figuratively." *Okay, this was definitely weird.*

"You mean you walk on fire?"

"Exactly, except they're actually red glowing coals from a fire that you walk through, not the flames."

"So, you did this and that got you over your fear of intimacy? That's it in a nutshell?" This did not compute in my world.

"No, there's more to it than that, a lot of mental preparation involved before you actually walk, but it's not a real complicated, lengthy process. It teaches you how your thoughts affect your life. When you change your thoughts, you change your brain and body chemistry which allows you to walk across the coals, facing your worst fears about being burned."

We talked more and she handed me a colorful brochure with an in-depth description, and the necessary details. I thanked her and we headed for the parking lot. As she got on her viper green Harley, I asked her what she did for a living.

"Oh, I'm a carpenter and I do woodworking in my spare time."

Wow, quite a little woman we have here. Samuel would be intrigued with this one. I pushed that thought out and replaced it with another as I drove home. I couldn't wait to tell Samuel I was willing to face the fire to save our marriage, that is if he came home tonight. The kids were due back the next afternoon, so we had to get everything patched up by then.

As I turned onto our street, I spotted Samuel's truck in the driveway. My heart fluttered as I mentally rehearsed my latest declaration to him. When I walked in, he was in the recliner going through the mail in that meticulous way of his, carefully slicing along the paper's edge with his pocket knife. I tore through envelopes so quickly that I sometimes damaged the contents. Whenever Samuel watched me, he would urge me to slow down as I discarded the remains of my frenzy in the trash, but I had little tolerance for paper clutter on tabletops and dressers.

I was tentative in my approach toward him. He looked up and then went back to the *Cabella* catalog. *Looking for rock climbing equipment, no doubt.*

"You're home," I said timidly. Without looking up he responded.

"Yeah, I've been here awhile. Where were you?" His minor interest in my whereabouts gave me a crumb of encouragement to feed off.

"Would you like some coffee, then I can tell you all about it."

"I had some downtown." *So, he's been downtown.* He didn't frequent there on the weekends unless he was with me. Did he continue his nocturnal soirée into the daylight? Coffee time was our sacred ritual together. We always had such intimate conversation and I felt slighted by him partaking without me.

"Well I haven't had any so I'm going to make some. I'll be right back."

He made no gesture toward me and I felt boxed out, like a point guard whose opponents had figured out a new strategy to deal with my speed and agility. It was rare that we did not greet each other with a light kiss or substantial hug after being apart. When I returned, he was still deep into his catalog. and I felt intimidated, afraid to push the envelope which was already so close to the edge. I sat down with my mug in hand.

"Let me know when you want to talk," I said with little force behind my words. He laid the magazine across his lap and finally met my eyes.

"I'm ready. What's up?"

He obviously had no intention of offering up anything about last night's whereabouts. Since I knew I was treading on very thin ice I dared not ask.

"A woman named Max from Mount Pleasant called. She had read my ad and wanted to meet halfway to talk."

"Is she a coach?"

"No, but she had dealt with some of her own fears around intimacy."

"I thought you were looking for a coach." He was obviously not too receptive, but I pressed on regardless.

"Yes, ultimately that is what I put out to the universe, but it's bringing me other things so I'm checking them out."

"Okay, so what did she have to offer?"

"She had tried a lot of different things and none of them worked, and then somebody told her about firewalking. It's a technique used to move through your fears by altering your thoughts."

""What do you mean by firewalking? It sounds a bit strange to me." Samuel had a very practical, logical side that usually presented itself whenever I came up with one of my spontaneous ideas.

"It sounded odd to me too, but the more she told me, the more sense it made. There is a lot of mental preparation involving your fears before you actually walk across the hot coals. But you *do* walk across the coals."

"And how is that supposed to get rid of your jealousy and insecurity about me? I don't see the connection."

Since I had just begun my investigation into the process, I didn't have all the answers. Sometimes talking to Samuel felt like being cross-examined on a witness stand. He was so thorough in his own decision-making process that he expected everyone else to be as well.

"I think when you learn to control your mind around a specific fear, like the physical pain of being burned; you can transfer that ability to other fears, like the fear of loss. Learn how to face one fear and you can face others in your life."

"Sounds like you have some homework to do." Felt like a real Frederick statement to me.

"Yes, I do. I'm going to make some calls as soon as we're finished."

"Well keep me posted on this because I am just about at the end of my rope here Olivia." His tone became dark and serious.

"I know, I can feel you pulling away. Where were you last night?"

"I went to the movies and spent the night at the Hampton Inn. I put the receipt on your dresser because I used the credit card." So, he had been at a hotel, but not a sleazy one. And it was close by, so he probably didn't have anyone with him.

"It would have been nice if you had let me know."

"I know but I was just too pissed. Next time I will." *Next time.*

There was an air of desperation in our house when the children returned from their dad's. They could feel the tension and hear the eggshells cracking beneath my feet. I tried to compensate by being extra attentive, loving and playful but somehow their sensitive nature picked up on my shaky signals. There was no fooling them. Samuel tried to get back into the family rhythm but whenever the kids returned it was harder for him to transition back into parenting than it was for me. "Being a stepfather is different," he would tell me when I asked why it was difficult to join us back in the dance. He would remind me of his decade of bachelorhood prior to our relationship, how his time was his own. He still put in the effort, took Julia and Adam kite flying at the park and read extra stories at night. He did love them in his own way, and they loved him back. Julia was fond of telling her friends that she had two daddies, one here and one up there, and she would point in the direction she imagined Dane to be in.

At the end of the summer Samuel signed up for a fall rock climbing weekend. We discussed it and reached the fragile but firm conclusion that if he denied himself the resentment would only poison our relationship further. I bravely agreed as I imagined packing nuts and berries for his first climb. Meanwhile I had contacted the firewalk people and registered for a workshop at the end of the month. Because we had children it was necessary to take turns doing what we needed to do for ourselves on weekends. It was clear to me that Samuel's needs were a priority at the moment, or I would lose him for sure. So out of sheer terror, I postponed my workshop, yet knowing full well I must continue to move forward in my process, or we were surely doomed.

As I feared and predicted, Samuel loved the rock climbing and wanted to do more. There were twelve people in the class, seven women. He had partnered up with a high school teacher named Elaine who was an experienced climber, so she showed him the ropes. As he described the day, I made a conscious decision not to ask anything about what the women looked like or how old they were. I needed no extra scraps to feed the demons who lurked in the basement. They always came around after one of Samuel's new experiences that I was excluded from. It seemed he could read my mind because he filled in the blanks with non-threatening descriptions like "She was on the scrawny side, or I was old enough to be her father, or I felt like I was with my grandmother." It was his kind and ever diligent way of reassuring me that no one had stolen his heart that day.

Chapter Thirty-eight

Leading up to the firewalk, I wrote in my journal and spent intentional time alone becoming more intimately acquainted with my fear. I took my lunch hour to journal, recording as much detail as I could about my jealousy, its origin and the sinister sound of its voice. Carving out time to be alone proved less challenging than I thought because I had formed very few authentic friendships with women here, unlike on Algonquin where I had Miranda and the walking gang. I used the excuse that most of the women I met down here were typical southern belles, concerned with primping, curling their hair and keeping their nails brightly polished, not to mention their staunch republican politics and fundamentalist religious beliefs being so different from mine. The truth was, they were either too interesting or too pretty. As I recorded some of my feelings about losing Samuel to another woman, it hit me like a boomerang at top speed slamming up against the back of my head. I had met women through work, parents of Adam and Julia's friends, at clean-up days at the park, or scout meetings, that I had not allowed into my life simply because they were attractive and single, attractive and talented, attractive and smart, the list went on and on. If there was even a remote possibility that Samuel would be the slightest bit interested in a woman, I kept my contact with her at a minimum. It was to the point if one of the kids needed to be picked up and Samuel was available, I went instead so he wouldn't end up in the driveway talking to some single mom with tight jeans and a fabulous smile.

I put my pen down overwhelmed by the number of pathetic scenarios that were trampling down the door of my memory now that I had invited them in. I felt a wave of utter and complete self-disgust wash over me like a cold, damp rain, the kind you want to get out of quickly. To think I had deprived my sweet, innocent children of certain social experiences and gatherings because of my own selfish, irrational fears. Sick at heart, I closed up shop and headed back to the office. Walking across the park, I saw a handsome man, two attractive women and a little boy feeding the ducks together. It all looked so relaxed and normal. They could have been sisters, friends since grade school, colleagues or neighbors. Whatever they were, they were a delightful threesome enjoying one another's company, seemingly without a trace of anxiety. How did *they* do it? In my probing, curious fashion I wanted to walk up, whip out my pen and begin interviewing each of them. Who are you? What made you this way? Can I have some, please? I felt like one of the poor, disheveled Italian children peering through the fence at the beautiful blond bathers in the film *Bread and Chocolate*. They had such vulnerable longing in their hungry eyes, wanting so badly to be like the fair-haired gods and goddesses they gazed upon; lean, confident and aloof, free from the messy entanglements that a fiery Mediterranean heart can bring.

The firewalk itself was anti-climatic compared to what led up to it. Not only did we write about, know and practically bed down with our fear, but we had to read what we had written, unedited, aloud to the group of twelve, the "dirty dozen" as we were referred to by our group leaders. We circled the glowing coals surrounded by large stones collected from a nearby river. I was seated next to a striking young man with dreadlocks traveling down the middle of his back, tied together with a thick piece of yellow yarn. He had a handwoven turquoise and black vest over his bare chest. His dark skin glistened in the fire's light and I could see his well-defined pectoral muscles when he turned to introduce himself. His brown eyes were warm, handshake firm, and his smile mischievous and friendly. The name Cortez made me wonder if he was part Latino. Whatever he was, he certainly was spectacular.

No one was spared from the hot seat; it was just a matter of time before your number came up. I didn't have my usual advantage of volunteering to go first so I could get it over with and sit back while the others boiled in their own juices. I had been the first person in the ropes course to do the "Leap of Faith" which gave me an edge over the testosterone fueled youth in my group. But as fate would have it, I was one of the last to go before the fire. After hearing all the other brands of fear that existed, when my turn came, the butterflies had subsided, and my words came out in a strong and steady stream. I spoke with strength and clarity out loud, for the first time, about my outrageous jealousy, about the demons that taunted me with their whispers of suspicion, their screams of doubt, their outright muti-lation of trust. I hardly recognized my own voice, its determination and steadiness. My cheeks flushed, no longer from shame but from the flame's heat against my skin. As I headed back to my place in the circle Cortez reached up, squeezed my hand, and nodded his quiet acceptance. Our eyes linked up briefly and a tiny spark flew between us. As I sat down a sense of relief permeated my entire being. Finally sharing my fear aloud felt like I had a rose-colored iguana hidden in my back pocket and she was finally out in the daylight. Initially she squinted and shifted her eyes wildly back and forth, but once she began to feel the sun warming her scales, she rolled over, belly up, and exposed her soft spot.

As each member of the dirty dozen walked across the coals, we were greeted at the other end with arms hugging, drums beating and hands applauding. I got lost in the rhythm of the drums and danced with Cortez and other members of the group. We eventually formed a circle and clapped to the beat while each of us ceremoniously found our way to the center and created a solo dance of celebration. As I did some version of the limbo and spun around, I was filled with pure joy by all the support and enthusiasm as the dirty dozen whistled, cheered and clapped wildly.

Joy was something I knew little about, no reference point. I didn't truly realize this until Sandra had asked me during one of our sessions when I felt joy in my life or what made me joyful. I was dumbfounded when I couldn't come up with an answer. The closest image I could conjure was watching Adam and Julia running toward a wave breaking on the sand and then allowing it to chase them back into my arms, giggling madly all the way. But it was their joy, not mine. I was hard pressed to come up with anything that belonged solely to me.

My mother rarely exhibited unbridled enthusiasm or joy about anything, even before Paul was diagnosed with epilepsy. After his diagnosis she had a built-in excuse that she clutched like a hand-bag at her side. She had a sick child and there was no cure for his sickness so she could never truly be free. There was that one time I saw her getting ready for her leading role in the church theater group as Eliza Doolittle in *My Fair Lady*. As she sat at her vanity applying the final touches of her stage makeup, I thought I saw the closest thing to joy flicker in her eyes and ripple across her face. It was breathtakingly beautiful, and so was she.

When I was driving home, I revisited each detail of the firewalk, from the time I entered the circle until we had our group hug at the end. I lingered when I came to Cortez, his impish grin and his shimmering brown skin. I had shared a brief connection with him that felt nice but not disruptive. I headed east on interstate twenty-six toward Charleston as the sun faded behind me.

I returned home that evening to a rousing welcome from my little family. Purple and gold balloons dangled from ribbon on the front porch heralding the heroine home. There were a mixture of carnations and sweetheart roses on the dining room table. Samuel was proud and amazed that I had the courage to go through with it after what he had read in the brochures.

We got the kids to bed a little early, so we had some time to-gether before the work week descended upon us once again. We made such sweet love that night, simultaneously climaxing not once, but twice. After matching our breathing pattern and letting my belly roll into the space his exhale created, he softly kissed my face over and over.

"So how do you feel now Firedancer?" He did have a way with words that fit so perfectly sometimes.

"I feel amazed, and I feel strong and more accepting of who I am now. I'm not as ashamed."

"Why would you be? You've faced the fire and walked right into it. That's hot stuff mama!"

"Yes, but that's not the part that did it."

"What do you mean? Who can beat that?"

"Well, it was saying out loud in front of a group of total strangers, that I was a jealous, out of control woman with all sorts of irrational fears and fantasies about my husband that have no real basis in reality."

"So, saying it in front of other people made it all go away."

"No, let me finish!" It was annoying when he jumped in when I was only halfway there. "It was the actual calm acceptance that I felt from the others after I admitted it, that allowed me to begin to feel it for myself."

"Well, it's easier for people that don't live with you and aren't directly impacted by the wound (as we had so fondly come to call my 'issue') to accept it."

He was resisting me here. I knew he ultimately just wanted it to vanish into the forest never to be heard from again.

"Of course, but it's the acceptance of myself that feels so good."

"Well, I'm proud of you girl. I knew you could do it. I know you're going to lick this thing, completely. One day you'll turn around and it will be gone."

He hugged me one last time before he rolled away into his usual night time reading routine. I let him have his illusion of my fear's total disappearance that night. He deserved it.

"Yeah, I'm making progress." I stroked the iguana across her rosy scales, placing her on my bedside table instead of hidden away in the drawer.

"Firedancer, yes, I'll call you Firedancer." I whispered in her direction.

That night I dreamt of misshapen but voluptuous women. They were draped in rose petals circling a pond, shedding their layers as they spun round and round, exposing loose flesh, crusty moles and winding scars. Their dance was a dance of imperfection, simplicity and wild joy.

Chapter Thirty-nine

I stayed pumped up for quite a while after the firewalk. I received a few e-mails from dirty dozen members as we continued to fuel each other's courage in the weeks to come. Cortez never responded to the one I sent but I savored the moment of his warm recognition that embraced me as I stepped off the hot seat that night.

For a brief period, life took on a peaceful, domestic glow. With Adam and Julia becoming more responsible we decided to adopt a cocoa colored mutt we had seen in the humane society's weekly ad. She had a fluffy white patch on her chest, so we named her Mocha. She was clumsy and lovable, falling right into our family circle. But it was only a matter of three weeks before I met up with my next challenge. I read somewhere in the interim that a soul mate is someone who forces you, by virtue of showing up in your life, to deal with your history and its repercussions. *In your life, it's more like in your face!* My dear soul mate Samuel definitely fit the criteria as he prepared himself, and me, for something bigger and better this round.

He had been climbing monthly and the regulars, a committed group of five men and three women were planning an ice climbing trip to Switzerland at the beginning of June. They had found some unbeatable deal on travelocity.com and they were all super charged about it. They would meet up with a group of highly experienced Swiss climbers that would introduce them to their version of mountain climbing, on the ice. The weather was perfect over there that time of year. Adam and Julia were going away with their dad, and his now steady girlfriend Sarah, to Disney world to start off their summer vacation. Samuel had just gotten his first big bonus after managing his job so tightly that profit margins were up, and he was rewarded accordingly. So, all ducks were in a row, the universe was clearly supporting this endeavor. I was a sign seeker from way back, and all the signs were pointing toward Switzerland and her majestic, ice-capped Alps.

The night Samuel broke the news to me I was pampered in every possible way, perhaps to cushion the fall. He arranged for a sitter and got us a room at the Hampton Inn, complete with Chinese take-out. As we ate, he made not so subtle sexual overtures which were unusual for a week night. That in and of itself aroused a little suspicion but my libido got the better of me, and as I finished off my egg roll, I followed him under the covers. We saved our fortune cookies for dessert and read them aloud after our quick and intense lovemaking. Sometimes you allow lust to have its way with you and you travel down that road, hard and fast. You grind, hump and the zipper can't make its way down soon enough so you can have him inside you, absorbing your vibration, taking you back down.

"So, what's your fortune sweetness?"

He always wanted the lady to go first, part of his traditional military upbringing.

"Wake up. You are under the lucky star now." That had a nice ring to it.

"How about you?"

"Your hard work is about to pay off."

"Well, you just got a bonus so that fits." He shifted onto his side and leaned up on his elbow.

"Yes, and there is something I'd like to do with that bonus."

We had decided long ago when he got a bonus, he would put a portion aside for himself, sort of a 'Samuel fun fund.' It would be there when he wanted to attend a workshop or buy a new vest from Filson's, instead of it just disappearing into the family pot. It was a good way to avoid future resentment since so much of our family finances were dependent upon his income.

"What's that?" I was concerned but not yet alarmed.

"Well Jason from the climbing group e-mailed everybody on Monday about an amazing ice climbing trip to Grindelwald, Switzerland when the kids are at Disney world with their dad and Sarah.

My gut tightened, not as badly as in the past, and the voices hissed from below.

"So, you want to use your bonus to go with them?"

"I'd like to, but I want to talk about it first. How do you feel about it?"

There were actually two opposing forces inside me pushing against one another.

"It's your money and you can do what you want." The ice queen suddenly made an unscheduled appearance

"Olivia, you're way beyond this sweetie, you don't need to shut down on me."

"Okay, okay. I think you deserve to do it. You've been working so hard. And the kids will be gone so they won't miss you."

"Will you miss me?" He started rubbing my back and drawing me closer to him so I couldn't hide out.

"You know I will, but I think the time is right." The other part stepped forward and pushed the ice queen out of the way.

"It's time for me to spend time alone and just deal with it, no children, no distractions, just me on my own."

"You can hang out with friends and do your clay when you're not working."

By now I did have some solid friendships forming in my life. I had stayed in touch with Max since the firewalk. Samuel thought she was cute and perky, but no great shakes like I thought he would. Linda from the dirty dozen had a fear of abandonment so we had common terrain that we traveled comfortably together over coffee and long walks. And my strange and wonderful collection of primitive clay figurines was slowly growing to the point where Samuel had built me a shelf to display them on.

"I'll be fine," I said while trying to convince myself that was true.

"I have no doubt you will."

"Call Jason and tell him you're in but know that we will need to dialogue again."

We had recently attended a workshop designed to give couples tools to create safety around difficult topics. I was usually the one that initiated the dialogue, but Samuel was always a willing participant. He was comfortable talking about anything without a safety net, but I still needed one. My father's unpredictable outbursts over credit card bills, charge accounts, and Sunday dinners that came out of the kitchen lukewarm, had made me skittish. And Samuel's occasional loud voice followed by sudden departure in his truck also contributed to that reluctance.

"Absolutely, we'll talk a lot between now and then. I just want to be at peace with us when I leave."

We gathered up our food cartons, fortunes and returned our key to the front desk. The young clerk smiled and winked assuming we were having an illicit meeting and now rushing back to our other lives and lies. We played along and told her we'd be back. She went back to her keyboard blushing with her assumptions.

Now that Firedancer the iguana was out and about, preparation for Samuel's mountain climbing expedition felt different. We dialogued about my fantasies and fears about him meeting up with some gorgeous, rugged, tan Swiss beauty who would take him to great heights. Instead of totally invalidating my terror and rationalizing why this could or would never happen, he just listened. Sometimes he couldn't contain himself anymore and his left-brain would kick-in, but he was better about just giving me the space I needed to share my crazy, wild images with him. As he listened it was like taking Firedancer out of her shoe box into my hand and stroking her scales.

The closer we came to departure day the more I distracted myself with shopping and packing for Adam and Julia's trip to Florida. They were reeling with excitement because they were staying at Discovery Cove where they would swim with the dolphins. We got underwater cameras, lime green masks and flippers. I put together goody bags with healthy treats along with some gummy bears thrown in for good measure. It was bittersweet for me because I had hoped it was a trip we would make as a family, but Dane and Sarah had secured a great package deal through the travel agency she worked for. It looked like I was being abandoned all the way around for great deals.

After the kids got on their plane, I drifted back to the car trying to figure out what was next. I needed to get my plans in order now so that I could survive the next week of their absence and Samuel's trip. Since I had devoted most of my time to getting Julia and Adam ready for their excursion, I had neglected myself. I called both Linda and Max when I got back. Linda was going on a business trip and would be away all week, and Max wasn't home. How was I going to fill all this free time? There are only so many movies, books and bowls of popcorn. I had talked a good game with Samuel about how important it was for me to deal with my stuff without distractions, but now that the days were closing in on me, I was becoming more anxious. I could work a lot more, earn some comp time and get a head start on the next issue of the museum's quarterly publication, or I could head to the craft store and get a fresh supply of clay. I could do a lot of things, or just let it unfold.

The afternoon before Samuel's trip we decided we would have an early dinner at our favorite Mexican restaurant after he put the finishing touches on his packing. It was within walking distance and the vision of us strolling back hand in hand grounded me even though uneasiness was descending upon me like an island fog at dusk. It was less than twenty-four hours before lift-off, so I was keeping more of a lid on it this time. Samuel had talked so much about wanting to leave in a peaceful, loving place rather than the tense discomfort that had permeated some of his weekend climbs and workshops. I fought with the ice queen as she struggled to make a last-minute showing. The voices beckoned her on stage, but I kept the curtain tightly drawn. While Samuel checked and re-checked his belongings, I thumbed through magazines from the basket next to our bed. Lying there on the satie, I surely gave the appearance of a relaxed, secure woman. Marianne Williamson, a spiritual writer, encourages her readers to "act as if," so I was trying it on for size this time.

Though it wasn't exactly a comfortable fit, I was wearing it as I casually thumbed through a copy of Spiegel and their new spring collection of walking shoes. That was about all my fleeting level of concentration could handle because the catalog pages were filled with bronze beauties like the ones you probably find in Switzerland, the ones who would make me look pale in comparison. But I must have disguised my worry because when I told Samuel I was looking for a new pair of shoes he went merrily along with his cross check and got ready for dinner.

We held hands on the way back, stopped a few times to hug and kiss, and threw a tennis ball for Mocha and her friends, two obsessive golden retrievers that lived next door. I had succeeded in getting through dinner without succumbing to my catastrophic fantasy of the sexy, Scandinavian beauty that would be at the other end of his rope, who would sit by the fire offering some exotic blend of whiskey to warm them up at night, who would laugh at all his simple jokes, and even be somewhat spiritual in her orientation to life. I kept her at bay though in my peripheral vision she was ever present, but not to the point where she was taking over.

"What are you thinking my love?" I had apparently been silent for too long.

"About the trip and the people you're going to meet and connect with." I was partially honest with him.

"The *women* I'm going to meet is really what you mean isn't it?" *Got me, good for him.* I actually wanted to be called on my own subtle deception, so it was liberating.

"Yes, the blond climber who will hold out her rope and you will follow her tight ass anywhere." *There, I had actually made a joke!*

"Has it occurred to you I might have a tight male ass in my face instead of a woman?"

"Samuel this is no time for your rational shit to kick-in. I need acceptance not logic!"

My honesty surprised me, but I felt better, stronger. Instead of hiding behind the face of indifference I let Firedancer out of her box again. She began tap dancing in the moonlight once she heard me singing my truth.

"Okay, you're right! I'm going overseas and meeting a group of climbers you don't know, and you're scared about what will happen, and if I'll be attracted to someone."

It was amazing to realize that my fear of losing him to another woman was far greater than my fear of him falling off the mountainside.

Much to my utter dismay we did not make love that night. Samuel's early flight and nervous anticipation outweighed his sexual appetite. That was a low blow my ego could barely tolerate, and I spent most of the night in the rocking chair staring at the moon while he snored his way into oblivion. I ended up sleeping in the guest room and when he came into awaken me it was everything I could do not to roll over and let the ice queen have her way. The only thing that kept my heart pried open was the thought of not talking to him for at least thirty-six hours and not seeing him for a week. When he gave me the last kiss, he knew I wasn't a hundred percent there, but it was good enough for him to leave intact.

I had finally accomplished something that had eluded me until that moment. I had feelings of anxiety sprinkled with love and I was able to align myself with my heart rather than my fear. I had silenced the voices and kept the ice queen from ruining my final act. I took a deep bow and let out a huge howl, dancing around the living room. Samuel was gone on an incredible adventure that would take him farther from me than ever before, and I was not in pieces scattered all over the floor. I danced my way into the kitchen for a second cup of coffee and a shortbread cookie. It was time to celebrate.

Later that afternoon I called Sandra anxious to report my progress. When she finally got back to me, I was beginning to descend a bit because the voices were slowly returning. They obviously wanted to drown out the sound of cheering and applause that came from the audience who witnessed my landmark performance that morning. Sandra was delighted, and not at all surprised that the sabotaging process had begun.

"You're changing a very familiar pattern here Olivia, and your ego will fight you tooth and nail." My heart sped up and some of the old ways my body used to respond were coming back into play.

"Just notice them but don't allow them to take over. The more you resist the more they will persist."

"It's like a catch-twenty-two. I can't completely surrender nor can I fight to push them away."

"Right, you've got it. Just observe the process without blame or shame. And remember Olivia, if you and Samuel didn't have such a deep, loving relationship, you wouldn't be afraid of losing him. Unfortunately, some of this goes with the territory of intimate partnership."

It wasn't exactly the most comforting conversation, but it left me feeling saner as I waited for Samuel's call to let me know he had arrived safely. It got later and later, and the call never came. There was obviously some delay in his flight, and he had been unable to call me, or had they arrived, and the blond bombshell had already swept him away to their quaint living quarters for the week? Was he sitting next to her having kaffee-fertig, a favorite drink among Swiss climbers?

I clicked on the television and surfed until I landed on the Discovery channel. They were having a special on Norwegian Fiord horses. As I watched the strong, stout golden animals cantering along a sloped area in the country I remembered back to my first love, Mike. When I was in second grade my parents took us to Cummings Cove Polo Club to watch the matches every other Sunday. My mother loved rubbing elbows with equestrians, and I loved watching the sweat glisten on the horse's back as they cooled down. My older sister Sienna knew the stable manager's son from confirmation class, so I got to walk the horses between chukkas. There was one Palomino named Mike that I took a special liking to and tended to him any chance I got. One Sunday he stepped on my foot and broke it in two places, but that didn't diminish the love I had for that noble beast.

The summer after my thirteenth birthday my parents sent me to a camp in the Adirondacks that had horseback riding. They thought my love affair with Mike would lead me to bigger and better things like dressage and show jumping. One afternoon we took a trail ride in the woods and I was riding a speckled Appaloosa named Screwball. The name was apropos as I found out five minutes into the ride when a chipmunk crossed our path. I was in the middle of the line and Screwball backed up into the horse behind him setting off a chain reaction of movement and partial hysteria since all of us were new to riding. But while the other horses calmed down Screwball continued onward, and eventually reared up again. I ended up in a nearby stream. I wasn't badly hurt, just a couple of nasty bruises on my shin and elbow which looked worse than they felt. But I didn't get back on the horse and my instructor didn't make me. Perhaps she was overwhelmed by sheer numbers, or maybe she wasn't as skilled as she could have been as a beginner's instructor. Unless a rider is seriously injured, you always want to encourage them to get back on the horse and finish the ride, so the fear doesn't set in and solidify.

While I got lost in the powerful, solid gait of the Fiords, the phone rang.

"Hey baby, I made it!" Ah, the sweet sound of his voice rang through me like a thousand delicate bells.

"Wonderful, where are you now?"

"At the airport waiting for our luggage."

"Is the team there to meet you?"

"Just two people came with a van."

"Are they nice? What are they like?" *Here it comes, get ready for round one.* I steadied myself.

"Yeah, it's a guy named Werner and his brother Klaus." *False alarm for now.*

"Well I'm so happy you made it, sweetie." I knew he could hear the tentative relief in my voice.

"Me too. Are you okay? What are you doing?"

"I'm actually watching a wonderful program about horses, and yes, I'm doing pretty well. I was getting a little nervous about an hour ago but then I rode it out."

"Yeah, we had to circle the airport for a while. Listen I'm really proud of you sweetie and I'm rubbing my heart." Rubbing our hearts was something we taught Adam and Julia to do when they first started traveling to see their dad. We told them whenever they missed us, they just needed to rub their hearts and that would bring us all closer together.

"I'm rubbing mine too."

A few nights later I dreamt of horses. Dozens of them cantered through a field of heather, sparks flying from their heels, with manes of fire. I watched from a nearby hillside in quiet amazement, yet unafraid. There was a secret desire building inside that wanted to burst forth, grab hold, and ride toward the horizon on one of them. I could feel my entire chest flood with energy as my heart throbbed along for the ride.

I awoke feeling exhilarated and restored. Before my second cup of coffee I spread the newspaper across the dining room table and prepared the space for clay work: wooden tools, bowl of water and my Windham Hill Sampler #86 CD for background inspiration. But I was already inspired as I shaped the moist terra cotta into so many of those stout, beautiful horse creatures. They spread themselves across the paper surface heading off to various destinations. It was two hours before I stopped and noticed the time. And with the time I thought of where Samuel might be, and with who. He was probably well into his climb by then, perhaps stopping for refreshment, taking in a breathtaking view, and talking to his team mates. While I prepared a late breakfast of shortbread and strawberries it occurred to me that I was really in a different place with all this. I had been able to sustain an activity for longer than an hour without collapsing into the fear, but not struggling to keep it away either.

The next week moved along as I met Max for a power walk along the seawall at High Battery, finished a novel by Anne River Siddons that I had been nursing along for months, and wrote a few poems while rocking on the porch swing with coffee. And Mocha and I had both gotten accustomed to our daily romps in the park just in time for the sunset.

It had worked out that Samuel's flight came in thirty-six hours before Julia and Adam would return home. That brief window was the gift of time we needed to reconnect without distraction or interruption. Whenever the kids came back from a trip Samuel always felt somewhat neglected by me and became ornery, like a troll under the bridge.

I carefully selected my outfit for the airport. I wanted sexy and casual. My short denim jacket with a coral tank top and snug black jeans felt just right. Looking at my profile it seemed like I had dropped a few pounds in his absence despite my shortbread breakfasts. When the plane landed, I felt like a schoolgirl again, waiting by my locker for Tim Dwyer to take my books and walk me home. Samuel was one of the last passengers to disembark. Judging from his ruddy complexion and healthy tan, there must have been plenty of sun. A smile spread across his face as he walked straight toward the window where I was standing. As if the glass had no business being there, he placed his hand on mine and his lips mouthed a kiss. I drove home and listened intently while he gave me a detailed description of each day. He was more excited than I had seen him in a long time, as well as more affectionate. It was late when we pulled in the driveway but even before we got out of the car, he was all over me.

"I want you," he said as he grabbed his backpack from the back seat.

"You got me." No time for cat and mouse tonight, the kids would be home tomorrow afternoon.

Our reunion was gorgeous, longer than usual as we prolonged and luxuriated in our foreplay, inventing new tricks as we went along. Because we were alone in the house we could be as vocal as we wanted so we howled like two wolves reunited. We lay quietly for a long time after that, listening to Lyle Mays and feeding each other the white chocolate cheesecake I had gotten for the occasion. I had been careful not to ask Samuel questions on the ride home that would rob him of the joy of his first overseas trip. Sandra had encouraged me to let him choose what he wanted to share on that first night. He broke the silence by telling me more about the people he had met, since initially he had focused mostly on the terrain and the actual climbing. He began to mention the names of a few women; Ursula, Monica and Erika, gently offering general physical descriptions of each. Two out of the three were peers and attractive. I began to feel the shift in my center, I was losing terra firma. It felt like he was leading me somewhere, and I wasn't sure I wanted to follow. Then it came spilling out. The chalet they stayed in on the last night had a hot tub and they all took one together. It was usual and customary in their country to do that naked. I was afraid to hear Samuel's response to my question.

"Were you naked too?'

"I was." He let out a big breath and rolled over on top of me.

"And I'm telling you because there was nothing to it and I didn't want to hide it from you."

I was supposed to appreciate his honesty now, but it was tough, very tough. I was falling into the quicksand and the voices were there to pull me under, to fill my lungs so I couldn't breathe, spill into my ears so I didn't have to hear the truth.

"Did you feel pressured to do it, or did it just come naturally?'

"I felt okay about it, but I wondered how it would affect you, that was my only hesitation."

"And you obviously thought it would be okay for me."

"I knew it would be challenging but I wasn't doing anything wrong, so, yes, I went ahead."

I didn't know where to go with this, but my flight mentality was at the launching pad ready for takeoff. He was appealing to my higher self, although at that moment I questioned if there was such a thing.

"Olivia, you've got to believe there was nothing to it. It was our last night together. We had accomplished great things as a group, and we wanted to celebrate and say goodbye." That just wasn't good enough.

"Did you find yourself getting turned on when you saw their bodies? I'm sure they were pretty hot if they were climbers."

"I noticed their bodies, and yes, they were in good shape, and no, I did not get a hard on."

It was all too much for me to take, too much too soon. But I knew enough to stop there.

Somehow, we ended up spooning and actually falling asleep. The next morning, I was truly amazed that I had slept at all, with no disturbing nightmares of tan, toned Ursula splashing about with my husband. Samuel was exhausted from his flight, so I put on my creamiest robe and got the coffee going. It was a fabulous day with an irresistible blue sky stretching before me. I headed out to the swinging bench and let the morning sunlight bake some sense into me. I was tickled with myself as I gently swayed back and forth. One of my monstrous fears had materialized and I was still sane enough to brew coffee in the correct proportions. Within a few minutes Samuel was up, joining me on the bench. He snuggled up close, testing the waters.

"Are you okay baby?" Part of me wanted to tease, taunt and torture the hell out of him, sort of like pay back. But another part of me was growing stronger every day.

"I am indeed, and it feels great to be okay." The air became palpable with his relief.

"I am so glad, so proud."

"So relieved?" I couldn't resist.

"Well, yes. Even though I knew where I was coming from when I chose to partake, I knew it would be rough for you."

"Don't get me wrong Samuel, it's not my first choice to have you sitting naked in a hot tub surrounded by awesome, attractive climbers, but you did, and I'm still here to tell the story."

"And more importantly, I'm here with you because I love you and none of those awesome, attractive climbers hold a candle to you."

"Now Samuel, you don't have to fib to make me feel good." It was still hard for me to take in that love on some level.

"It's the truth, and someday you'll know it."

We spent the rest of the morning hanging out. I was a bit miffed that Samuel didn't bow down and kiss my ass, but he was comfortable enough with our resolve that he unpacked instead. There was a part of me that wanted to be treated with kid gloves and chocolate because of my hard-earned accomplishment, but soul mates leave you to reward yourself. And so I did. On the way to the airport I got a tall latte with a gooey, blond brownie on the side.

Chapter Forty

Naturally it was wonderful to have the children back. They were brown as berries and had mesh bags filled with treasures from the deep green sea and Mickey Mouse's palace. I smothered them with all the hugs and kisses I could get away with before they had their fill, which was always long before I did. Samuel took them to the park while I got dinner and did their laundry from the trip. Their little pockets were filled with sand, candy wrappers and the tiniest of shells. I pictured Dane leisurely strolling along the beach helping them hunt for booty. He was always so patient and involved.

As I transferred their clothes from washer to dryer, I watched Samuel take each one by the hand to cross the street. He was cautious and protective whenever he was with them. I would have to say he was as caring as any step-dad could be; knowing full well he had no legal rights to them should anything ever happen to me. Sometimes he would tell me how hard it was to love them, knowing they could be taken from him in a heartbeat. That was one trial I knew nothing about, but I came to appreciate his position more and more as our longevity increased. But Samuel never let his mind dwell in areas he couldn't control, namely the future. That was a skill that I was slowly developing.

One afternoon in July when I was busy making travel plans for Julia and Adam to travel to Algonquin for their two weeks of summer vacation with Dane, Miranda called and invited herself down for a visit. She thought she could tie it in with the children's travel arrangements and escort them back to the island instead of me. For our peace of mind and their safety, Dane and I would each fly with them one way rather than doing unescorted minor trips and entrusting them to the airlines. But Miranda's offer had some appeal since we could use the extra time and money to remodel their outdated bathroom while they were away. I checked with Dane and he was comfortable, not thrilled of course because Miranda was now just *my* friend, no longer a mutual one, but he still trusted her. She had been there for us when the twins were born, when we desperately needed down time, extra milk or liquid Tylenol.

"By the way," he said casually, "Sarah and I are busy making plans for a small wedding when the children get here." I was stunned by his announcement, yet I should have expected it from the way the children were talking when they returned from their Disney trip. Julia mentioned something about the pretty ruby ring dad had given Sarah.

It wasn't until I was putting clean sheets on the guest room bed for Miranda that I got a slight tingle in my belly. Beautiful, self-sufficient, single Miranda, who had slept with my husband, was coming to spend three nights under our roof. Oh, she had dated in our absence, and there was one that had looked quite promising, but didn't pan out in the end. She was still footloose and fancy free with similar interests to Samuel. When I got into bed that night, I asked him if we could use our dialogue tools. Because it was nearing his reading routine, he was less than enthusiastic. He reluctantly agreed if we kept it to under thirty minutes.

"Honey, I'm feeling a bit strange about Miranda coming."

"She's your old friend, what's the strangeness about?"

"The usual. She's a single, attractive woman, and you happen to have a past with her." By now I was able to state my case more easily, without all the shame bogging me down.

"Honey, the key word is *past*." He was getting activated, using rationalizing again.

"Samuel, remember the tools, no rationalizing, just validation here."

"Okay, I acknowledge that because she is a pretty, single woman that I had more than friendly contact with one night you are feeling insecure about her staying in our home."

"That's right. I'm afraid that having her around for so long, walking around in her pajamas and stuff will create a problem."

"Well, I can understand your fear, but I can assure you that it won't be a problem for me because my heart is right here." He put his hand on my heart and kissed my forehead.

"Now what do you need from me to feel safe while Miranda is here?"

"I just need you to be aware that I'm scared and check in with me."

"And you need to check in with me too. Don't leave it all up to me."

When Miranda arrived later that week, I went to the airport by myself. I decided I would broach the subject with her to avoid any possible discomfort once we got to the house. She was surprised by my concerns and immediately tried to brush them off in her rather cool and playful manner.

"An old lady like me, I don't think so! Besides it's abundantly clear that Samuel only has eyes for you my dear." She pinched my cheek as if to say, 'get over it sweetheart.'

Back at the house Samuel had the kids engrossed in a game of monopoly. When we walked in Adam was buying Park Place and feeling pretty cocky about his holdings. Julia was always a better loser than him so despite her losses she was still rather chipper.

"Look how much you've grown! You're both gorgeous!" Miranda dropped her Gucci bag in the foyer and went toward them with open arms. Samuel stood up and embraced her like the gentleman he always was. She kissed him on both cheeks and then bent down to greet Adam and Julia. Samuel winked at me over her shoulder.

After the children were in bed the three of us lingered over decaf, catching up on the island gossip. Miranda had just started talking about an advanced woodworking class she was taking when Adam called down to me. He rarely had trouble falling asleep, so I went to see what was bothering him. It turned out that I was up there for quite a while. He had chosen the privacy of his room and the anonymity of darkness to relay a bullying incident that happened on the playground at recess. The lioness in me emerged as I listened and rubbed his back, throwing out a few suggestions here and there. But even as I did that, I could feel a part of myself drifting down the stairwell to Samuel and Miranda. When Adam fell asleep and I headed back downstairs I was ashamed of myself for being even slightly distracted from his concerns. Miranda and Samuel were deep in conversation when I got back, and they obviously hadn't missed me.

"Everything all right, sweetie?" I decided to soak this one for all it was worth and break their little woodworking spell.

"Actually, no. Some kid in Adam's class was harassing him out on the playground. He was pretty freaked." Samuel shifted his posture away from Miranda and toward me. *Got him!*

Miranda gathered up the cups and saucers and headed into the kitchen.

"We'll finish up some other time, Miranda." Samuel said. She turned and flashed him one of her famous smiles.

"Absolutely, I want to hear the rest."

"The rest of what?" I asked in a suspicious tone directed toward him only.

"Oh, we were talking about a particular finish for mahogany."

"Is she working with that now too?"

"She just recently started experimenting with different types of wood in her class." *She is the renaissance woman isn't she*, I thought.

While I was in the kitchen preparing the coffee for the next day, I heard Miranda come out of the bathroom. I glanced over and she had changed into a pale peach short nightgown and was heading down the hall. She paused in front of our bedroom door.

"Good night Samuel. Thanks so much for answering all my amateur questions. It was a big help." Her voice faded a little and I couldn't figure out why, so I started down the hall. When I got to the door of our bedroom, she was taking her arms from around Samuel's neck. I bristled and instantly felt sick to my stomach.

"I was just giving your man a big hug for helping me out tonight with all his years of experience." I could hardly look my dear old friend in the eye. Something had taken over me to the point where I didn't recognize her, or myself.

"Well, you're welcome Miranda, it was no big deal. But tomorrow is an early one for all of us, so I'll say goodnight." I don't think she even noticed that I didn't speak at all, but Samuel was acutely aware of my silence. I slammed my dresser drawer shut and pulled on my leggings and tee-shirt, not a very glamorous combination for night wear.

"Hey you, get over here." He grabbed me and sat me down. I didn't want to look at him, but he turned my face toward his.

"What the hell was that all about?" I fired away.

"What was what about?"

"You know exactly what I'm referring to. What was she doing in our bedroom, in her night gown with her arms around your neck?"

"I guess that was her way of thanking me though I thought it was a bit overdone."

"Well you certainly weren't discouraging her from where I was sitting."

"She caught me off guard and I didn't want to make a big deal of it."

"Samuel, are you still attracted to her?" I had to know.

"Olivia, Miranda is an interesting, attractive woman, but I am not attracted to her." All I heard were the words interesting and attractive. The rest was lost.

"Olivia, do you understand the difference?" I struggled to get away from the place that I was being pulled back into after so much supposed progress. And Miranda was my old friend.

"No, I don't. If you were attracted to her before, why wouldn't you be now?"

"Because my heart is with you, my connection is to you. I am full inside. Yes, I still find other women attractive, but I am not open to them in that way."

I was silenced by my fear and confusion, so he continued trying to soothe me.

"Let me give you a real good example. I was riding home from work the other day and there was an attractive woman riding her bike in front of me. Her hair was blowing in the wind and she had on tight Lycra shorts that revealed plenty. As I drove past her I didn't even glance in the rearview mirror. Now when I was a bachelor, I would have figured out a way to turn the truck around and meet her. But I just headed on home, looking forward to seeing the woman that was waiting for me there." A convincing vignette on some level but I still did my usual probing.

"In other words, being with me has closed off a part of you?"

"I prefer to think of it as our relationship fulfills me on so many levels that I'm not out there looking." My shoulder dropped and I felt myself breathe again. I was starting to have a glimmer of understanding about what he was saying. Somehow, he could shift his attention temporarily to another attractive woman, but he would be back. I flashed on Cortez, the drums by the fire and the wild dancing. I found him intriguing and sensual, but I came home all the same.

When we got up the next morning, I tried to occupy myself with the final stages of packing for the children. I kept my contact with Miranda brief as I went about my domestic duties while she tried to engage in conversation. I felt angry and betrayed on some level. She had known from our first conversation about her past with Samuel that maintaining our friendship would be a challenge for me. How could she be so cavalier last night in our bedroom and take the liberties with Samuel that she did? But I refused to have any tension before the children left for two weeks, so I had to stuff it.

Samuel left early and simply waved to Miranda from the front door as he was leaving for work. He made no effort to connect with her. When we were driving to the airport, she cautiously brought up the subject.

"Are you upset with me?" Her voice was low and timid. The children were busy with their new dry erase boards, so I responded, in the same low voice.

"I am but we don't have time to get into it now."

"Was it the time I spent with Samuel last night?" She asked in a rather innocent way.

"No, that was fine. It was going into our bedroom in your night gown and kissing him goodnight." She took her time responding.

"I just felt so comfortable with all of you and it had been such a great visit. It seemed, well, natural, I guess."

"With all I've shared with you about my fear and your past with Samuel it feels pretty insensitive and thoughtless." I was becoming louder now. But she was always so good about controlling her emotions, so she kept her voice soft and smooth, like liquid silk.

"Maybe I was a bit careless; I hope you'll forgive me." She put her hand on my shoulder and patted it. I knew it would take me awhile to forgive, and even longer to forget, but in order to feel good about her flying with my precious cargo I once again acted "as if."

"We've been friends for a long time, been through so much so I'll let go of it. Just give me some time."

When the plane lifted off and they were out of sight I immediately went back to reviewing the incident in my mind. I was furious, disappointed and hurt, yet I loved her dearly. I felt like I had made so much headway with the hot tub incident in Switzerland, weekend rock climbing and Samuel's growing interest in Shamanism. Why did she have to go and throw a wrench in the works and give me something else to contend with? This time I hadn't gone looking for anything, one of my best friends hand delivered it right to my bedroom door.

Amazingly enough, Samuel and I were able to work through it that night and enjoy our two weeks without the kids Even though we weren't going anywhere because we needed the time and money to work on their bathroom, we still managed to enjoy ourselves and create the feeling of a vacation. We went out to eat a lot, watched sunsets from the porch with wine, smoked skinny cigars, and had more than weekly sexual encounters in a variety of locations.

One evening after the ball of fire had disappeared behind the clouds, I felt a burst of unusual gratitude about my life. Samuel was working late, and we were meeting at our favorite Italian restaurant on Church Street. I loved getting dressed up and having a rendezvous downtown. It still felt new and mysterious, and I was grateful those kinds of feelings were possible after ten years. And I was thankful we continued to work through all these ancient wounds that we both carried.

Through my stuff Samuel had also uncovered issues of his own, like being accused of stuff he didn't do. My unfounded jealousy triggered his reaction of being unjustly blamed. It happened to him a lot when he was growing up. Somehow with a pile of siblings he came out looking guilty in a lot of situations and took some pretty severe beatings for them. But he had long ago put that away somewhere until I came on the scene and blew the lid off. Though we activated each other, we also acted as healing agents. Now that was something to be thankful for, and I felt it all the way down to my toes.

I arrived ten minutes late, partly because of traffic and partly because I wanted to make a grand entrance in my short red linen skirt and low-cut black top. Samuel gave me the once over I was hoping for and then landed a big, wet kiss on my neck.

"You look gorgeous as usual."

"I'm so glad you agreed to meet me Mr. Ferrell. I have a project that I hope will interest you." From time to time we would slip into roles that would titillate us during our evening alone together. He followed along ever so playfully and willingly.

"Please, tell me all about it. You have my undivided attention." The evening continued to be magical, fun and erotic. When we got home we ended up on the dining room table. Needless to say, he got the job.

Chapter Forty-one

Julia and Adam came home healthy, heavier and unenthused about starting school again. Southern schools started almost a month before the north and they were still in their vacation mode. The older they got the harder it was to leave their dad and they talked about wanting to spend a month with him next summer instead of just two weeks. They mentioned Miranda coming by and taking them for ice cream one day. My contact with her had been a little superficial and less frequent since her visit. I didn't want to deal with it long distance so I figured we would talk more about it when I brought the kids up for Thanksgiving. But I had already begun to grieve the loss of the way our friendship had once been. It didn't feel quite the same anymore; we rarely discussed Samuel or the latest man in her life. We used to go on and on, sharing intimate details about our men, our relationships, our lives. I wanted to get back to that place.

For Halloween we really did it up that year. We carved four elaborate pumpkins, filled bags with sand and candles along the path leading to our door, and dressed as Pocahontas and John Smith. At ten and eleven Julia and Adam were not enamored with our costumes but we hammed it up anyway. When I came back from replenishing our candy supply, I noticed Samuel on the sidewalk talking to Little Bo Peep without her sheep. She pulled something out of her bag and handed it to him. When her sheep returned, she waved and led them away with her staff.

"Who was that honey?"

"That's Margie, the one who does drafting part-time for us out of her home."

"Oh, was that something work related she gave you?" My curiosity was moving in.

"No, it's information about a week-long workshop in Florida next summer. Some shamans are coming over from South America to a retreat center down there."

"Is Margie into shamanism?" Now my curiosity was beginning to go to another level.

"No, her husband is. She and I talked one morning when she saw the calendar with the shaman paintings you gave me. She knew she would be trick or treating in our neighborhood tonight, so she brought it along."

"That was nice of her. You never told me about that conversation."

"Olivia, I don't have to tell you everything now do I?" He was joking on the one hand, but serious on the other.

"No, but I guess when its important stuff that has to do with your spiritual path, I like to be kept up to speed."

"Okay, but our conversation was so brief it didn't seem significant." Our spiritual focus was gradually assuming a powerful position in our lives, but for very different reasons. I was reading more Deepak Chopra, Thomas Moore and Marianne Williamson, practicing yoga, and seeking more intentional solitude to better manage the fears triggered by being with someone like Samuel. It was ironic that when he first came into my life, I saw his masculine tenderness as a safe haven. As I looked over at him devouring the new brochure, I laughed at the cosmic joke that had been so cleverly played on me. I fell hook, line and sinker.

I flew up with the kids for Thanksgiving and reluctantly agreed to stay the night at Miranda's. She was all excited about her latest love Gabe, a lawyer that had moved his practice to the island from Bangor to scale down and simplify his life. It had a nice ring to it. We all went to Logan's for dinner, one of the more expensive restaurants on Algonquin. I didn't bring anything dressy, so I rifled through Miranda's closet for something to wear. She was two sizes smaller than me, so I needed something on the less fitted side. Her black cashmere dress worked, and as we put on our makeup, she babbled on about how wonderful Gabe was.

The evening flowed along with Pinot Grigio, fresh seafood and easy conversation. Gabe was attentive, interested enough, and had a great sense of humor. Miranda was glowing in her ivory silk blouse and it looked like this could be the real thing. After he left, we spread out in her queen size bed eating white chocolate truffles and reliving all the details of our dinner. We giggled about his gorgeous blue eyes, the gold ring on his pinkie finger, and the way he held his coffee cup slightly tilted. It felt just like it used to between us. Then she did something totally out of character. Perhaps it was the wine, or her new-found love and contentment, but whatever the reason, *she* brought up her visit last summer in Charleston.

"Olivia, have you let go of what happened last summer?" I was definitely blindsided by this one. Miranda had avoided confrontation at all costs for as long as I had known her. I didn't know how to answer. If I had let go of the incident, I wouldn't have had reservations about staying with her, and I did. I reached for the bottle of Perrier on her night stand and took a long sip.

"I guess I'm still confused about what motivated you. I had shared my fears on the way back from the airport and you knew I was stretching to have you there."

In some of my sessions with Sandra we had discussed Miranda. Sandra said some women would have let the friendship die a natural death once we had left the island. It would have been an easy, uncomplicated way of ending it, just chalking it up to long distance and all. But I had chosen to press on because of our long and rich history. Miranda and I had often fantasized about being two old widows sipping good wine in Portofino.

"It's hard to say. I guess it had been a long time since a man had really paid close attention to what I had to say. It felt so good to have that focus and attention. My response was to thank him in the way that felt most natural to me, a hug and kiss."

"And what about me Miranda? What about my feelings about your particular brand of gratitude?" She snapped back.

"I wasn't thinking about you right then. It's not always all about you." That was unexpected and it stung like a hungry yellow jacket coming out of nowhere on a hot summer day. I wanted to slap it away but instead I retreated into a place of shame. I looked back at Miranda, feeling a bit embarrassed by my self-absorption.

"You're right, sometimes I overreact and expect too much from people. Maybe your gesture was no big deal."

"For some people it probably wouldn't have been. After all, I've known Samuel for a long time, and it wasn't that strange." I felt boxed in by her cool, logical approach.

"I'm sorry about my reaction, but now that you have Gabe in your life, he'll be hanging on your every word and you'll have gobs of attention." My words were a few steps ahead of where my heart lingered, but I was determined to have them catch up realizing that I almost lost a dear, old friend because of this unwieldy fear of mine.

"Yes, it seems like he could be the man I've been putting out feelers for all this time. It's so great that you got to meet him."

"I like him, and he comes with a lot of what you said you wanted. He's older, no children, well established, and very comfortable." Miranda always said she wanted someone who was on the mature side, and therefore probably older than she. Gabe was nine years her senior. and his salt and pepper hair accented those blue eyes, making them jump right out the first time he smiled at you. He obviously had a very successful law practice because he was driving a Lexus and had just purchased a large, newly restored house on the cliff overlooking the harbor.

When Miranda dropped me at the airport the next day, she kissed me on both cheeks as she was accustomed to since her year abroad in France. I hugged her tightly and it felt like we had hurdled something major. She was meeting Gabe for brunch at Ollie's Grille, so I told her not to bother parking.

Waiting for the plane I wondered what my children were up to at this hour. It was close to ten-thirty in the morning, so they were probably just waking up. Since they started middle school with their hormones kicking into high gear, they required much more down time. I wondered what their now stepmother, Sarah, had planned for their breakfast, or should I say brunch, when they finally made it out of bed. She and I had managed a cordial relationship in our brief conversations. I had tried to push beyond that and learn more about the woman my children were spending significant time with, but she remained very reserved. The limited information I had gleaned from Dane and the kids was that she was from South Dakota and had come east to start her life over after her husband was killed in a plane crash. I knew she worked as a travel agent, played the accordion, and loved her African Gray Parrot, Simon. She had no children of her own so all I could hope for was that she was good to mine.

Chapter Forty-two

It was a brutal winter for South Carolina. There was a wave of ice and snowstorms that swept across the country leaving power outages and stranded tractor trailers in its wake. With the fierce cold and consistently low temperatures Samuel's rock-climbing trips were seriously curtailed. But he always found something to occupy his mind and hands. He had finished the children's bathroom and was now building book shelves for the living room. The number of spiritual books he was purchasing steadily increased and they needed a home. With the rock climbing taking a back seat, his interest in shamanism now moved to the forefront. His appetite for more knowledge about the South American shamans coming that summer from Ecuador and Peru became insatiable. Many a night he was up late reading or looking at websites about them.

"Find out anything I need to know about?" I came up behind him late one Saturday evening and looked over his shoulders. On the screen were scantily clothed men with dark skin and painted faces with brightly colored head bands. They stood around a fire.

"Oh, this is a very famous Spring ritual that is performed by the shamans in their villages. It's amazing. Take a look at their faces;

they are so beautiful and intense." He was totally absorbed by what he was seeing. He journeyed in his mind to faraway places more and more now.

"Take me with you," I said aloud. He turned immediately and put me on his lap.

"You are always with me, baby. I am not leaving you behind." I know he was convinced that what he was saying was true. The rock climbing, trip to Switzerland, the Miranda fiasco, and weekend shaman workshops had taken us much farther than I dreamed we could ever go, surely farther than I thought *I* was capable of going. With his weeklong trip to Florida looming in the background I was still able to stay relatively calm most of the time. But those wild colors and painted faces by the fire with eyes staring right through your soul made it scary to imagine Samuel among them. He squeezed my hands with reassurance.

Despite the horrendous, frigid conditions some of our crocuses, daffodils and tulips prematurely popped their heads out in late February and still managed to survive. With Julia and Adam doing more with their friends and less with us, I had taken to the earth and found tremendous comfort there. I brushed and cleared away old leaves and tiny branches, smoothed the soil over, making way for the glorious parade of flowers that were humming in the distance. I had planted a variety of perennials one Sunday afternoon in September while everyone else had somewhere to be. The satisfaction of seeing them poke through and reveal themselves was sublime. They were coming to greet the world with heads of orange, yellow and pink. I had nestled those bulbs down under all by my lonesome and now I sat back, leaned against the steps and took it all in.

"Look at my little gardener here." Samuel joined me on the porch when he got home from work.

"How was your day handsome?" We performed our greeting and parting ritual, a feather kiss. If he started out the door in the morning without one, we would laugh and recite the Chinese proverb, "He who forgets to kiss his wife in the morning have bad luck all day." We would not have that.

"Good, busy as always. We finally got a new administrative assistant to replace Donna." Donna had left to join her husband who had been a Professor at the College of Charleston for thirty-six years and was retiring. First thing on their agenda was a Safari to South Africa, a long-time fantasy of mine as well. Donna was in her early sixties, soft spoken and extremely efficient. She would be missed, especially for her famous homemade cinnamon swirls that she brought in weekly for coffee break.

"What's the new person like?" There was a slight tingle down there, but nothing major. If I hadn't been paying attention, I might not have noticed it at all.

"She seems nice. Her name is Karen and she has a good, strong background. She worked with a restoration crew after Hurricane Hugo so she has a real sense of what goes into it."

"That sounds helpful. Why did she decide to switch over to administrative stuff after doing hands on?"

"I'm not sure; we only spoke for about five minutes. I'll learn more at the staff meeting Wednesday." I became mildly curious about Karen's age, looks and marital status, but not enough to raise the questions. The answers would present themselves soon enough. I went back to gently weeding and removing the remains of winter from my garden as Mocha rolled and moaned in the grass next to me.

~

Sarah's family had rented a house in the Florida Keys for a spring break reunion. Adam and Julia were thrilled with the idea of being on the water, fishing, snorkeling and meeting more cousins. Dane was very vague about the details except to say that they would fly into Charleston, meet the kids at the airport and go on to Florida from there. Sarah had made all the arrangements and the itinerary was on the way. They would have electronic tickets and could only have one carry on. I craved more specifics about how many cousins, siblings, aunts and uncles would be there, but Dane gave me only the necessary information and signed off. It was still hard for me not to know more details about his life. We had been so close and then parted sadly, but not in an ugly, violent break like so many others we knew. But now that he was remarried, our rapport had become short and almost businesslike. Samuel said that was healthy, and I knew he was right, but it still felt like a loss.

The kids didn't call to say they arrived safely, which was a pet peeve of mine when they were traveling. I finally called and one of Sarah's relatives answered and said Adam and Julia were already out swimming with their new cousins. I hung up and felt so disconnected from them. What bathing suit was Julia wearing? Was she feeling brave enough to try her new flowered turquoise two-piece? Had Adam eaten enough? He so grouchy when his blood sugar dropped. Were they on the bay or ocean side? Over a simple pasta, garlic, tomato, and olive oil entrée Samuel sensed my preoccupation.

"You miss the kids, don't you?"

"I miss hearing from them, knowing what they're up to. I just wish they would call." I heard myself whining and it was unpleasant.

"They're having too much fun to call. Remember they're adolescents now. We're the last ones they are thinking about."

"I know, I know. But I wish Dane would encourage them to stay in touch more when they're with him." He took my hand and rubbed it.

"Olivia, that's unrealistic. Dane is with his new family and you are not part of that picture."

"But I'm their mother."

"Yes, you are, so call them when we finish dinner if that will put you in a more connected place."

I called and the kids were outside playing "Capture the Flag". It took quite a while for Julia to get to the phone. I could hear lots of laughter and clatter in the background. Julia was breathless and unenthusiastic when she got on the phone. She couldn't hang up fast enough, and Adam never made it. He had the flag and couldn't stop just then, but he would call back later. He never did. Samuel temporarily distracted me with a massage that led to other places, but as I lay back on the oriental rug my mother had sent us as an anniversary gift, I felt the world gradually shifting beneath me.

About two weeks after the kids returned, having bonded nicely with their stepmother's family, Dane called and left a message saying it was important I get back to him. I put down my shopping bags, let Mocha out, balanced the cordless under my chin and dialed his number. Adam and Julia were at soccer practice and I had about thirty minutes to put away groceries and squeeze the call in. It was unlike Dane to have such urgency in his voice, so I hoped nothing was wrong. After the fourth ring I started to click into worry mode when he picked up.

"Dane, is anything wrong? Are you and Sarah all right?"

"Fine, we're fine. I was just down in the basement and couldn't get to the phone. How about you? Everything okay with the kids?" His tone seemed a bit warmer and more accommodating than usual.

"They're at soccer practice, trying to get back into the flow after being on vacation."

"Yeah, we all had a good time."

"It's hard to get any details from them but they both seem to like Sarah's family. They said her brother Everett is hilarious."

"Yeah, he's quite the character. Listen, did the kids mention anything about the summer or the next time they're coming up?" This was definitely leading somewhere. Dane never mentioned the next visit until we were about a month away and under the gun to make flight reservations. It was a sore point with us from the beginning, even when we were married. I was a planner and he allowed things to just unfold.

"No, why? Do they want to stay longer this time? I figured that was in the making. We added on a week last summer, so I was anticipating a month this year." He was quiet, except for an audible sigh.

"So, what's up Dane? You obviously have something on your mind." I noticed that as I got scared, I pushed harder, an old habit coming back into play.

"Well, when we were down in the Keys we talked about Adam and Julia coming to live with us." He paused and let that hang in the air for a minute. "It's a good time with them both about to start high school." I sat down on the floor and dropped the bag I was holding. Everything around me started to spin and go out of focus.

"Olivia, are you there?"

"Yes, I'm still here." I wasn't ready to face something that I had known was possible from the day I left Dane, and then moved away. But I had only known it in my head, nowhere else, not on paper, not in reality, certainly not in my heart, where it counted. Their bright, bold drawings and photographs, long ago tacked on the cork board in the kitchen, fluttered in the breeze blowing through the back door. Mocha was back and my world was caving in.

"I was sure the kids would say something to you and Samuel when they got back." As I did a fast rewind, I remembered them talking a lot about some of their new cousins moving to Algonquin, and how much fun it would be to see them more often.

"No, they didn't mention it specifically, but I think you should be the one to tell me anyway. You're the adult."

"Well, what do you think?" Only a millisecond to respond about the departure of my two babies? They were always my babies when I was going to be away from them, or when they were sleeping, or sick.

"I think I need some time to digest this. I realize we have joint custody, so this has always been a possibility that existed out there somewhere."

"That's fine Olivia; we'll talk in a week. It's just that I know how you plan in advance and I didn't want you buying round-trip tickets for the summer if this was going to happen."

"If this is going to happen, Samuel and I will be driving them up. They will have so much to bring, and we'd like to see where they're going to be living." There was no way that I could live without a visual of where my children would be.

"Okay, well, hang in there. I'll call in a week or so and we'll start to make some plans. I'll need to register them for school." I was blown away that he was even thinking along those lines already. He obviously didn't expect any strong resistance at my end. Then

again, Julia had mentioned that one of Sarah's brothers was an attorney so perhaps while they were fishing in the Keys he got some
free legal advice about his position in all this.

"Yes, we'll be talking again. How about next Monday after dinner at about seven?" I wanted to pin him down.

"Sure. I'll talk to you then. Give my love to the kids." That was
it. He hung up after rearranging my entire life in a ten-minute
phone conversation. But what I had done certainly created a bomb
cyclone in his, so it had finally come back to devastate mine.

That night when Samuel found the dog food in the freezer and
the ice cream under the sink, he wondered what was amiss. He tried
to make a joke, but I clearly wasn't going there.

"Where were you when you unpacked the groceries today?" He
smiled innocently and held up the mushy carton of ice cream and
the frozen pellets of dog food. I walked out of the kitchen and mumbled, "In a place I hoped I'd never have to go." He put the sticky carton in the sink and followed me down the hall for an explanation.

Chapter Forty-three

Driving to work the next day I made a wrong turn and rolled right through a stop sign. My mind was overloaded with the anticipation of Julia and Adam going to live with Dane and Sarah. *Accept loss forever*, wasn't that some kind of Buddhist saying I had heard or read somewhere? What would our home be like without the phone constantly ringing for Julia, and Adam's muddy soccer cleats in the hallway? My insides coiled in retaliation at the utter silence of it all. So much of my life was filled with them, their sounds, smells and touch. I always knew if Adam hadn't washed his hair when the oil slid through my fingers as they brushed lightly across his forehead in passing. Julia was now obsessed with masking her natural scent, and as she experimented with different perfumes, I could track her mood: sexy, sporty or sensual, by how she smelled that morning for school. My heart ached with the emptiness to come.

When I got into my office there was a sticky note from Dwayne saying he wanted to see me as soon as possible. *Now what?* I certainly didn't need any more curve balls today, this week, this month, whatever. I buzzed him and he told me to come on up. I stopped for a cup of coffee, my third for the morning, which was highly unusual. I always watched my caffeine intake because it interfered with my blood sugar level. I usually waited until between two or three in the afternoon when I hit a low energy point, and then indulged in my third and final cup of the day.

"Olivia, I've got a sensational idea for our centennial quarterly." Dwayne was more jazzed than I'd seen him in a while. He opened up to the centerfold of another museum's glossy publication. There was a gorgeous layout with a series of portraits. Their faces beamed up at me from the page below.

"I would like you to look at the roster of trustees. Some of them are related to our founding members of a hundred years ago. I would like interviews with photographs in the centennial issue. Let's feature the people that are linked to our beginnings."

I felt something percolate inside. I had wanted to be a journalism major in college but mid-way through my sophomore year I became interested in psychology and switched over. My original fantasy had been to work as a photo journalist for *Life* magazine. I could envision tea cups and hear classical music in the homes of people to be interviewed. I would play with the lighting and arrange the background appropriately, capturing their true essence. It went back to those birthday trips to New York City with my Aunt Joanne when my sister and I would meet her in Grand Central Station under the clock. My old composition book collected the secret lives of strangers I had spotted in the crowd and wrote about. I would read aloud to my Aunt over Manhattan clam chowder at the Oyster Bar, and she was always enthusiastic and intrigued.

"Dwayne, I love the idea and I really need something I can throw myself into."

"Why? Aren't I working you hard enough?" He flattened the edges of his mustache and smiled.

"Hardly, it's just that Dane called yesterday, and he wants the kids to come live with him. I'll need a major distraction to deal with this one."

"But wasn't that always a possibility? Besides it will give you and Samuel more time to pursue your own interests." That's why Dwayne was the boss and I wasn't. He could be so damn logical, detached and calculating. They weren't his children, so it was easy for him to be cavalier. He didn't have any of his own, but his two Russian Blue cats were his treasured babies.

"Well, I'll start doing my research now and see who looks interesting. When I come up with a list of potentials, I'll get back to you."

"Perfect. See if you can have that by the end of the week. And you'll be fine, Olivia. Think of all the splendid possibilities that await you with all that free time!" Starting down the hall I shivered as the all-encompassing loneliness descended upon me again. It was gray, cool and thick, very thick. It felt like a damp, outdated trench coat that had come to rest on my shoulders. The pockets were worn thin and empty.

I dove into the project deep and fast. I read short biographies on all the trustees, their families and histories. By late morning Thursday I had generated a list of eight potential interviews and delivered them to Dwayne by noon that day. He was delighted and surprised with my speed and efficiency. By Monday of the next week we had narrowed it down to six that I needed to prioritize in terms of who would be most interesting. One woman stood out above the rest, Miriam Hazelton. She lived north of Charleston on Goose Creek. Her father had been one of the founders of the museum and she was in her late seventies. I called and scheduled a time to meet the following week. She was very willing and suggested two in the afternoon for tea. I could already see the light filtering through the French doors reflecting off the golden edge of her tea cups.

Driving north to Goose Creek I had a feeling of pleasant anticipation. My Pentax camera was on the seat next to me, along with my tape recorder. I had checked the batteries and loaded my film before leaving the office. As I advanced the film, the clicking sound brought such sweet satisfaction. Doing anything technical without assistance always gave me such a sense of accomplishment. Samuel had taught me everything I knew about the camera and taking photographs. It all came so easily to him, but I needed to hear it, see it and do it several times before I finally got it right. Now I was on my way to my first interview and photo shoot, with all the necessary equipment that I had prepared all by myself.

To get to Miriam Hazelton's I had to cross an old covered bridge, white with a red tin roof. Her property was surrounded by cottonwood trees and hemlocks. A wooden sign outlined in dark pink hung on the fence post read "Rosewood Junction." That had a friendly, inviting ring to it. I curved around the gentle sloping driveway that led to her "heart of pine" house from the colonial period. It was friendly from the start with its pineapple welcome flag, and the sound of a dog accompanying her to the door. The bark was one of excited curiosity rather than fury. A petite woman with snow white hair, pulled up and back with combs and bobby pins, greeted me with a soft smile. She was wearing a denim shirt rolled up at the sleeves with worn out khaki pants, more casual than I expected for an older, southern female.

"Come in, you must be Olivia. This is Buster, my very harmless canine." I bent down as I had been taught so long ago, greeting Buster at his level so he wouldn't have to jump up to get a better sniff.

"Yes, I'm Olivia from the museum. Your home is so warm and inviting." She showed me into the casual but elegant living room with French doors that led to a stone patio. It sloped down to a garden, creek and what looked like a pasture.

"What a beautiful setting. Do you have cows out there?" She smiled.

"No, I raise Norwegian Fiords."

"Oh, I saw a special about them on the Discovery channel not too long ago."

"They are the gentlest, yet strong horses, great for trail riding. Do you ride?"

"No, but I've always loved horses. There was a white horse in my past but that's a story for another time." Somehow, I already knew there would be other times, lots of them. As we sipped our jasmine tea and indulged in her delicious shortbread cookies, she answered all my questions with such grace and ease. I felt a sense of comfort and peace that I hadn't known since I first met Dane. It was pleasantly eerie, so effortless to listen to her, to stay present. She knew her family's history in detail, and never skipped a beat. When she went into the kitchen to get us a refill I got up and started looking at the photographs on the end tables. In a teak frame there was a very handsome older gentleman with his arm around a striking younger man. They appeared to be somewhere tropical.

"That's my husband Dirk and my son Will. They were in South Africa." She was so matter-of-fact.

"Where are they now?" She paused a moment and put the tray down.

"They're both gone. They died in a plane crash on the way home from that trip." I was stunned and wished I hadn't been so damn inquisitive. She sensed my discomfort and carried on.

"Dirk was a doctor; after Will was born, he became very active in the 'Doctors Without Borders' program. He traveled all over the world wherever natural disaster struck. Will became a photographer for *National Geographic* and went to take pictures of his work in Mozambique. They were flying out of Nampula on one of those small planes and ran into bad weather. That picture was taken by one of the nurses the day before the accident. They were a dynamic duo, those two." She finished with a wistful smile as she dusted off the frame with her cloth napkin. I was still back at the part about him traveling around the world with other people, obviously some female doctors and nurses. A nurse had taken that picture. How did she cope with his absence, not to mention the women?

"That must have been so hard, having him gone all that time." I waded in gently.

"It was at first but then I learned…" Her voice trailed off and she glanced in the direction of the garden filled with yellow trumpet-shaped Jessamine. Two mourning doves perched on the feeder. There was already so much I wanted to know about this woman. She was a gem, a treasure trove that I had randomly selected from a list of names and unknown faces. Even after our second cup of tea we had barely scratched the surface.

"Miriam, you seem to be such a fascinating woman. There is so much more I'd like to know, but I am running out of time for today. I want to take a few photographs, and then perhaps we could schedule another time." Her eyes twinkled, as if reflecting her soul's joy at its recognition.

"I would love it, my dear."

She sat in the rocker by the window and I took eight shots, hoping I had kept her in focus. My mind was racing with the possibilities of our next contact. She graciously wrapped half a dozen

shortbread cookies up in foil after I told her that they were my favorites. We parted with a date set for two weeks from then. I got in
the car and cruised back to Charleston, playing Pat Metheny's music all the way home. I hadn't thought about my kids leaving, nor
Samuel's trip to Florida, since I had arrived at Rosewood Junction.

Dwayne was pleased with the interview and the photographs of
Miriam were crystal clear. He wanted to hear more about her father,
one of the founders of the museum, and less about her husband
and son, so I had a legitimate excuse to return.

Two weeks later Buster greeted me in the driveway as if he had
seen me yesterday, and Miriam had freshly baked apricot cookies
and coffee waiting on the patio. It was a warm, clear day and it felt
so right to be there. I had allowed myself over two hours for our
visit so I could get the historical data on her father behind me, and
then move on to the real reason I was there. She wove her story like
a tapestry before me, a brilliant combination of colors and texture.
She had grown up in Charleston as one of seven children. Both of
her parents were artists. Because of their devotion to one another, their art, and having six other siblings, Miriam had fended for
herself much of the time. Throughout her life she had become well
acquainted with the region's history and folklore. When she answered my last question, we both sat back in our Adirondack chairs
basking like sea lions on the rocks in Santa Cruz.

"Miriam, would you mind if I got a bit more personal?"

"I thought you'd never get there young lady!" She laughed. This
woman was more intuitive than I realized. She knew I had a mission other than gathering facts about her father and his artwork. It
was as disconcerting as it was comforting. Goose bumps peppered
my forearms.

"I'd like to hear more about Dirk, your marriage and how you dealt with his adventurous spirit." She nestled back in her chair, cradled her coffee mug and closed her eyes. The sun reflected off the silver and turquoise medallion strung around her neck, throwing sparkles across her face. Buster rested his head on her lap.

"Well, you can see from Dirk's picture he was terribly handsome, with equal amounts of charm and wit to match that face. He knew just the right thing to say, blended with touch of humor whenever it was appropriate. Oh, how he kept me laughing, even in the darkest of times." She hesitated for a moment and then continued.

"You see we had two miscarriages before Will came along, both girls. Dirk was away for the first one. He was so mad at himself, but we both knew it went with the territory."

"What was the territory, exactly?"

"When I met Dirk as a medical student in Tampa, Florida he was dedicating endless hours to a clinic for low income families. I knew right then he was married to his patients first. From the very beginning I recognized him as a true healer." I rarely heard anyone in the states refer to doctors that way. Samuel used that word when he spoke of the shamans and medicine people he was learning about. He said it was their purpose, the reason they came here. I wondered if that was where Samuel was headed.

"And being with someone like that didn't scare you, knowing his world was much bigger than you?" She smiled and that twinkle reappeared in her eyes.

"I was in love my dear." She leaned forward and patted my hand. Perhaps I was barking up the wrong tree. Maybe Miriam was much stronger, more sane and secure than I was, and therefore wouldn't be able to relate to my howling insecurity.

"It's time for me to feed and water the horses. Would you like to join me?" She switched gears on me.

"Sure, I've got time." We walked to the barn in silence. White wispy curls blew free from her combs. She took off her denim shirt and tied it around her waist, revealing an old beige sleeveless cotton shirt. As she entered the barn, she playfully called out the names of her four remaining Fiords. She had scaled down her numbers in the last few years having only a part-time assistant working with her. The sweet smell of hay surrounded us and crackled beneath our feet.

"Would you like to help me feed them?" The memory of Mike's soft nose nuzzling crept back into my palm. I loved bringing him apples and soft peppermints, listening as he crunched them between his long teeth. The Fiords were closer to the ground and seemed more approachable, different from huge speckled Screwball who towered over me in the woods that day, just missing my head with his left front hoof.

"I'll follow along and watch this time." After the first two, Miriam was letting me split off the flakes of hay and walk into the stalls, placing them in the corner. I filled their buckets with fresh water and listened as they lapped it up. We went into the tack room where she had rectangular baskets with dividers which separated brushes, combs, picks and fly sprays. Each one had a name tag fastened to its handle: Cleo, Tara, Beep, and Monti. Above each basket was a hook holding halters, lead ropes, bareback pads, and western saddles. We spent our last hour grooming Cleo and Tara. I watched the first time, and when we got to Monti, she handed me the curry brush and told me to go ahead. Smoothing Monti's coat I felt the sleek gold of Mike run through my fingers all over again. I had missed those four-legged creatures that ran with the wind. When we parted Miriam invited me back to talk some more and help with the horses. Walking to my car I was struck by her quiet confidence. She never even asked what had happened to me with the white horse in my past.

Chapter Forty-four

As hard as I tried to hold it back, like weeds in my garden, the summer was encroaching upon me anyway. Brown envelopes arrived from Triple AAA containing maps from South Carolina to Maine. Samuel and I put in for our vacation time to take the trip, while the kids just kept right on living. Coming home from work I gathered boxes from behind liquor stores which always had the best sizes for packing.

The closer we got to departure day the less time I had with Miriam and the horses. I had progressed to the point where I was riding in the ring at a slow trot. Those visits had become like an elixir to my soul and I started to go into withdrawal without them, becoming cranky and impatient. There were numerous trips to shopping outlets where Julia couldn't spend fast enough, while Adam had to be forced into the dressing room. How very different they were. During our drive north while Julia talked incessantly about making friends at her new school, Adam did Eddie Murphy and Jim Carey imitations to pass the time.

Their stepmother was more guarded about showing us the children's rooms than Dane was. It was a strained morning, but we all managed to behave, exchanging polite trivialities as we settled them into their new living quarters. When we finished Dane abruptly announced they had lunch plans at Algonquin Yacht Club with his parents. The kids were ravenous as always, and the cheeseburgers at the club were an absolute favorite. In a split second there were quick hugs, kisses and "I love you mom," as they got into Sarah's silver jeep and faded into the distance. My cheekbones ached and the tears were about to crest over the edge of my lower lids. Samuel held my hand tightly, trying to keep his finger in my dike. My heart stretched and snapped back like a rubber band, stinging painfully.

My body got in the front seat of our van, but my mind lingered behind. Aboard the ferry moving farther away my babies, I held tighter and tighter, struggling to retrieve every last facial expression and word I could grab hold of. But those final moments were so fleeting I couldn't bring them back. I retraced my steps over and over, but I could not capture that last glance of my children.

"Honey, are you okay?" Samuel reached over and put his arm around me.

"No, I'm not. It was too fast, I wasn't ready."

"It was a quick exit, but do you think you ever would have felt ready?"

"Well, I don't know, but I needed time to prepare myself so I would have known those were our last words, touches, smiles, whatever. I can't remember their last expressions."

"I do, they were both smiling, entering their new life with excitement, and the necessary tinge of fear about the unknown." I was astounded that their stepfather was more in tune with my children than I was.

"How did you do that?"

"I was just there, nowhere else. I focused on just what was happening." I was furious with him for being so together, and disappointed with myself that I allowed the moment to pass me by. I was so worried about when it would arrive that I wasn't there when it did.

When we pulled in the driveway I didn't want to face going inside. I sat in the car looking up at my children's bedroom windows, dark and empty. The next day when Samuel left for an early meeting, I felt lost and disoriented in my own house. I sat in Julia's beanbag chair and picked up her favorite doll. Her red hair was snarled from neglect. Untangling the knots with my fingers I remembered the day we got her. We were out buying winter boots and Julia had been so patient and cooperative. Rather than reward her with sweets, I wanted to give her something lasting and special. In the toy department Julia let out a squeal when she spotted the redheaded, soft doll flopped over sideways on the shelf. Her green-striped jumper and white apron were dusty indicating she had been there awhile. From that moment on she had a permanent home in Julia's heart. Now she looked like an abused child whose mother watched too many soap operas, eating too many chocolates.

Three days of solid rain was not cooperating with my urgency to move out of my sorrow. It held me down in its cloudy, damp grip. Miriam wasn't answering her phone and she didn't believe in answering machines. "If it's really important they'll keep trying," she would say. And I kept trying, throughout those first long days, trapped by this new emptiness that seemed to go on forever despite the fact I was working. But one evening I began to hear something besides the sigh of my own sadness. I stepped away from my grief and stepped more into the present. I became aware of water traveling through our gutters and soaking into the earth. Cars splashed their way into the puddle in front of our driveway leaving the sidewalk to lap up the remains. Mocha shook the moisture off her light brown coat, rolling and wiggling on the doormat after returning from doing her business reluctantly. She hated going out in the rain.

I tried Miriam again ready to hang up after the third ring.

"Hello," her voice reached out to me like a raft to a breathless swimmer. I grabbed hold.

"Miriam, it's Olivia. Where have you been?"

"Yes dear, I know it's you. I was visiting my niece Caroline in Columbia. She is one of my few remaining family members in the area."

"Can I come over tonight for a short visit?"

"Not this evening, Olivia, I'm tired from the trip and need to rest. How about tomorrow?" I was slipping under again. Tomorrow I had two appointments back to back, and I had run out of excuses to visit Miriam. The centennial issue was proofed and ready for the printers.

"I could come for just a short visit after you've had some time to yourself."

"Let's make it next weekend, a nice long one. You can come for lunch and we'll work some more with the horses." My last visit I had gone into detail about being thrown in the woods and she clearly had something more up her worn denim sleeve.

"All right, what time would you like me to arrive?"

"Noon will be just fine. By the way, how was your trip north with the children?" *It wasn't a trip; it was an amputation of not one, but two limbs.*

"The traveling was fine, but I miss them terribly, and it's so quiet here."

"That's good dear, that's the way it needs to be." *For who or what?*

"I'll see you next Saturday." She hung up and I sat listening to the dial tone as if trying to decipher Morse code. What did she mean by 'needs to be'?

Samuel was preparing for his shaman gathering at the end of the month, so he didn't mind me going to Rosewood Junction on Saturday. Usually he coveted our weekends alone together, but now that the kids were gone it wasn't as much of an issue. I grabbed my water bottle and journal this time. The interview was long over but there might be something to record, to remember about this Indian summer day. Samuel was at the dining room table with multi-colored stickies lined up like paper soldiers. They were marching toward the three books he was reading in preparation for the gathering of the eagle and the condor, the healers of North and South America coming together, which was the conference theme.

Crossing the covered bridge into Miriam's cottonwoods, they embraced me like old friends as I approached her driveway. The door was open, and Buster appeared out of nowhere. Miriam came to the door before I was out of the car, welcoming me back to her sacred chambers. We hugged and she smelled of oatmeal soap and talcum powder. She didn't believe in deodorant. She said it kept all the toxins in instead of letting them out. "Sweating is necessary," she said.

"How about some coffee before we go down to the barn?"

"Love it, and I brought some blueberry scones to go with it." When we were seated in our Adirondacks once more, she left the space wide open for me to enter.

"Miriam, when we first met you said you learned how to deal with Dirk's adventures, but you never elaborated. Would you mind telling me more about it now?"

"I feel that heavy weight you're carrying around, Olivia. Yes, it's time to put it down, rest awhile." I took that as a yes.

I traveled into her world following her vivid trail of memories of meeting Dirk, miscarriages and finally Will's birth. When Dirk was at home there were long walks, fresh flowers and timeless intimate interludes. When he was gone, there were love letters, charcoal sketches and handmade souvenirs that came to her in crinkled brown packages with his hand prints all over them. He adored her and their son, but something else called to his soul that he had to answer. She recognized if she got in the way of that calling, their life together would have become a prison for him, and he would have thrashed wildly against its walls. Realizing this, she had to come up with a way to love this adventurous healer and let him go.

"But how did you do it Miriam? Weren't you afraid you would lose him to some exotic native woman or beautiful doctor?"

"Yes, at first, of course it was threatening to me. I felt so small. But he wasn't willing to coddle me, just to love me."

"So where did you go with your smallness?"

"One night before he left on a sudden trip to Nicaragua, he gave me a clue about how to live bigger."

"Will was in a deep sleep by then. I listened contentedly to the gentle song of his sleep. His night breathing was one of my favorite sounds. I could lose myself in it. The silk edge of his pale blue blanket hung from the corner of his mouth, lightly coated with saliva. The sound of the phone jarred me while I covered up his tiny fist. I pulled the blanket over his shoulders as I overheard Dirk talking to someone about Nicaragua, a flood and the next flight out. I froze in the shadow created by my son's starry night light. *Not now, not yet, you just got back home to us four days ago.* I closed Will's door and Dirk met me in the hallway."

"My love, there's been a flood in Nicaragua, a huge landslide and they need us. I've got a flight out at eleven." It was now seven-thirty which meant he would be gone in a matter of hours. I suddenly re-membered there was a new medical student, Cassandra, who was to join them on their next trip. I was well acquainted with everyone else on Dirk's team but her, and it left a kind of gaping hole inside me not having met her.

"Will Cassandra be joining you this trip?" He stopped short.

"Yes, but why does that matter?"

"I just like to know everybody that you go into these dangerous situations with. It makes me feel better." My words seemed flimsy compared to the weight of my fear. He rested his large hands firmly on my shoulders.

"Get a hold of yourself Miriam. There will always be new wom-en, new places and faces. This is the life we have chosen." He had little time to make things right, so he didn't mince words.

"I know but sometimes I'm afraid you won't come back."

"Miriam, that's always been a possibility, but it won't be be-cause of another woman. There's no more room in here for anyone else." He traced the periphery of his heart.

"Sometimes I just don't feel as visible and important as all these doctors, nurses and medicine people you work with. I can't compete with their mission, their zeal, their commitment." I was shaking now. Dirk's huge brown eyes filled, and he allowed the tears to spill over onto his angled cheekbones. He held my face firmly in his hands.

"Miriam, there is no one that can replace you, ever. But you must know your own goodness, go to the place where you feel emp-ty and then learn to fill it up. I can't do that for you, no one can."

"His truck backed out of our gravel driveway and the headlights were swallowed up into the darkness. That night I slept on the floor in Will's room under a quilt that Dirk's mother had made when he was born. She was so creative with her hands. She spent hours crocheting delicate snowflakes for our Christmas tree and no two were ever alike.

"Dirk's office called the afternoon before he was due home to say he had been delayed for at least another week. The fresh scent of his homecoming zucchini bread that I had just removed from the oven filled the first floor, Will woke up from his nap with a screaming earache, and my heart longed for its partner across the globe. The rest of the day seemed to plod along forever, even though I had plenty to do nothing fully engaged me. I went from room to room, filling a hot water bottle for Will's ear, then sewing a patch on Dirk's gray woolen cardigan, the one he always wore reading by the fire, or in his study. The hours felt like a bottomless pit that I was tumbling into, further and further. My voice made no sound as I silently screamed from the dark place I was in, begging for someone, anyone, to save me, from myself.

"That night I got Will to bed early and drank a cup of warm milk with Amaretto. When that didn't put me to sleep, I started rummaging through Dirk's extra medical bag in the closet for something that would. I don't remember falling asleep, but I awoke to the sound of my sweet Will wailing in pain from a place that seemed oh so far away. I felt as if I were wading through molasses to reach him. He had caught his head between the wooden crib slats trying to climb out. How long it had taken me to wake up I know not, but he was in a panic, as if I wasn't coming for him. Rocking him back to a calmer, secure place I knew something had to shift in my heart. There would be other stale zucchini breads, earaches, long days, and even longer nights.

"Three days later Dirk called somewhere between elation and exhaustion. His work both fortified and drained him. He would be home in two days. A piece of me fell back into place making it easier to go forward with my day. Will and I were on our way to welcome our new neighbors and their horses that had moved in down the road. I never did any formal riding as a girl, but my parents had dear friends who owned a horse farm where they raised Appaloosas. I spent a lot of time there helping with grooming and feeding when school got out for the summer. There were also those occasional but wonderful trail rides up to the old cabin on their property that had a great view of the Cooper River.

"Will took to the horses, and our new neighbors the Galloways took to him immediately. They had no children of their own, so they were enchanted by all his childish antics. They invited us back and said they always needed someone to exercise the horses if I was ever interested. On the walk back I imagined myself up on the chestnut Pasa Fino, who danced around the field doing her own version of the two step, and I became quite excited by the prospect.

"Dirk's homecoming was a tender and joyous occasion. There was a fresh loaf of zucchini bread waiting on the windowsill, warm to the touch when he lathered it up with butter. His face was dry, bronzed and unshaven. He looked rugged and handsome as he took me in his arms and lifted me clear off the ground. We held each other tightly and I welcomed him back into the deepest part of me. Oh, how I had missed his touch! We opened our curtains and let the moonlight cast its silver glow onto our bed as we fell into a peaceful, deep, and sound sleep. The next morning, I got up first and had a cup of coffee before he even opened his eyes. Just as I finished the last sip Willie was up looking for his cinnamon raisin biscuit. Dirk hadn't yet lifted his cup from the saucer and my curiosity was already alive and brimming."

"So how was it? Did the new team work well together? What's Nicaragua like? Did anyone speak English? Were their many fatalities?" He put his index finger to his lips.

"I'm waking up, my sweet, Miriam. Give me time and I will answer all your questions. We'll take the film to be developed later so you can see some of the brilliant, colorful visuals. It was amazing." Will climbed under the covers next to him and I fetched his biscuit. The two men in my life were gradually waking up and I was there to soften their start, make it easier to join the world. I loved that part of my life, feeling so necessary and fulfilled in my role.

"My parents treated me as if I was the oldest child, giving me responsibility for my younger siblings. I often diapered my brother and gave my sisters their bottles when my mother was in her studio. I combed hair, mixed farina with honey and milk, and read "The Princess and the Pea" over a hundred times. I always felt special doing it; I was the "little mother" of the house. Mother and father were always grateful when I stayed home from dances or Saturday outings with my friends so they could attend some important artists' gathering. Once my father painted me a picture of purple morning glories climbing across a fence as a thank you gift. When I wasn't being useful, I felt sort of clumsy and out of step.

"Dirk spread the photos of Nicaragua across our Shaker coffee table into a brilliant, colorful fan. The landscape was breathtaking, and the people were beautiful, even in their terror and displacement. Will poured over them like a little old man. He would pick one up and bring it close to his face and then hold it at a distance. He would sort them into two stacks, one for pictures with faces and one without. He pulled one from the pile of a stunning woman with a head full of dark, thick curls holding a bandaged infant.

"My she's lovely? Is she Nicaraguan?"

"No, that's Cassie."

"Who's Cassie?"

"You know, Cassandra, the new intern that joined us for the first time." If she took my breath away in a photograph, how was my husband able to survive two weeks in the muddy trenches sharing a group tent with her?

"I know what you're thinking Miriam, and no, you needn't worry, and yes, she's going to make a great doctor." I wasn't nearly convinced.

"She *was* a great doctor, and a great person. I cautiously came to know her at family gatherings that the team held four times a year. You couldn't help but be drawn to her, the way she laughed at silly jokes, and looked you right in the eye when you spoke to her. She loved listening to Will, and as he grew, she took a genuine interest in what was then a hobby for him, photography. The more I allowed myself to embrace who she was, the more genuine she became, and in turn, less threatening when she was off with Dirk to faraway places.

"Will's interest in photography grew through his adolescence and he pursued it in college. He did a dual major in journalism and photography which eventually landed him a job at *National Geographic*. He followed in his father's footsteps around the globe, coming home for short visits and warm zucchini bread. I missed our long conversations by the fire and the trail rides we took through the woods. You see our neighbors with the Pasa Finos became dear friends, and we spent long days with them when Dirk was gone that made them feel shorter just being there.

"My first trail ride happened one April morning when Dirk was in Bali after a fire that burned out of control. While he bandaged charred limbs, I rode through the woods upon Tita, the lively mare.

I merged with her eyes and ears, alert to sudden passing chipmunks or the wind rustling through the pine trees towering above us. I surrendered to her gait and made it my own, moving as one large graceful animal. Sissie Galloway insisted I ride with a fleece bareback pad, the closeness allowing me to lose track of where Tita left off and I began.

"Time had no place there as we followed a stream bed to its fragile source, pausing long enough to feel the mist spray into our faces. Entering the horse's world, I could taste the cool moisture against my lips. I felt myself gradually go to a new place, beyond my own skin, a place empty of anything else. This place allowed me to be fully present with my horse and the surroundings. Giving birth to Will I experienced something close to this during labor. In order to allow him entrance into the world I expanded past what I knew as the boundaries of my own skin. But when he came out with a bloodied cry I was instantly filled again by his being. Here the emptiness of anything or anyone but this moment filled me totally, in a most unique way. On the way out of the woods as the wind picked up, Tita suddenly broke off into a fast trot. Breathing through her unexpected friskiness, I tightened one hand on the reins while the other remained relaxed at my side. I sailed along with her, the exhilaration and connection overriding my fear.

"That next Friday Dirk returned from Bali and the Galloways were leaving for a trip. Dirk's team had planned a birthday gathering for Cassie at the lake that Sunday. I sent my boys off without me because Sissie asked me to look after things while they were gone. I had stalls to clean, hay to get out, and horses to exercise. I baked two extra-large zucchini breads for the celebration and made a card out of layered tissue paper and doilies for Cassie. She was forty and still single, married to her adoring patients all over the world."

"You'll be missed sweetheart," Dirk said as he squeezed me goodbye.

"He and Will waved from the porch as I got into our clunky old Land Rover with a basket full of ripe apples and carrots. Backing out of the driveway I realized it hadn't even occurred to me that I would be missed. My mind hadn't gone galloping into fearful projections about what might happen if I wasn't there. Pulling the reins in on Tita when she suddenly became high spirited had helped me to tame the wild horses that roamed my mind. The basket bumped along in the front seat as I made my way around the next curve and an apple rolled onto the floor."

Miriam was exhausted after our trip to Nicaragua and back. She leaned back in her chair and purred like a kitten as she fell into a peaceful sleep, the sun fading behind her. I covered her with Will's quilt and said my good byes to Buster who barely lifted his head from her lap as I got up to leave. I scribbled a note of thanks and left it on the tray by her side. The sky opened up and melon laced its way through teal. It was getting close to sunset, so I pulled over and found a perfect spot facing west. As the crimson ball dropped into the horizon's arms, my cell phone rang.

"Hey baby where are you?" It was a worried Samuel.

"Oh, I stopped to watch the sunset on the way back from Miriam's."

"It's almost seven and I was getting worried. Are you okay?" I knew the closer we got to his departure the more sensitive he became about my behavior, assuming the demons were back.

"I feel better than ever. What's for dinner, I just realized I'm starving."

"Well, I was hoping to have you for dinner, what did you have planned?" That felt inviting, and I loved the spontaneous edge.

"How about having me for dessert and getting take-out at Angelo's?"

"Perfect, I'll order, and you can pick it up on your way in."

"Sounds good, I'll have Eggplant Parmesan."

"See you soon, don't dilly dally. I want my dessert."

Chapter Forty-five

Samuel's trip to Florida was less than two weeks away and I planned my Saturday visit to Miriam's without even asking what he was up to. When he pouted around the house Friday night, I was confused.

"I thought we could go on a hike and picnic. This is our last weekend before my trip." This time *he* was whining for a change.

"Can't we do that tomorrow? The weather is supposed to be perfect all weekend."

"I guess so, but I thought we'd sleep in and spend some time in bed."

"I think we can manage both, and don't forget there's always the possibility of hot sex in the woods." I winked.

"Why do you have to go out there today? Can't you spend time with her when I'm gone?"

"I'll be doing that too but being with Miriam is critical right now." It hadn't occurred to me until just that moment as the image of purple velvet flooded into my consciousness.

"Why is that?"

"Because, she's the *wizard*, that's why." He nodded and there were no further questions.

I awoke with the sun in my eyes the next morning and couldn't wait to get up and moving. Coffee tasted better than usual, and I was excited to get to Miriam's and see what she had in store for me. I would stop at the bakery and get sticky buns as a special treat for us. We both deserved one. While I was showering Samuel got in. He knew I came alive in the water and he started licking the wet droplets from my ears, neck and shoulders. It was sensual and stimulating but *I* was being called away. I moved back, attempting to postpone his intentions.

"Let's wait until I get back. We'll have more time."

"Why are you in such a hurry?"

"Miriam is a morning person and she gets very tired after lunch. I want to be with her while she has the energy."

"Okay, I hope I still have some energy left when you get back." He was half kidding, half serious.

"Well, I'll just masturbate, and you can watch. How's that?" I think he was startled by my frankness, as well as being turned down, especially on the heels of his trip. I surprised myself as I reached for a towel and got out.

Miriam was filling the bird feeder when I arrived. She turned and waved me into the backyard. Wrens fluttered around and picked at the seeds dropping at her feet. She exuded such peace. It was still hard for me to imagine that she had lost her beloved Dirk and Will all at once, and yet she carried on so beautifully. She got up each day, watered the garden, cleaned the stalls, rode the horses and dozed with the sun at her back. The courage it must have taken to get through those first shocking, silent days, and black nights, surrounded by memories in the darkness. And to think I was crumbling because my kids went to live with their father. It still ached inside, and sometimes I still went into their rooms at night burying my face in their pillows, trying to catch their leftover scent. We talked every Sunday, I sent weekly greeting cards, and I looked forward to our next vacation together, but I was beginning to accept and appreciate the gift of time their absence had thrust upon me.

I walked toward her and opened my arms, the white bag of sticky buns crinkling in our embrace. "Good morning my dear," she chirped like one of the wrens balanced gently on the peak of the bird house.

"Good morning, how about some sticky buns to start this amazing day?"

"I was hoping we could get out on the trail first thing, before it gets too hot." She hadn't mentioned riding outside the ring. I was comfortable in the arena having ridden there several times now, but I wasn't sure about going beyond that gate. My adrenaline surged, and time sped up.

"Cleo and Monti really need the exercise. Why don't you groom Cleo and get her tacked up. We'll use the western saddles."

She was trying to lead me down the high road to bypass my fear. She calmly instructed me without room for discussion or hesitation. I knew Cleo would be able to sense my anxiety, so I spoke softly to her while I made circular motions with the curry brush across her shoulder. She loved the attention and she gave herself over to me. I conveyed my fears, but she seemed indifferent to them. She just wanted me to keep on brushing. I had Miriam cross check the girth to make sure it was tight enough and then I led Cleo out to the mounting block. As soon as I was on, she wanted to get moving, but I held her back.

"That's right Olivia. Let her know she can trust you to lead her. Do it with your intention, voice and body, and you won't need to use force." She was so at ease up there on Monti, her floppy straw hat shielding her from the bright sunlight the day had bestowed upon us. We headed up a gradual incline that led to the trail entrance. Looking ahead I saw a few more hills and it suddenly dawned on me that we would go up, and therefore have to go *down* those same hills. My heart spiked, putting my body on high alert. My sweaty palm rubbed Cleo's neck as I told both of us, "Good girl, good girl," as we made our way onto the trail. She gracefully stepped over stones and roots, losing her footing only slightly at one turn.

"How are we doing?" Miriam turned back and smiled.

"Hanging in there." I replied still on the edge.

"Breathe, relax and look around at this view, Olivia. It's gorgeous." She took her hand and carved an arc in the air.

Remembering to breathe was helpful and I started to feel my connection to Cleo as we descended into the earth. I could feel my hips swaying with her and started to notice what was around me. It was magnificent as far as you could see. The creek was close enough to hear its voice bubbling up and over stones in its path. As the trail narrowed the foliage thickened and it became harder to follow. But I finally relaxed into Cleo's rhythm as we found our way. The saliva came back into my dry mouth and the hair on my arms was no longer standing on end. My frontal cortex was back on line, and fight and flight were turned down. I was actually enjoying myself.

Passing a cluster of sweet gum trees, my reality was quickly altered when Cleo backed up a few steps and reared into the air. I pulled back on the reins and attempted to turn, but her dance of panic was underway so my pleas to "whoa!" fell on frightened ears. Somewhere in the background I heard Miriam's voice telling me what to do, but I could only make out sounds not words, as Cleo bucked. Coming from somewhere inside I heard "emergency dismount" but by then Cleo had already released me. The side of my face lay against the ground where I came face to face with the culprit, a black snake slithering in my direction.

"Olivia, not to worry. It's a black garden snake." Somehow Miriam had managed to secure Cleo and she was already kneeling beside me loosely holding the reins of both horses.

"Are you all right my dear? Does anything hurt?" Before she reached me, I was unaware of my physical body. Bringing it back into focus I felt soreness in my cheekbone that had hit the ground, along with my left elbow being out of sorts.

"My cheek and left elbow are sore, but I'm okay." She looked closely at my face and carefully touched the periphery of my elbow. When I didn't scream out in pain, she stood up.

"I think you'll be just fine, Olivia. You handled that situation beautifully."

"What do you mean? I got thrown off!"

"Yes, but I watched, and you didn't freeze up. You talked to her, and you were in the process of doing an emergency dismount, but she got you there first." She was grinning from ear to ear. She was right, I hadn't totally lost it. I was able to continue thinking.

"So now are you ready to go on with the ride?" I was stunned. She didn't really expect me to carry on with this.

"Miriam, my elbow is sore, and I only have one arm to work with." Now I was moving into my dance of panic. I couldn't do this. I needed to go back and have a warmed sticky bun, take a bubble bath, and call it a day.

"Olivia, you were riding with one hand before it happened. You can do it." She wasn't going to coddle me either. I brushed the stray grass from my shirt, and I looked down at the Dublin Ladies River Boots Samuel had given me as a gift to encourage my riding. At some point Miriam came up behind me and handed me Cleo's reins. I stood there, frozen, avoiding her eyes. The person I had to face now was me. Cleo eventually got bored and nudged me while I was in the middle of my calculations about how long it might take me to walk back on foot, leading her behind me.

"Well, let's go, Olivia. The horses are getting restless." The nerve of this old woman, pushing me like this. I wasn't an experienced rider like she was. We were at an impasse.

A small breeze beckoned me and blew Cleo's forelock gently against my bruised cheek. In that instant I knew there was only one way that I would ever become like Miriam, experienced at riding, at living, at loss. I took Cleo's face into my hands, breathed into her nostrils and reconnected with her. She dropped her head, connecting with me once again. I climbed back on. The rest of the ride was uneventful in comparison, though we did spot a mama quail and her little ones waddling off into the brush.

When I unhooked Cleo's girth, I felt Miriam's hand on my shoulder. She held it there for a moment, solid and warm, underscoring my triumph. After the horses were fed, we sat back to our Adirondack chairs, gloating and enjoying our warmed sticky buns. Licking my fingers, I let the feeling of wellbeing permeate me, like butter melting into toast. When I left that afternoon, Miriam gave me an especially long, firm hug as she whispered in my ear, "That's how it's done, Olivia. That's all there is to it. Now you know, my dear."

Chapter Forty-six

We made love the night before Samuel's departure and the next morning too. His appetite was a pleasant surprise given his nervous anticipation about the trip. He was embarking on something that both excited and frightened him all at once. The calmer I became the more excitement he revealed. I gifted him with a blank journal covered in soft green leather with ferns imprinted on it. He promised to sketch and record his experience, assuring me that I would share in all the details upon his return. He would be gone, ironically, on our wedding anniversary. He had given me a fire pot as a gift and with it a box of river sticks. He had tied a piece of colored yarn around each one. He said as he tied the yarn, he had a loving thought about me or us, and he wanted me to burn them whenever I felt the need to connect with him. I was so touched by his incredible thoughtfulness. After he left for Florida, I sat on a bench in the backyard admiring the primitive clay fire pot and the pile of precious sticks he had carefully chosen from our favorite picnic spot by the Kanawha River. I felt such abundance well up from deep inside. Even though there was no one to share it with, I still felt it throughout my entire being.

I called Julia and Adam, hoping to pass some of the feeling of fullness on to them, but all I got was their answering machine. I didn't bother to leave a message because I knew it would lose its original flavor. I truly missed that daily contact, but I had learned to let go more and connect deeper when I was with them. It had all become so much easier, thanks to Miriam. I would call her after I took Mocha for a jaunt in the park.

Miriam was asleep when I called. It was late morning and she usually napped after lunch. She sounded groggy and confused, complaining of a headache. I wanted to go over and fix her some soup, but she was adamant about wanting to be left alone. I felt a bit miffed knowing that she was fully aware that Samuel had just left for his next big adventure. I was hoping for a little more support. The next day I tried several times and there was no answer. Perhaps she needed a break from my intensity. Maybe all my questions had exhausted her. I would hold back for a while. The garden needed weeding and there were bulbs to plant and bed down. The soil would feel good between my fingers.

Heading out the door for work the next morning the phone rang. Could it be Samuel this early? It seemed unlikely because they had morning rituals with the shamans that weren't over until about nine. Perhaps it was Adam or Julia finally returning my call of a few days ago. But they were in school by now.

"Hello, is this Olivia Demarco?" It was a woman whose voice I did not recognize.

"Yes, this is Olivia."

"Hello. My name is Carolyn Hazelton, I'm Miriam's niece."

"Oh, yes, I've heard her speak of you. You live in Columbia."

"Yes, that's me. My Aunt Miriam passed away last night in her sleep." A tremor of disbelief shook through my body, my heart cracked open and my knees buckled. I slid down the wall to the floor. This wasn't possible.

"Was she alone? What happened?"

"Buster was by her side, as always. His continual barking late at night brought the neighbors around because it was so unusual for him to behave like that. The doctor said it could have been a brain aneurysm or a massive stroke. The autopsy report will be completed sometime later tomorrow." There was so much I wanted to say but tears were streaming down my face and nothing made its way out of my mouth.

"Aunt Miriam was so fond of you, Olivia. You were such a bright spot in this last year of her life. She spoke of you frequently with great fondness and warmth in her voice." I was beginning to heave inside. I struggled to express myself.

"She was a total gem, and she taught me so much. I will treasure my time with her, always."

"I'm so glad your paths crossed. I'm sure she had very specific wishes about her death and how she wanted it handled. During our last visit she told me where she kept her important papers so when I have gone through them, I will be in touch about any kind of memorial service she may have wanted."

She had that same quality as Miriam. Being matter-of-fact and sincere at the same time must run in their family.

"Okay, thanks so much for calling. I'm sorry for your loss."

"Thank you. You probably spent more time with Aunt Miriam in this last year than anyone so we know you will miss her."

"Yes, deeply." *Desperately, I will miss her desperately.* She had so much more to teach me, I had so much more to learn. How could she leave me now? We weren't finished. She brought me to the edge of myself, now what do I do? *Damn you Miriam!* I slammed the receiver down and sobbed myself into a slippery ball. After I wiped away the remains of the deluge, I phoned the office and said I would be late, there had been a death in my family. She was family, family of my heart, teaching me more than my mother had been able to do because of her own fears. I had created a place inside myself where she would remain forever.

I left a message at the gathering for Samuel to call me that night. He would find it on the bulletin board and wonder what was wrong. The rest of the day was a blur, with Miriam's face overshadowing everything I did. Looking out the window of my office I saw her soft white wisps in the clouds, her watery eyes reflecting from the lake at Middleton Place Gardens where I went to lose myself after work. I had no use for food, but a cup of special French Roast decaf comforted me as I rocked on the porch that evening. Someone once told me that when a person dies their soul lands somewhere in the sky. I searched the heavens for a star that resembled Miriam's presence. The loud ringing of the phone jolted me away from my silent scanning.

"Olivia, is everything okay sweetie?" Samuel's voice was concerned and unsettled. He probably thought the demons were visiting.

"Miriam's dead. Her niece Carolyn called me this morning."

"Oh baby, I'm so sorry. I wish I were there with you."

"Me too but I'll be okay."

"I know you'll be okay, but I still want to be there to hold you. I know how connected you and Miriam were."

"Yes, we were, and now she's gone." I broke down again.

"What can I do Olivia?" I wanted to lash out and scream, "*Come home where you belong!*" But I remained silent for just long enough.

"Nothing really. I'm glad you called. Carolyn will get back in touch in a day or so to let me know about her memorial service."

"Honey, I know you're hurting, and I wish I could do something to comfort you."

"Me too, but everything happens for a reason. I guess I'm supposed to go at this one alone."

"Perhaps, but I still wish I was there." I knew he meant it.

"Are you having a good time?" It was hard for me to ask but I pushed through my own drama long enough to do it.

"Yes, the shamans are amazing, so full of wisdom, yet so humble and simple in their ways."

"I'm happy that you're enjoying them." And I meant it, despite my desperation and sadness. I had reached a place that was bigger than my own stuff, at last.

"Thank you for that Olivia, it means a lot."

"I know."

"I love you and I miss you, and I want you to call if you need to."

"I will, and I love you too."

I have no idea how long I sat on the couch with the phone cradled in my lap. Time had stopped and something else had taken over that was unfamiliar, but not uncomfortable. Retrieving my coffee cup from the porch I took one more look toward the heavens. Out of my peripheral vision I saw a shooting star skirt across the skies and plunge brightly into the darkness.

"Thank you old woman, thank you for all your gifts."

That night my sleep was sporadic and restless. I had a dream that went from disturbing to soft and comforting. At some point I was in a lush green meadow and as I rolled onto my back and looked up, white threads wove themselves into a quilt and slowly descended upon me. When I awoke, I felt warm and safe. With my eyes still closed I ran my fingers across my chest, expecting to feel the silky white strands rippling beneath them, but it was the same old duvet, complete with Mocha's saliva and scent. She had taken to sleeping with me when the kids moved up to their dad's and Samuel was away.

Two days later Carolyn called. Miriam had died of a cerebral embolism, quick and painless, thank goodness. She had requested nothing more than to be cremated and scattered in the creek on her property. Since Carolyn was the only local relative, she asked me if I would join her at sunrise on Saturday to honor Miriam's memory and send her on her way. Of course, I would be there. Daybreak was Miriam's favorite time of day. She would often sit with her eyes closed and listen to the earth awaken to another day. "No two mornings are ever alike if you truly listen," she told me.

I arrived early on Saturday and headed straight for the patio of memories. The bird feeder was empty, so I went to the shed in search of a new bag of seeds. I cut the edges with Miriam's orange gardening sheers, remembering the texture of her withered, tanned hands. I spilled the contents into the tiny house, letting the overflow drop to my feet. I went straight to the Adirondack chair and closed my eyes, allowing the sounds of dawn to travel through me. Sitting very still I could have sworn a faint, warm breath whispered across my forehead. When I opened my eyes I was still alone, goose bumps rose up on my forearms and the hairs stood at attention.

Carolyn made it with about ten minutes to spare before sunrise. She was tall, handsome and had the same blue eyes as her aunt. She carried an oval basket draped with a navy and yellow batiked fabric.

We walked in an easy silence down to the creek and found the spot where it widened and ran at a good clip. There was a small sandy spit just big enough for our two pairs of feet.

"This is the perfect place, don't you think?" The red highlights in her hair sparkled as the sun crested in the background.

"Absolutely, Miriam would approve. She often stopped here to refresh the horses when she was out on the trail."

She removed the scarf from the basket, revealing a pile of ashen colored chips. I had never seen cremated remains and it was unnerving to see what a brilliant life is reduced to. I expected them to be soft and flaky, more like leftover ashes from a fireplace or campfire. But when I reached in and took a handful from the basket, they were gritty and tough, like tiny shell parts you sift through on the beach when searching for shark's teeth. My fingers had known that texture because sifting had been one of Adam's favorite beach pastimes. He would meander by the sea scooping up fistfuls of sand until he found something that resembled the tooth of a shark. I missed that once little hand in mine.

While Carolyn knelt down and spread her share of the ashes into the creek, I quickly stole a second smaller scoop and poured it into my jacket pocket. I had my own idea of how to keep Miriam alive in my life. Scattering the other portion in a circle I watched it become part of the stream itself, flowing along and disappearing beneath the rippling surface. We each said our own private farewell and headed back to the house. When we reached the circular driveway, she took my hand and held it tightly.

"My Aunt Miriam went through a lot in her life and she allowed very few people into her world. You must be very special indeed."

"I feel honored that she opened up to me."

"When I go through all her papers and belongings I will be in touch. I'm sure you'll want something to remember her by."

"Yes, definitely. That would be wonderful." We said our good-byes and she went back into the house. I wanted to stay and linger on the patio, weed some in the garden, and watch the wrens feasting on their morning banquet, splitting the sunflower seeds apart, and letting the shells scatter beneath them. Slowly pulling away I looked at the faded pineapple flag blowing in the breeze and wept all the way home.

Chapter Forty-seven

Samuel came in a few hours earlier than expected. Someone from the workshop was passing right through Charleston and they left Florida just in time to escape the commuter traffic pouring in and out of the city. He called to me as he came through the front door. I was back in the den diligently writing down everything I could recall about my time with Miriam. I wanted to savor every moment I had in her presence. When I heard his voice, I had a mixed reaction, I wanted to complete my sentence, yet I was delighted to have him back. I didn't get the usual heart palpitations, but I felt warm and fuzzy inside. I scribbled a note on a post-it and stuck it on the bottom of the page marking where I left off. As I got up from the futon, Samuel was already halfway down the hall. He lifted me into the air.

"God, I missed you woman!"

"Look at you, all tan and handsome." When my feet touched the ground, I stood back to take him in, but not in my usual suspicious manner, like a dog sniffing for signs that her territory had been invaded.

"Yeah, it was sunny and hot all week."

"Well, tell me, was it all you imagined?"

"Yes, and much more."

We grilled tenderloins on the porch and drank wine while he shared one amazing tale after another about the timeless wisdom of the shamans. He talked about the rituals he participated in and the connection he felt to "the group." As soon as the word connection was spoken, I felt a slight stirring inside.

"Did you connect with anyone in particular?" He didn't respond immediately, but then he took my fork out of my hand and laid it across my plate. Taking both of my hands in his, he moved his chair closer to me. A subtle ripple began inside my heart.

"Olivia, we did an exercise in partners called 'opening the heart.'" Waves passed through me. He paused and kissed my forehead, one of my soft spots. He felt me shifting from my center.

"I was sitting next to a Cuban woman named Isabella. Her uncle got her out of the country when she was seven and she hasn't seen her family since. The connectedness of the group allowed her to feel part of a larger circle for the first time since she was a child."

I sat quietly and very still. My mind roved frantically at first, but then found a resting place. There in that spot instead of finding a dark, exotic beauty I came upon a small girl disguising her sobs as she stole away in the darkness, leaving all that was familiar behind. Samuel must have been holding his breath while I traveled there and back to him.

"Are you okay baby? Where were you?"

"I was with that little girl on a wooden boat heading out to sea, wondering how she was able to part with her family at such a tender, vulnerable age. It's been hard enough for me to part with my children as an adult. It must have been devastating for her." He exhaled.

We had turned the corner as if smoothly rounding a curve on a bicycle built for two. He went on to tell me how his conversations with Isabella throughout the week had been very healing for her and she was grateful for his focus and concern.

When he was finished, he started to weep, softly at first, but then he broke into loud sobs and his chest began to heave up and down. I did not try to comfort him because I had learned that touching could interrupt the releasing process, knowing he was experiencing the ecstasy of freedom. Soon after, I joined him, unlocking the chains that had bound me for so long. Lighter than air we floated into each other's arms and on to the bedroom.

Right before Thanksgiving and the return of my children, Carolyn called.

"Olivia, I have wonderful news! We've settled Aunt Miriam's estate. She left Rosewood Junction to you." In a split second I was everywhere, passing the hemlocks, on the patio, in the shed, and out to the barn with Monti, Cleo, Beep and Tara.

"I don't know what to say, are you absolutely sure about this? What about the other members of your family?"

"After Dirk and Will died, I was the only one that Miriam remained in close contact with. Six months after she met you, she changed her will. Originally, she was leaving everything to 'Hope Springs,' a therapeutic riding program. But now it's all yours to do what you wish."

I thought I might have a scarf or the silver necklace with a turquoise stone embedded in the center to remember my beloved mentor. The thought of her sanctuary being passed into my hands rendered me speechless.

"Olivia, I'm sure it will take a while to digest all this. We'll need to meet as soon as possible to sign over the deed, etc." I caught my breath and put it back, ordering it to stay there.

"My children will be home for Thanksgiving. Could we do it right after that? I don't want to give up any time with them."

"That suits me just fine. Miriam's lawyer is Mr. Dockery, and his office is located on Archdale Street. I'll get a date and time and get back with you."

"That will work. Carolyn, I can't thank you enough. I'm overwhelmed by Miriam's generosity."

"I'm delighted for you. It will open so many doors." She had a dose of that same intuition that her aunt possessed.

Thanksgiving roared in with great abundance and excitement from the moment we picked Adam and Julia up at the airport. They slept in until almost noon each day, consumed more food than we could keep in stock, and watched old videos until the wee hours of the morning. I managed to bribe them into one game of monopoly, promising the winner a real cash prize. Family game night always meant a lot to me, a time when we had light playful exchanges and munched on popcorn. I choose that evening to share the news about Rosewood Junction being gifted to me. Samuel and I had decided to do some necessary repairs on it over the next year, put our house in Jericho on the market in early spring, and be settled in our new home a year from Christmas. Julia's only concern was that we would be forty-five minutes from the closest mall. Adam who had always enjoyed the outdoors accepted the change in stride. They both loved the idea of horseback riding whenever they were home.

It was easier to send them off this time. Our connections felt more solid and I had gotten some one on one time with each of them. Samuel had purchased some fine, slender Cuban cigars and Adam and I smoked them under the stars one night talking about sports, his anal math teacher, and the latest Robin Williams movie. Shopping and lunch at the mall were the only way to lure Julia into my clutches. Over oriental chicken salads in the food court with rock music blaring in the background I listened to her concerns about her weight, the cliques, and how adorable the assistant track coach was. When I waved goodbye as they passed through the security check point my heart was full and satisfied. Samuel put his arm around my waist.

"You okay sweetheart?" My hand slid into his back pocket.

"I'm fine, just fine." And I meant it in every fiber, though I didn't completely trust it yet.

Chapter Forty-eight

I started going to Rosewood Junction on Friday afternoons after work and staying until Sunday before dinner. Sometimes Samuel would join me, but there were weekends that projects had to be done on our house to get it ready to be sold. A routine created itself with a rhythm all my own, beginning with morning coffee on the patio, checking the bird feeder, grooming the horses, and letting them in or out of the pasture. I usually exercised two in the arena in the morning and took two trail rides in the afternoon. My reluctance about being alone on the trail gradually diminished to the point where I eventually lost it for good.

By late spring we had a buyer for our house who was flexible enough to allow us to stay until the end of the summer. This gave Julia and Adam Easter break to say their farewells, pack boxes, and get rid of anything that no longer seemed relevant or sentimental in their eyes. I always felt closure was necessary with both people and places. Having unfinished business was like cold leftovers. You eventually had to get back to them and decide their fate.

Now that our house was sold Samuel turned his focus toward Rosewood Junction and getting her up to speed for us to move in. On an exceptionally warm day he took a break from his work on the roof and joined me for ice coffee and zucchini bread on the patio. I had found Miriam's recipe in a wooden box in the pantry and tried it one rainy weekend. From then on, I was hooked. As we both indulged, we delighted in the tremendous good fortune that had come into our lives at this early stage. We had fantasized about having a place like this someday when the kids were out of college but never dreamed it would come while we were still in our prime, with so much time and energy to enjoy it. I leaned back between his knees and his fingers traveled through my scalp, massaging me gently.

"Olivia, we're definitely going to make enough money on the house for you to stop working if you want to." It hadn't crossed my mind that Miriam's generosity was also about the gift of time, to do what I wished. The real estate market had been soft for a while so we weren't sure how it would look after our remaining mortgage balance and the realtor's commission were paid. But the market had spiked in the last few months and we were pleasantly surprised by the profit when all was said and done. Doing whatever I wanted seemed so foreign to me. It was a difficult place to go in my mind.

"That's almost too much to think about, let alone imagine."

He persisted in his playful but direct manner.

"Olivia, just let your mind run wild like the horses do when you set them out in the pasture. It will come to you." And it did. Being with Miriam and the horses had helped set me free from fears, doubts and limitations. It was more powerful than talking to a therapist, a ropes course or a year's supply of anti-anxiety meds. Miriam had her own wish about leaving Rosewood Junction to 'Hope Springs' for children with physical and mental limitations. My mind started sprouting possibilities like thousands of new varieties of flowers in a fertile garden plot. They were endless, and they kept on coming. I finally settled on one special theme that felt so right, like it had been there waiting for me all along. The power of fear in my life had almost succeeded in totally dismantling me, my marriage, and my family. It almost destroyed a valuable friendship, kept me from conversations, new events and experiences. If it had done that to me surely it was ravaging the lives of other woman, robbing them of opportunities and possibilities. It would crop up like weeds in their garden, strangling the closest thing of beauty in its path. Jealousy, fear and insecurity were rarely part of everyday conversation among women, but I would find a way to reach them. The name of my Equine Assisted Personal Growth program would be called *Freedom Reins*.

When we combined our French Country furniture with what remained of Miriam's pieces everything fit together beautifully. Our hand-woven rugs and her wall hangings all blended nicely in their lovely pastel colors. The first night Samuel and I spent at Rosewood Junction as our permanent home I filled every room with fresh flowers from the garden. I opened all the windows and let the breeze push the sweet floral scent through the hallways. We decided on Chinese take-out by candlelight since we were too tired to cook and clean up after the move. Linking our hands across the table we talked about what we were grateful for, how far we had come, and how much we appreciated Miriam's incredible benevolence. Samuel had more to say.

"Olivia, with the money we made on the house I'd like to take my long-awaited trip to Peru. There's one coming up in October with the same group that sponsored the shaman gathering in Florida." No wonder his parents nicknamed him the "bombshell kid." In the middle of a seemingly peaceful celebration he kicks it up a notch. Hadn't I seen the sign on his bulletin board when I first met him, 'Rock the boat.' I knew he had been working up to Peru, but it seemed much further down the road. He was talking about five short months from now. But when we spoke about it in the past, we hadn't anticipated the windfall that Rosewood Junction delivered to us. Was this Miriam's own version of the cosmic joke?

"How long will you be gone?"

"It's a three-week trip which includes Macchu Picchu and Lake Titicaca, two places I am very drawn to." Yes, drawn to. No matter how I tried to push it out of my mind sometimes I had to remember that my beloved soul mate was called away to lush, overgrown places that held the mystery of ancient indigenous shamans and the sound of their drums and rattles. And it was that depth that drew me to Samuel in the first place and made him so compelling to be with.

"What about work?"

"Well now that we're not under the gun financially I can take two weeks paid and one unpaid."

"Will you still be able to have time off at Christmas when the kids come home?" My mothering instinct was rising up and taking her stand. This would be our first time at Rosewood Junction as a family and Christmas was always very special to me.

"Honey, of course, I know how important that is for you. I'll be there with bells on, and my reindeer tie." He gave me that irresistible grin of his. The image of Samuel following some dark, sensual medicine woman down a narrow, tropical path into sacred territory faded out and became Christmas morning in my fleece robe, French Roast in hand, rocking in front of twinkling lights that adorned our magnificent tree.

My fascination with Christmas lights began about age five while riding back from my grandparents at night. My siblings would be sleeping, and my parents would be bickering about something my uncle said, and I would be mesmerized by the light show outside the car window. I would blur my eyes and enter the colorful, fuzzy world and get lost in the reds, blues, greens and whites. While my parents continued their heated discussion, I floated and swirled in the dance of lights.

Rosewood Junction had nine-foot ceilings so our tree would be grand and glorious, placed in the very center of the room. I would position the teak rocker and end table directly in front of it so I could enjoy many cups of coffee while admiring her.

Autumn descended upon Rosewood Junction in all her brilliance. The fields were ignited in orange and crimson. Trail riding was as invigorating as it was irresistible. I spent mornings with the horses and afternoons working on my marketing plan. My target audience would be women entering mid-life still carrying past baggage that had grown so heavy it held them back from their creativity and dreams.

While I was engrossed with "Freedom Reins," Samuel poured through books and websites on Peru and its sacred sites. He had been corresponding with the two people that would be leading his excursion, Carlos and Lena. One night he asked me if I would like to see what their website was like, and her green eyes beckoned me from the corner of the screen. Her credentials were as impressive as her natural beauty: an anthropologist fluent in Spanish as well as the Ketchua tribe's language. She had spent a year living with them in the Amazon. I wondered how tall she was, probably slender, and no frizzies in her long, sleek auburn hair. But very quickly I realized what an asset she would be to Samuel and his group, creating the cultural bridge that was necessary for them to cross. Samuel's curiosity and yearning about their lifestyle, rituals and spiritual practices would be answered. A part of me was rising to meet his dreams and embrace them. I felt a sun shower wash over me, brilliant and refreshing, and allowed it to cleanse me over and over.

As the time closed in on us, Samuel and I moved in tandem with our individual pursuits, like two rock climbers on the same face, waving from our separate locations as we headed to the summit. We celebrated our anniversary by having massages together and a catered dinner for a small group of friends. Miranda and Gabe, who were married now, flew down for the occasion and it was wonderful to have them with us. As I took in the people seated around our table, I saw a soft, warm light framing each of their faces. The sound of laughter and conversation became almost musical. Two of our very creative, attractive, and talented friends, Kate and Lyle, played a flute and cello duet before coffee and dessert. Kate's frosted hair cascaded down around her black strapless dress as her flute moved me to tears. She had never looked so alive and beautiful, and it was a pleasure to witness, for the first time. Samuel bent over and kissed my neck.

"Happy Anniversary baby, from one lucky guy."

"I love you Samuel." I returned his kiss and we applauded their exquisite performance. The carrot cake and café latte were a sweet and scrumptious ending to a perfect evening. Life was overflowing with abundance. After putting away the last wine glasses, hugging Miranda tightly before they left for their hotel, and wrapping up the rest of the cake, I stood at the glass doors leading to the patio. The moon was nearly full, and the stones were painted in its silver glow. I whispered,

"Yes, Miriam, now I know."

Chapter Forty-nine

October appeared out of nowhere along with the two oversized pumpkins sitting on our doorstep. Samuel was taking an early morning flight out of Charleston to Miami then on to Lima. I awoke before the alarm went off at five-thirty and rolled over to face my snoring soul mate. I watched his bare chest rise and fall, listened to the sound of his noisy breathing and shivered. This trip had its own set of dangers, a foreign country with political and economic instability, and traveling off the beaten path to primitive locations where tourists rarely venture without a specific purpose. Part of me knew he was in capable hands and another part feared what he might encounter. There were so many possibilities, from parasites to polluted water, and adjusting to high altitudes. And when at last he reached the summit of Macchu Picchu, what would greet him there? He was so compelled to make this journey, I imagined part of his destiny anxiously awaiting his presence. Another chill ran down my spine as I thought about all the courage it took for him to make this trek and follow this persistent call. I was fortunate to know and love such a man who had the strength to pursue his vision.

He made the long, arduous trip through security, blew me several kisses and disappeared into the mob of travelers. He became one of the many headed for some unknown destination, be it mundane or treacherous, they were all on their way to somewhere. I watched mothers coaxing small babies to wave to their daddies, silver-haired couples hugging adult children after a long awaited but most likely short visit, and young lovers wrapped in passionate, prolonged kisses. I headed to the coffee shop to comfort myself with a latte. Our tradition when any member of our family was flying was to wait until their plane left the ground before leaving the airport. When I checked with the agent and the computer indicated lift off had taken place, the tears rolled down my face with the realization of what we were both about to encounter. It was truly the next step. I sat back down in one of the white rockers to finish my coffee. A tall, bearded man reading *Newsweek* leaned over to inquire about my emotional state. I assured him I was fine and sat back absorbing my new reality.

On the way home I passed Avery's Nursery and decided to make a stop. I wanted to buy a magnolia to plant on the edge of the patio. Since I had pocketed Miriam's ashes that morning, they remained in a small red box lined with silk in my bottom drawer. There they patiently waited to be settled from whence they came. I knew that I would have plenty of time to create my own version of honoring her memory when I was alone in the coming weeks. When spring came each year, I would see Miriam's wavy white hair as the ivory blossoms took shape, renewing the gifts she had bestowed upon me. I went into the greenhouse and chose a seedling that appeared to be strong and capable of producing the results I desired. It rode home with me in the front seat happy to be on its way.

Driving along, the expanse of time spread itself before me like a long highway with endless destinations. I had given my notice at the museum and stopped working last month. I had been getting my marketing plan for *Freedom Reins* off the ground and trail riding with Samuel, so my days were productive and full. But now I had a stretch of three weeks completely to myself to design however I wanted. A slight tinge of anxiety bubbled up at the thought of it all, but the myriad of possibilities came alongside it and like rain on the windshield, it was wiped away.

When I got to Rosewood Junction, I would put in a call to Ms. Kitty's tattoo parlor which was discreetly located in an alleyway off King Street. Max had told me about it a few months after we met. She had a tattoo of a Celtic cross on her left wrist. I remembered my judgmental reaction when I first saw it. At the time it seemed unrefined and taboo, so I chalked it up to her being younger and more daring. But secretly I harbored a fantasy about getting one myself someday. That time had arrived, and I knew just what symbol I wanted as a permanent statement on my body. I would have a tiny purple horse drawn on my right hip in toward my abdomen. When I laughed heartily or cried madly the horse would be in motion, set free across the flesh hills that my body created in mid-life. It would be an erotic companion riding along with Samuel as he moved inside me.

When I passed through Rosewood Junction's gateway it was obvious that the horses were eagerly awaiting my return. On my way through the dining room I noticed a small ivory envelope on the table with Samuel's unmistakable handwriting on it. It was leaning up against a slender cobalt blue vase containing a single iris. I would let the envelope sit unopened in delightful anticipation as my gift on this first of many new days on my own. For now, Cleo and the gang needed grooming, and she was first in line for a long, vigorous trail ride. I walked out the French doors toward the stable.

Cleo greeted me with a strong nuzzle as I reached out to her. I held her face between my hands and exchanged a few, warm comforting breaths. We were both ready for a lively excursion into the woods. I picked up the curry brush and circled it across her back as we both relaxed into the motion.

"...our inner dragon is only tamed when we choose to ride it."
Michael Brown, *The Presence Process*